Consultant: Ann Bobker

Copyright © 2002 **Popular Book Company (Canada) Limited**

Printed in China

Contents

Overview

Section I provides children with opportunities to develop and practise addition and subtraction skills up to 100 with carrying and regrouping.

In addition, the Geometry units teach children how to classify 2-D and 3-D shapes, and find lines of symmetry.

Data Management topics include charts, pictographs and bar graphs. Children are encouraged to use real objects, pictures or bars to show information. At this stage, the number of items for comparison is limited to no more than 4.

In the Measurement units, children learn to select appropriate non-standard units for measuring the passage of time, length, weight and height of different objects.

Money applications include sums up to 100¢.

1 Addition and Subtraction to 20

Use the family of facts to fill in the missing numbers.

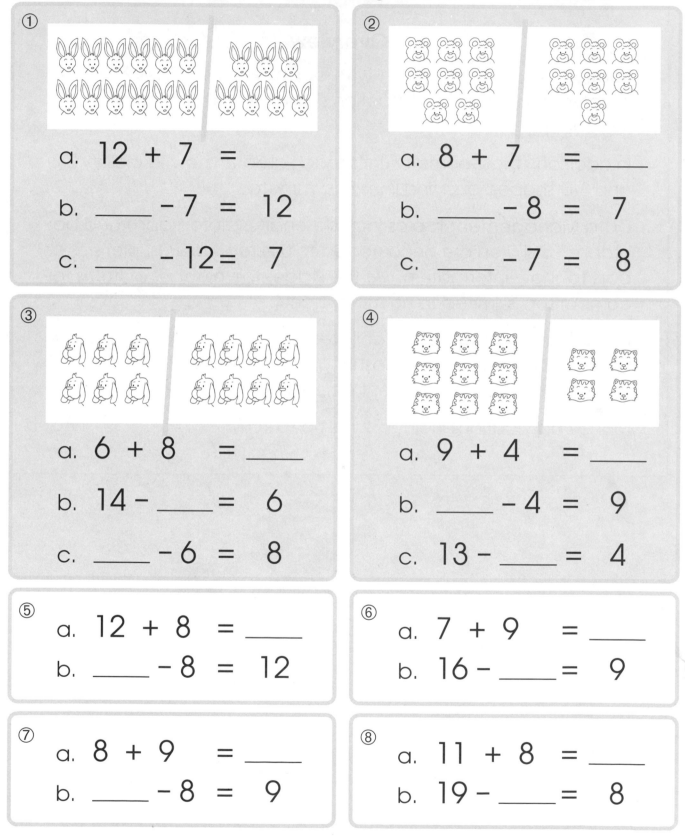

① a. 12 + 7 = _____

b. _____ – 7 = 12

c. _____ – 12 = 7

② a. 8 + 7 = _____

b. _____ – 8 = 7

c. _____ – 7 = 8

③ a. 6 + 8 = _____

b. 14 – _____ = 6

c. _____ – 6 = 8

④ a. 9 + 4 = _____

b. _____ – 4 = 9

c. 13 – _____ = 4

⑤ a. 12 + 8 = _____

b. _____ – 8 = 12

⑥ a. 7 + 9 = _____

b. 16 – _____ = 9

⑦ a. 8 + 9 = _____

b. _____ – 8 = 9

⑧ a. 11 + 8 = _____

b. 19 – _____ = 8

Look at the pictures. Then answer the questions.

⑨ How many 🐦 are there? _____ 🐦

⑩ How many 🐦 are there? _____ 🐦

⑪ How many 🐴 are there? _____ 🐴

⑫ How many 🐴 are there? _____ 🐴

⑬ How many birds are there?

_____ + _____ = _____   _____ birds

⑭ How many more 🐦 than 🐦 are there?

_____ – _____ = _____   _____ more

⑮ How many horses are there?

_____ + _____ = _____   _____ horses

⑯ How many more 🐴 than 🐴 are there?

_____ – _____ = _____   _____ more

⑰ How many animals are black?

_____ + _____ = _____   _____ animals

2-digit Numbers

Fill in the missing numbers.

① | 38 | 39 | | | 42 | | | 45 |

② | 29 | | 27 | | | 24 | | 22 |

③ | | 57 | | | 54 | 53 | | 51 |

Put the numbers in order from the biggest to the smallest.

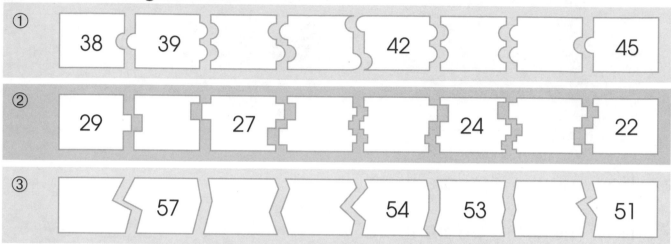

④ 42 23 54 37 : ____ , ____ , ____ , ____

⑤ 25 11 64 50 : ____ , ____ , ____ , ____

⑥ 30 47 81 90 : ____ , ____ , ____ , ____

Help the bird count by 4's to get to the nest. Colour its path.

⑦

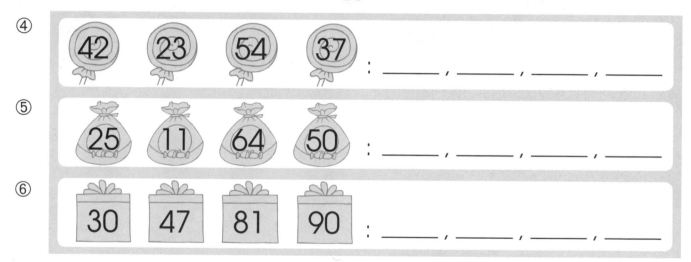

4	8	12	18	24	30	38
6	10	16	20	22	36	40
12	20	22	24	36	40	44
16	14	24	28	32	42	48

Fill in the missing numbers in the patterns. Then circle the correct words and write the numbers.

⑧ 12 , 14 , 16 , 18 , _____ , _____ , _____

Pattern : increase / decrease by _____

⑨ 55 , 50 , 45 , 40 , _____ , _____ , _____

Pattern : increase / decrease by _____

⑩ 20 , 30 , 40 , 50 , _____ , _____ , _____

Pattern : increase / decrease by _____

⑪ 85 , 84 , 83 , 82 , _____ , _____ , _____

Pattern : increase / decrease by _____

Colour the flowers. Then answer the questions.

⑫ Colour the 19th 🌼 blue and the 21st 🌼 yellow.

⑬ How many 🌼 are there from the 15th to the 20th? _____ 🌼

⑭ How many 🌼 are there in all? _____ 🌼

⑮ How many more 🌼 must Sally plant so that there are 29 🌼 in all? _____ 🌼

Fill in the missing days. Then answer the questions.

⑯

September						
SUN	MON	TUE	WED	THU	FRI	SAT
	1	2				6
	8		11			
14		17			20
			25	26		
28		30				

⑰ Debbie's birthday is September 18th.
 What day of the week is it?

_____

⑱ Tommy's birthday is September 27th.
 What day of the week is it?

_____

⑲ How many Mondays are there in
 September?

_____

⑳ How many Fridays are there in
 September?

_____

㉑ Lucy's birthday party is on the 3rd Sunday
 in September. What is the date of her
 party?

_____

㉒ Prima's birthday party is on the day after
 September 23rd. What is the date of her
 party?

_____

㉓ What day of the week is October 1st?

_____

㉔ Matthew's birthday party is on the day
 before October 3rd. What is the date of
 his birthday?

_____

Write the numbers for the children.

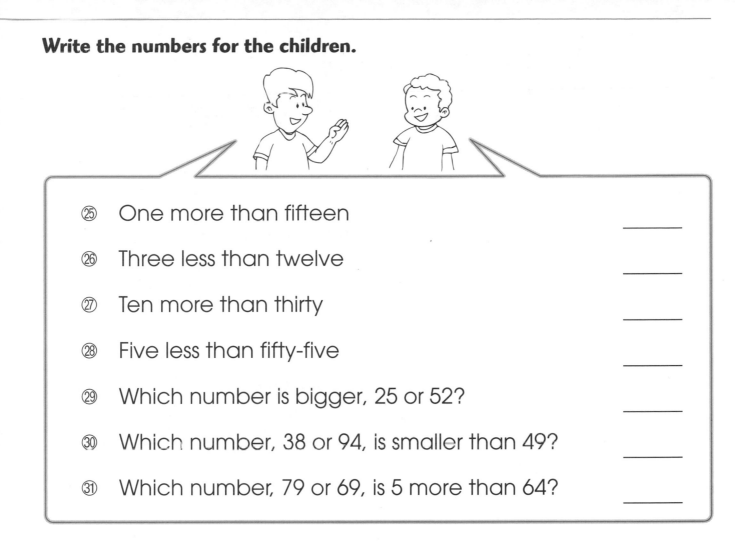

㉕ One more than fifteen _____

㉖ Three less than twelve _____

㉗ Ten more than thirty _____

㉘ Five less than fifty-five _____

㉙ Which number is bigger, 25 or 52? _____

㉚ Which number, 38 or 94, is smaller than 49? _____

㉛ Which number, 79 or 69, is 5 more than 64? _____

Cross out ✗ the wrong number and write the correct one in the box for each chain.

㉜ 41 ~ 40 ~ 39 ~ ✗36 ~ 37 ~ 36 ~ 35 ~ 34 ☐

㉝ 86 ~ 84 ~ 88 ~ 80 ~ 78 ~ 76 ~ 74 ~ 72 ☐

㉞ 50 ~ 45 ~ 40 ~ 38 ~ 30 ~ 25 ~ 20 ~ 15 ☐

㉟ 78 ~ 79 ~ 82 ~ 84 ~ 86 ~ 88 ~ 90 ~ 92 ☐

㊱ 32 ~ 28 ~ 24 ~ 22 ~ 16 ~ 12 ~ 8 ~ 4 ☐

Addition to 100

Count the blocks. Write the numbers in the boxes .

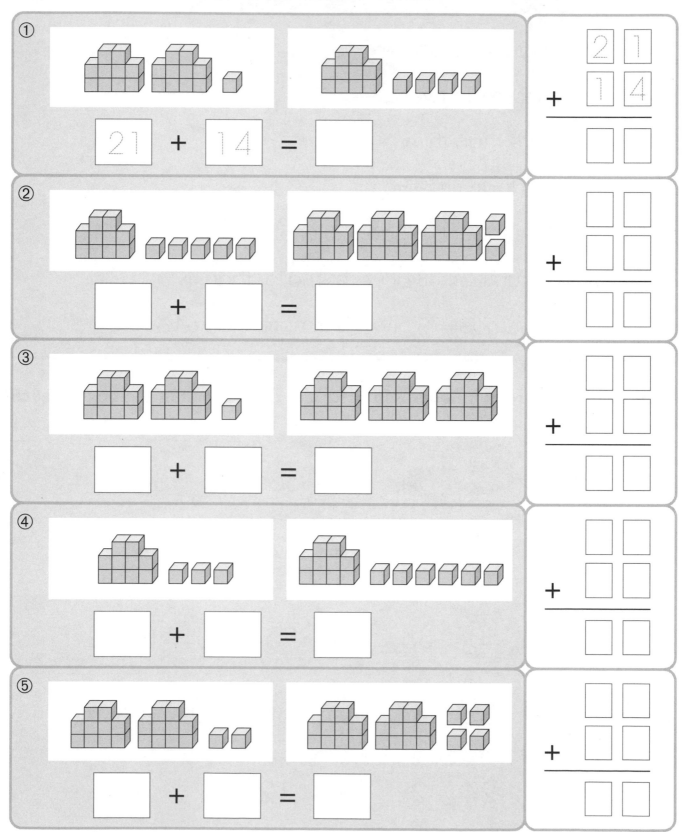

In each group, circle ten marbles not in the bottles and add the numbers.

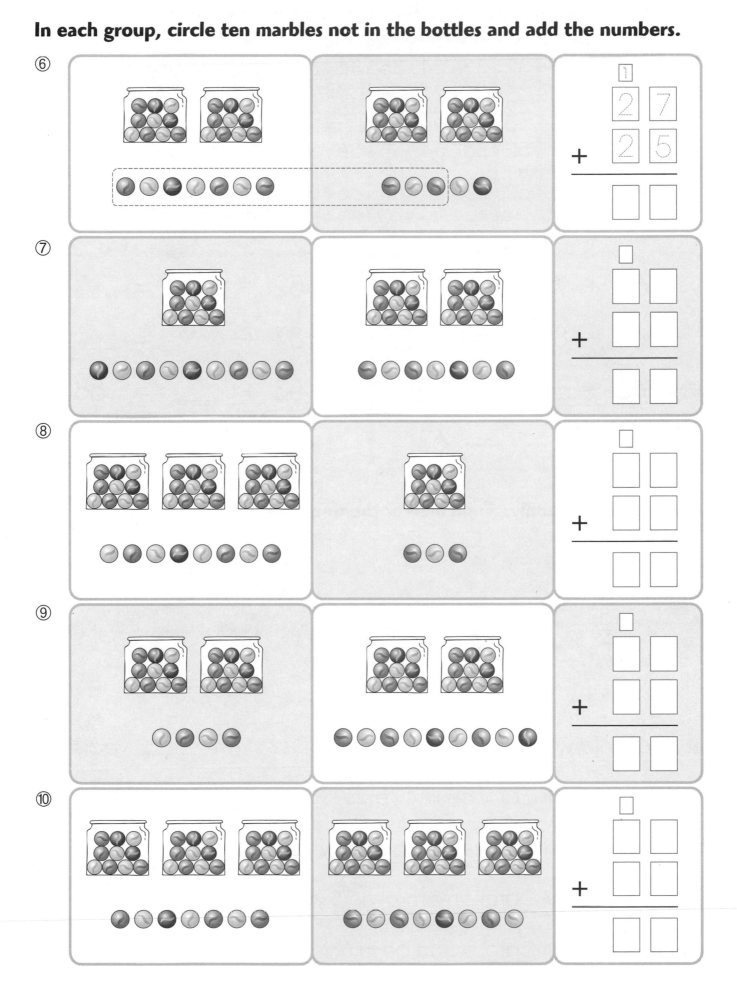

Fill in the missing numbers with the help of the number chart.

31	32	33	34	35	36	37	38	39	40
41	42	43	44	45	46	47	48	49	50
51	52	53	54	55	56	57	58	59	60
61	62	63	64	65	66	67	68	69	70

⑪ 61 + 7 = _____

⑫ 52 + 3 = _____

⑬ 45 + 8 = _____

⑭ 37 + 4 = _____

⑮ 43 + _____ = 49

⑯ 53 + _____ = 58

⑰ 54 + _____ = 63

⑱ 58 + _____ = 66

Look at Carol's family. Then answer the questions.

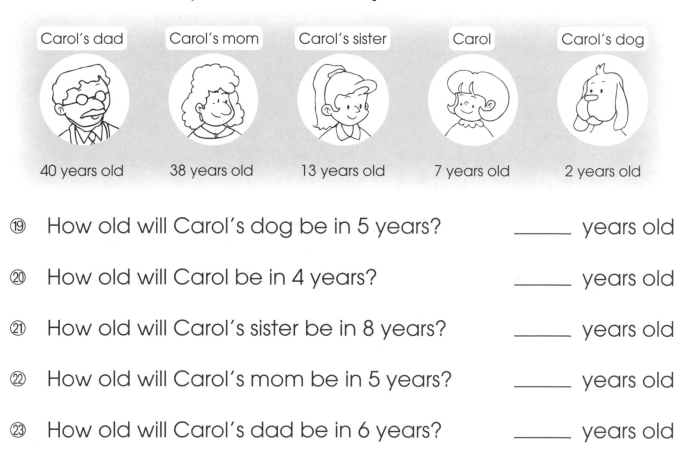

| Carol's dad | Carol's mom | Carol's sister | Carol | Carol's dog |
| 40 years old | 38 years old | 13 years old | 7 years old | 2 years old |

⑲ How old will Carol's dog be in 5 years? _____ years old

⑳ How old will Carol be in 4 years? _____ years old

㉑ How old will Carol's sister be in 8 years? _____ years old

㉒ How old will Carol's mom be in 5 years? _____ years old

㉓ How old will Carol's dad be in 6 years? _____ years old

Complete.

㉔ Sarah collects 12 🐚 . Joe collects 25 🐚 .
How many 🐚 do they collect in all?

____ + ____ = ____

They collect ____ 🐚 in all.

㉕ Bobby has 34 📚 . Stephen has 21 📚 .
How many 📚 do they have in all?

____ + ____ = ____

They have ____ 📚 in all.

㉖ Lucy has 35 🧁 . David has 12 more 🧁 than
Lucy. How many 🧁 does David have?

____ + ____ = ____

David has ____ 🧁 .

㉗ Tom catches 16 🐟 . Pat catches 36 🐟 .
How many 🐟 do they catch in all?

____ + ____ = ____

They catch ____ 🐟 in all.

㉘ Aunt Betty bakes 35 🍪 and 28 🍪 . How
many 🍪 🍪 does Aunt Betty bake?

____ + ____ = ____

Aunt Betty bakes ____ 🍪 🍪 .

Subtraction to 100

Write the numbers with the help of the number chart.

21	22	23	24	25	26	27	28	29	30
31	32	33	34	35	36	37	38	39	40
41	42	43	44	45	46	47	48	49	50
51	52	53	54	55	56	57	58	59	60

① 5 less than 47 _____

② 6 less than 59 _____

③ 4 less than 40 _____

④ 2 less than 55 _____

⑤ 6 less than 31 _____

⑥ 3 less than 42 _____

⑦ 7 less than 53 _____

⑧ 7 less than 35 _____

⑨ 52 is _____ more than 42.

⑩ 45 is _____ more than 43.

⑪ 32 is _____ less than 39.

⑫ 35 is _____ less than 40.

Count how many stickers each child has. Then fill in the blanks.

⑬ Sam gives 10 ☺ to his friends. He has _____ ☺ left.

⑭ Tina gives 4 ☺ to her friends. She has _____ ☺ left.

⑮ Felix gives 6 ☺ to his friends. He has _____ ☺ left.

Cross out X the correct number of cookies. Find the differences.

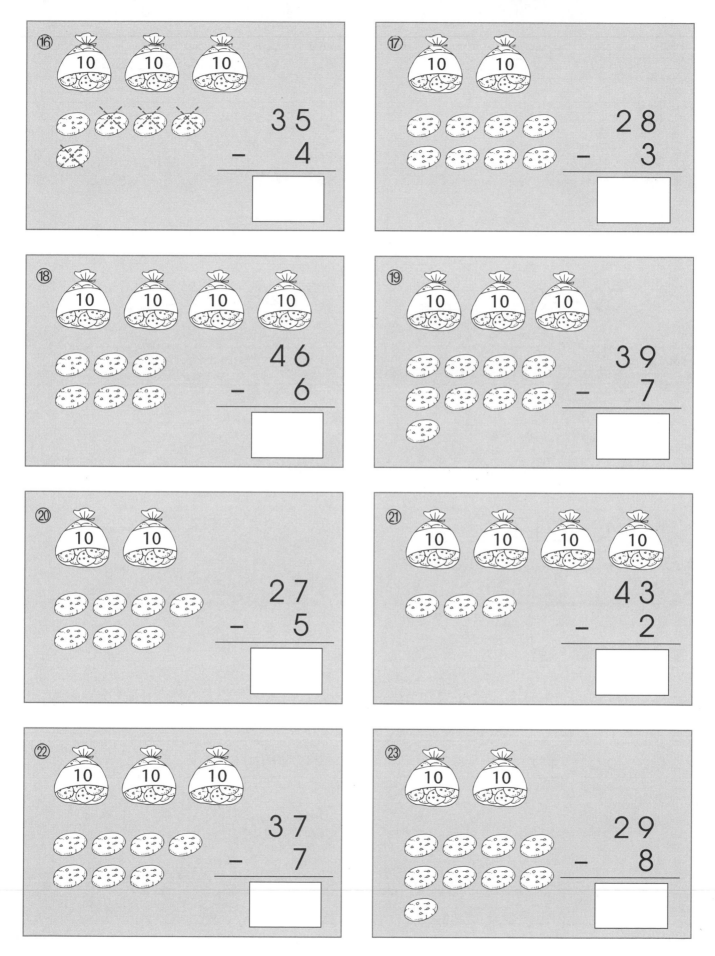

16.
$$\begin{array}{r} 35 \\ -4 \\ \hline \end{array}$$

17.
$$\begin{array}{r} 28 \\ -3 \\ \hline \end{array}$$

18.
$$\begin{array}{r} 46 \\ -6 \\ \hline \end{array}$$

19.
$$\begin{array}{r} 39 \\ -7 \\ \hline \end{array}$$

20.
$$\begin{array}{r} 27 \\ -5 \\ \hline \end{array}$$

21.
$$\begin{array}{r} 43 \\ -2 \\ \hline \end{array}$$

22.
$$\begin{array}{r} 37 \\ -7 \\ \hline \end{array}$$

23.
$$\begin{array}{r} 29 \\ -8 \\ \hline \end{array}$$

Cross out X the correct number of flowers. Find the differences.

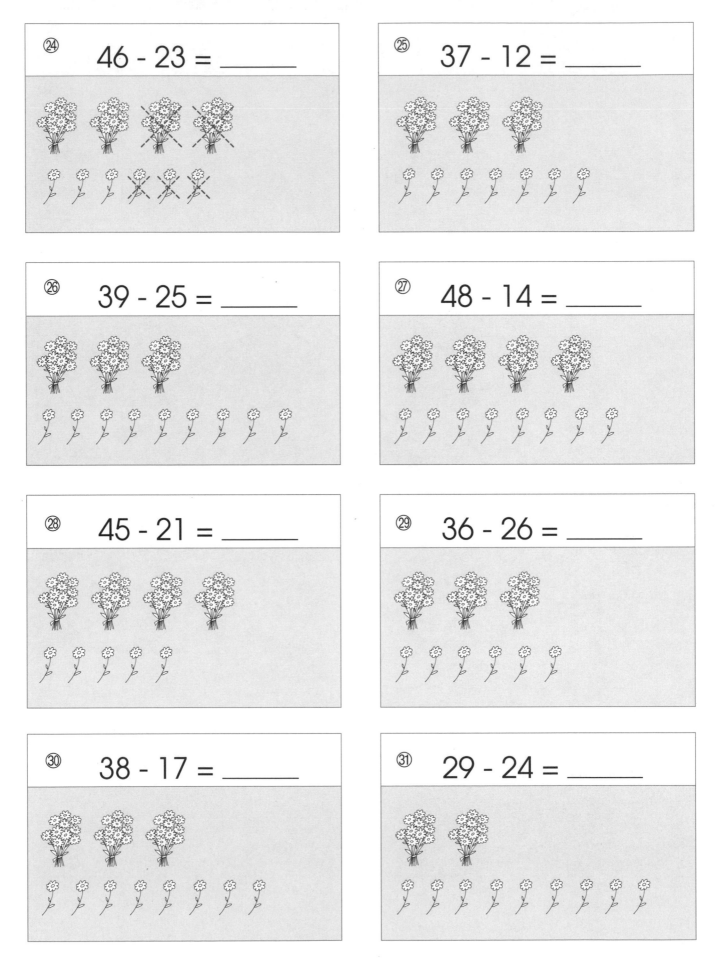

㉔ 46 - 23 = _____

㉕ 37 - 12 = _____

㉖ 39 - 25 = _____

㉗ 48 - 14 = _____

㉘ 45 - 21 = _____

㉙ 36 - 26 = _____

㉚ 38 - 17 = _____

㉛ 29 - 24 = _____

Complete.

32. Cathy has 32 🍭 . She gives 2 to Billy. How many 🍭 does Cathy have now?

    _____ – _____ = _____

    Cathy has _____ 🍭 now.

33. George has 45 🪙 . He has 4 more than Joe. How many 🪙 does Joe have?

    _____ – _____ = _____

    Joe has _____ 🪙 .

34. There are 56 🧁 in the store. Uncle John buys 5 of them. How many 🧁 are left in the store?

    _____ – _____ = _____

    _____ 🧁 are left in the store.

35. There are 38 👦 and 6 👧 in the class. How many more 👦 than 👧 are in the class?

    _____ – _____ = _____

    _____ more 👦 than 👧 are in the class.

36. Aunt Betty has 68 🍪 . She gives 8 to May. How many 🍪 does Aunt Betty have now?

    _____ – _____ = _____

    Aunt Betty has _____ 🍪 now.

Shapes

Circle the correct name of each shape.

① Pentagon
Hexagon
Circle

② Square
Rectangle
Triangle

③ Hexagon
Square
Rectangle

④ Pentagon
Triangle
Hexagon

Draw the line of symmetry on each letter.

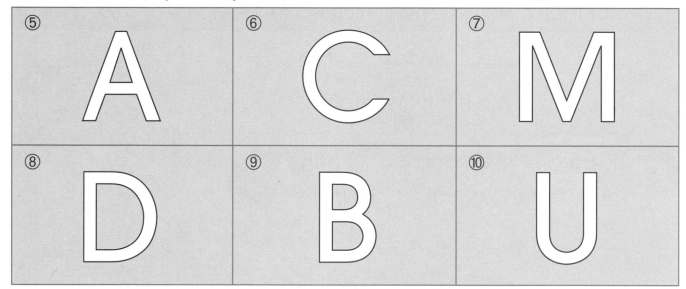

⑤ A ⑥ C ⑦ M

⑧ D ⑨ B ⑩ U

Each letter has two lines of symmetry. Draw them.

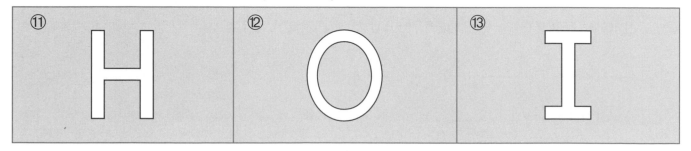

⑪ H ⑫ O ⑬ I

Look at the pictures. Then write the number in the box to tell how many lines of symmetry each picture has.

Write the name of each shape.

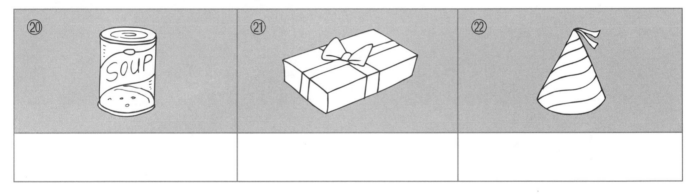

Colour the shapes.

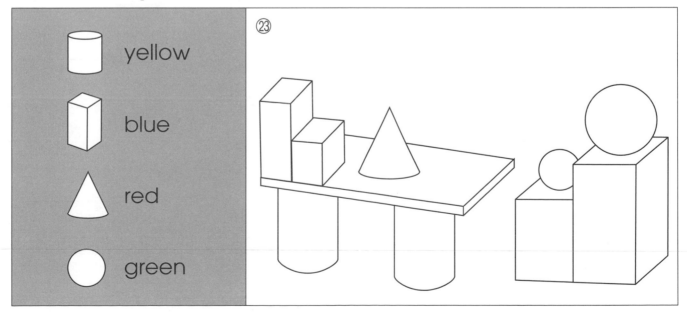

Count by 2's to help Little Squirrel find the food he likes. Colour the path.

①

2	4	5	7	9	11	13	26
6	6	10	12	28	30	32	34
12	8	6	14	26	30	33	36
14	10	12	18	24	25	27	29
16	12	16	20	22	26	29	30
20	14	16	18	22	24	26	28

Use the numbers to answer the questions.

44   66   50   96   9
14   39   8   54   70

② Which number is the largest? _____

③ Which number is the smallest? _____

④ How many numbers are smaller than 60? _____

⑤ How many 2-digit numbers are there? _____

⑥ Which number is 10 less than 76? _____

⑦ Which number is 5 more than 65? _____

⑧ Which number plus 20 is 70? _____

⑨ Which two numbers should be put in the following pattern?

____?____ , 24, 34, 44, ____?____   _____ ; _____

Count and write the numbers. Find the sums.

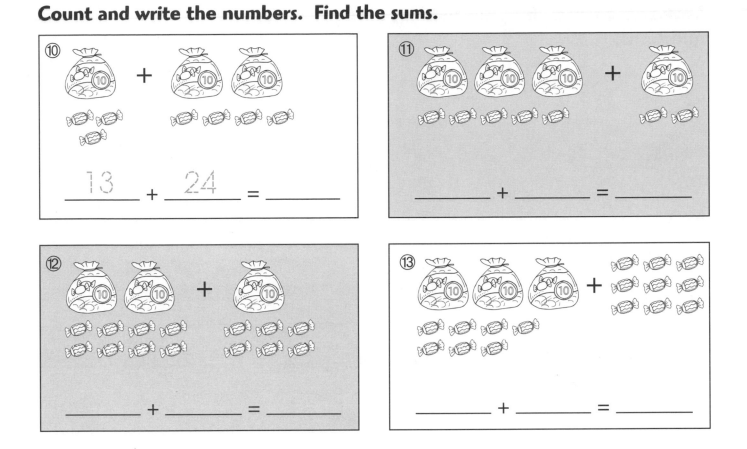

⑩ 13 + 24 = _____

⑪ _____ + _____ = _____

⑫ _____ + _____ = _____

⑬ _____ + _____ = _____

Count and write the numbers. Find the differences.

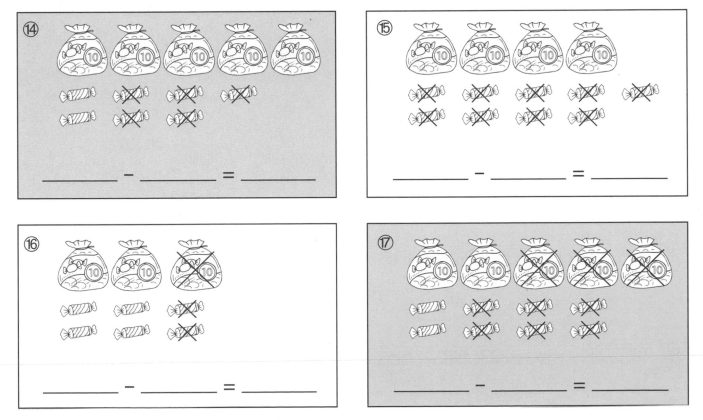

⑭ _____ − _____ = _____

⑮ _____ − _____ = _____

⑯ _____ − _____ = _____

⑰ _____ − _____ = _____

Look at the treats that Jake and May have got at Halloween. Then answer the questions.

⑱ How many treats has Jake got?

_____ + _____ = _____   _____ treats

⑲ How many treats has May got?

_____ + _____ = _____   _____ treats

⑳ How many  have the children got in all?

_____ + _____ = _____   _____

㉑ How many more  has Jake got than May?

_____ – _____ = _____   _____ more

㉒ How many  have the children got in all?

_____ + _____ = _____   _____

㉓ How many more  has May got than Jake?

_____ – _____ = _____   _____ more

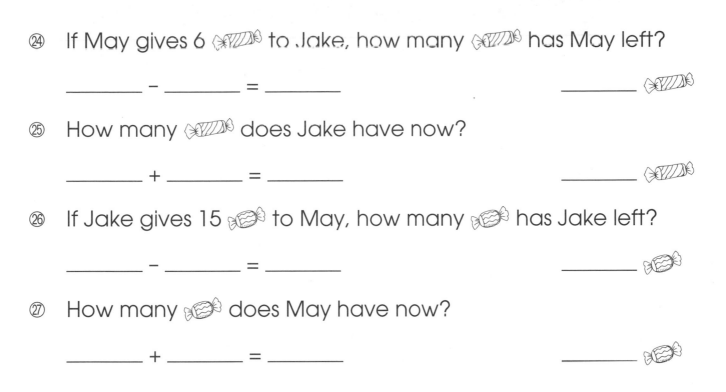

㉔ If May gives 6 🍬 to Jake, how many 🍬 has May left?

_____ – _____ = _____   _____ 🍬

㉕ How many 🍬 does Jake have now?

_____ + _____ = _____   _____ 🍬

㉖ If Jake gives 15 🍬 to May, how many 🍬 has Jake left?

_____ – _____ = _____   _____ 🍬

㉗ How many 🍬 does May have now?

_____ + _____ = _____   _____ 🍬

These are Jake's containers for holding his candies. Write the name of each shape.

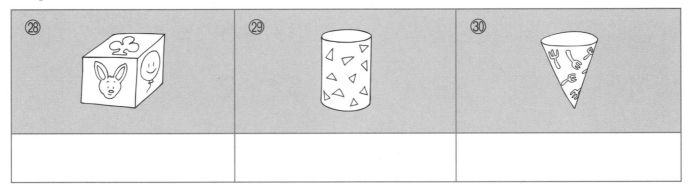

㉘	㉙	㉚

Look at the pictures on the containers. Draw their lines of symmetry.

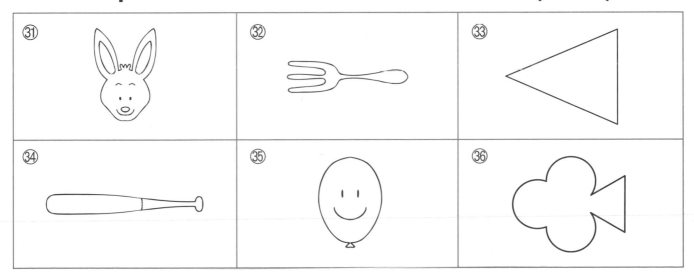

More about Addition and Subtraction

Use Eva's decoration to find the sums.

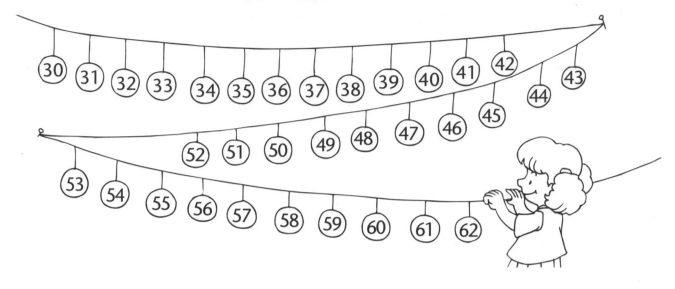

① 35 + 3 = _____

② 46 + 2 = _____

③ 53 + 4 = _____

④ 57 + 5 = _____

⑤ 49 + 8 = _____

⑥ 32 + 9 = _____

⑦ 33 + 5 = _____

⑧ 44 + 8 = _____

⑨ 47 + 11 = _____

⑩ 36 + 13 = _____

⑪ 35 + _____ = 39

⑫ 42 + _____ = 50

⑬ 55 + _____ = 56

⑭ 33 + _____ = 36

⑮ 47 + _____ = 51

⑯ 58 + _____ = 64

⑰ 32 + _____ = 33

⑱ 43 + _____ = 53

⑲ 49 + _____ = 61

⑳ 36 + _____ = 51

Use Little Squirrel's maze to find the differences.

58 59 60 61 62 63 64 65 66 67 68 69 70 71 72 73 74 75 76 77 78 79 80 81 82 83 84 85

㉑ 73 – 2 = _____

㉒ 63 – 3 = _____

㉓ 84 – 3 = _____

㉔ 78 – 6 = _____

㉕ 70 – 5 = _____

㉖ 82 – 4 = _____

㉗ 63 – 5 = _____

㉘ 81 – 2 = _____

㉙ 77 – 9 = _____

㉚ 67 – 8 = _____

㉛ 65 – _____ = 63

㉜ 84 – _____ = 81

㉝ 77 – _____ = 72

㉞ 79 – _____ = 70

㉟ 62 – _____ = 59

㊱ 80 – _____ = 73

㊲ 71 – _____ = 63

㊳ 64 – _____ = 58

㊴ 82 – _____ = 70

㊵ 79 – _____ = 69

㊶ 77 – _____ = 65

㊷ 84 – _____ = 71

Complete each family of facts.

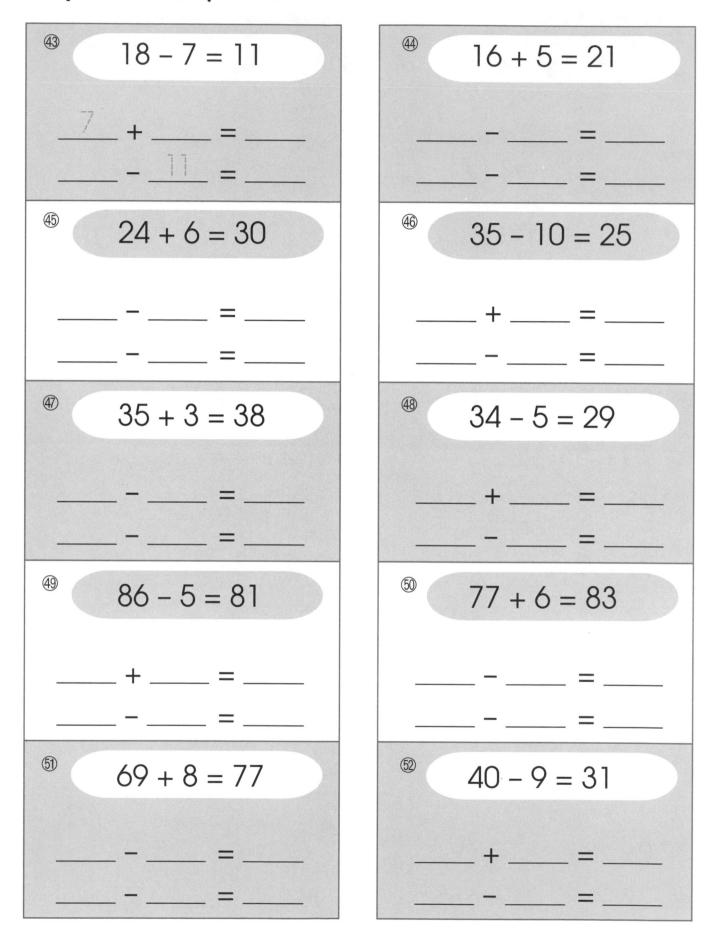

43) 18 – 7 = 11

___7___ + _____ = _____
_____ – __11__ = _____

44) 16 + 5 = 21

_____ – _____ = _____
_____ – _____ = _____

45) 24 + 6 = 30

_____ – _____ = _____
_____ – _____ = _____

46) 35 – 10 = 25

_____ + _____ = _____
_____ – _____ = _____

47) 35 + 3 = 38

_____ – _____ = _____
_____ – _____ = _____

48) 34 – 5 = 29

_____ + _____ = _____
_____ – _____ = _____

49) 86 – 5 = 81

_____ + _____ = _____
_____ – _____ = _____

50) 77 + 6 = 83

_____ – _____ = _____
_____ – _____ = _____

51) 69 + 8 = 77

_____ – _____ = _____
_____ – _____ = _____

52) 40 – 9 = 31

_____ + _____ = _____
_____ – _____ = _____

Count and write how many stickers each child has. Then answer the questions.

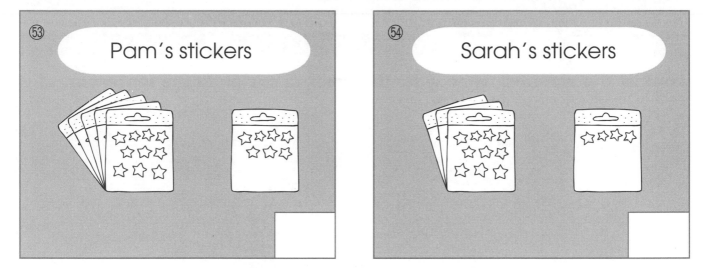

⑤⑤ How many ☆ do the children have in all?

_____ = _____   _____ ☆

⑤⑥ How many more ☆ does Pam have than Sarah?

_____ = _____   _____ ☆

⑤⑦ A sticker album has space for 60 ☆ . If Pam pastes all her ☆ in the album, how many more ☆ can she put in?

_____ = _____   _____ more

⑤⑧ If Sarah also pastes all her ☆ in the album, how many more ☆ can she put in it ?

_____ = _____   _____ more

⑤⑨ If Pam gives 15 ☆ to Sarah, how many ☆ has she left?

_____ = _____   _____ ☆

⑥⓪ How many ☆ does Sarah have now?

_____ = _____   _____ ☆

Measurement

Look at the pictures. Then write the times to complete the sentences.

① Jeffrey goes to bed at _____ .

② Jeffrey watches TV at _____ .

③ Jeffrey eats lunch at _____ .

④ Jeffrey wakes up at _____ .

See how heavy each person is. Then write their names to complete the sentences.

⑤ Rita and _____ weigh the same.

⑥ Sam is heavier than _____ .

⑦ Alan and _____ are both heavier than either _____

or _____ .

⑧ The lightest person is _____ .

Gordon uses his lollipops to measure the lengths and widths of the pictures. Help him fill in the numbers and circle the correct words.

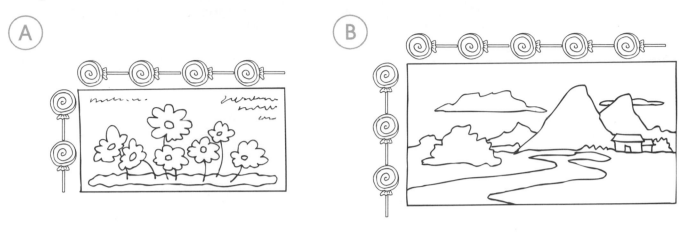

Ⓐ

Ⓑ

⑨ The length of A has the same length as _____ 🍭 .

⑩ The width of A has the same length as _____ 🍭 .

⑪ The length of B is a little longer than the length of _____ 🍭 .

⑫ The width of B is almost equal to the length of _____ 🍭 .

⑬ The length of A is _____ shorter / longer than the length of B.

⑭ The width of A is _____ shorter / longer than the width of B.

In each group, check ✔ the one that holds the most water.

⑮ Ⓐ Ⓑ Ⓒ Ⓓ

⑯ Ⓐ Ⓑ Ⓒ Ⓓ

Money

See how much money Sean has in his piggy bank. Answer the questions and check ✔ the correct answers.

① a. How many does Sean have? _____

   b. What is the total value of the ? _____ ¢

② a. How many does Sean have? _____

   b. What is the total value of the ? _____ ¢

③ a. How many does Sean have? _____

   b. What is the total value of the ? _____ ¢

④ Which coin has the biggest size? Ⓐ Ⓑ Ⓒ

⑤ Which coin has the greatest value? Ⓐ Ⓑ Ⓒ

⑥ Which coin is worth less than 5¢? Ⓐ Ⓑ Ⓒ

Show 2 different ways the children can pay for their food by checking ✔ the coins used.

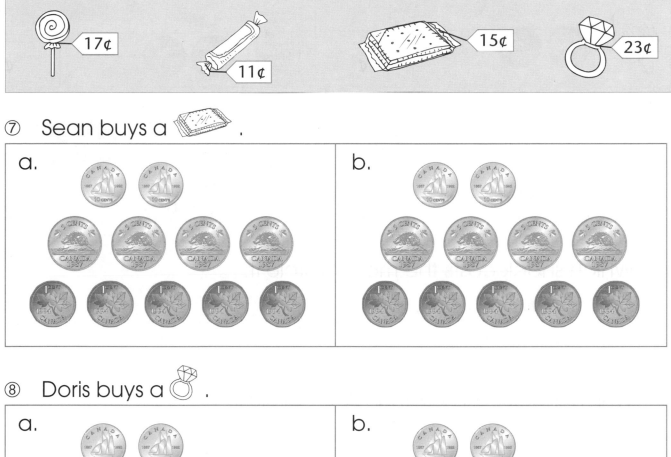

⑦ Sean buys a 🍪 .

⑧ Doris buys a 💍 .

⑨ Matthew buys a 🍭 and a 🍬 .

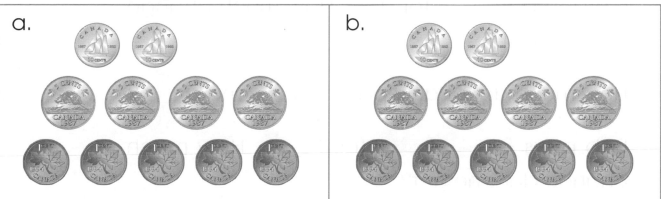

Write how much each snack costs. Answer the questions.

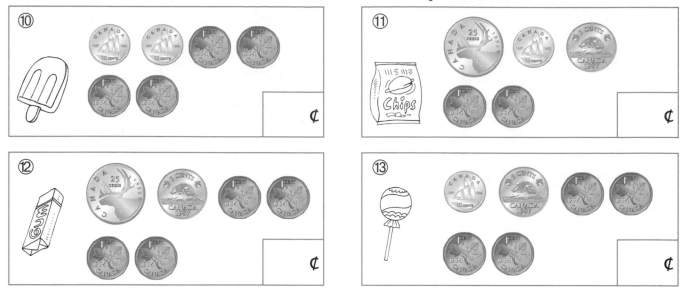

⑭ Which snack costs the most? Circle it.

⑮ Which snack costs less than 20¢? Circle it.

⑯ How much more does a  cost than a ? _____ ¢

⑰ Peggy has . She wants to buy a . How
     much more does she need? _____ ¢

⑱ Gordon pays for a 🍭. How much change
     does he get? _____ ¢

⑲ How much does Paula pay for a 🍦 and a 🍟 ? _____ ¢

⑳ Bob pays 🪙 🪙 🪙 for 3 🍦 . How much
     change does he get? _____ ¢

See how much Uncle Anthony and Aunt Sandra have. Answer the questions.

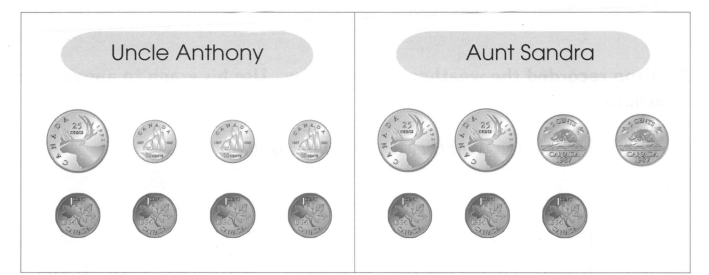

㉑ How many coins does Uncle Anthony have?   _____ coins

㉒ How much does Uncle Anthony have?   _____ ¢

㉓ How many coins does Aunt Sandra have?   _____ coins

㉔ How much does Aunt Sandra have?   _____ ¢

㉕ How many more coins does Uncle Anthony
    have than Aunt Sandra?   _____ more

㉖ How much more does Aunt Sandra have
    than Uncle Anthony?   _____ ¢

㉗ Uncle Anthony buys a [Gum 28¢]. How much
    has he left?   _____ ¢

㉘ Aunt Sandra gives 27¢ to Tommy. How much
    has she left?   _____ ¢

㉙ After giving the money to Tommy, does
    Aunt Sandra have enough money to buy a
    [Coffee] for 45¢?   _____

Pictographs

Mr Vann recorded the weather on his holiday. Use his graph to answer the questions.

Weather on Mr Vann's Holiday

① How many days were ☀ ? _____ days

② How many days were 🌧 ? _____ days

③ How many days were ☁ ? _____ days

④ How many more days were ☀ than 🌧 ? _____ more

⑤ How many more days were ☁ than 🌧 ? _____ more

⑥ How many days were not 🌧 ? _____ days

⑦ Was there more 🌧 than ☁ on

   Mr Vann's holidays? _____

⑧ How long was Mr Vann's holiday? _____ days

⑨ Which weather occurred the most? Colour it. ☀ 🌧 ☁

Use the graph to answer the questions.

Number of Pets in Pet Shop

⑩ How many cats are white? _____ cats

⑪ How many cats are black? _____ cats

⑫ How many dogs are white? _____ dogs

⑬ How many dogs are black? _____ dogs

⑭ How many cats are there in all? _____ cats

⑮ How many dogs are there in all? _____ dogs

⑯ How many more dogs than cats are there? _____ more

⑰ How many pets are white? _____ pets

⑱ How many pets are black? _____ pets

⑲ How many more pets in black than in white are there? _____ more

⑳ How many pets are there in the pet shop? _____ pets

See how many boxes of drinks Aunt Daisy buys. Colour the drinks to complete the graph and fill in the blanks.

㉑

Number of Drinks Aunt Daisy Buys

㉒ How many boxes of 🧃 does Aunt Daisy buy?   _____ boxes

㉓ How many boxes of juices does Aunt Daisy buy in all?   _____ boxes

㉔ How many boxes of 🥛 does Aunt Daisy buy?   _____ boxes

㉕ How many boxes of milk does Aunt Daisy buy in all?   _____ boxes

See how many cards Julia has. Help her colour the graphs and fill in the blanks.

㉖

Number of Cards Julia Has	

Cards in White	Cards in Black

㉗

Number of Cards Julia Has	

Heart	Diamond

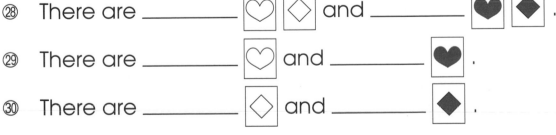

㉘ There are _____ ♡ ◇ and _____ ♥ ◆ .

㉙ There are _____ ♡ and _____ ♥ .

㉚ There are _____ ◇ and _____ ◆ .

㉛ Julia has _____ cards in all.

 **Probability**

Look at the spinners. Then check ✔ the correct answers.

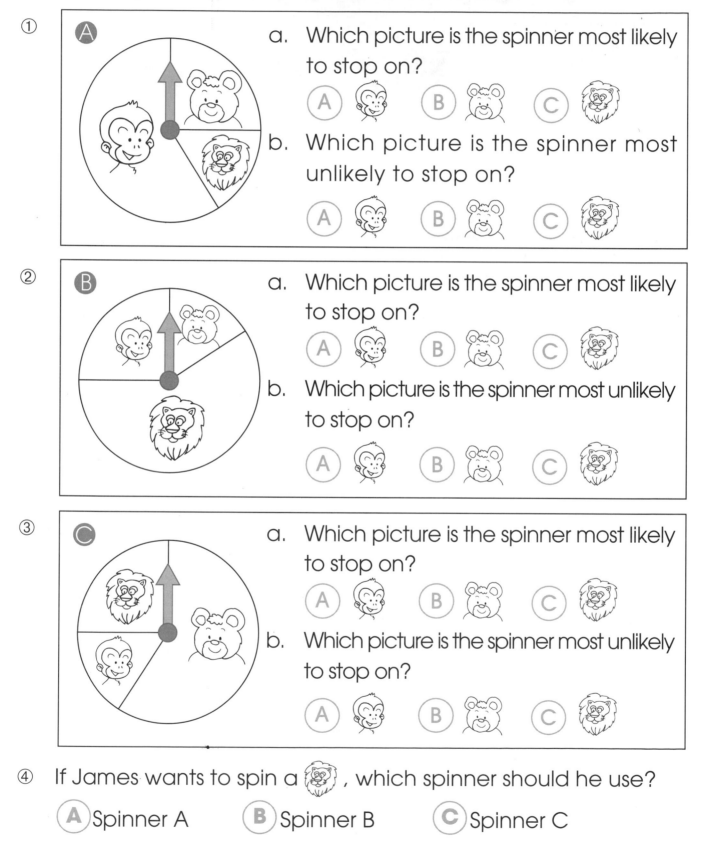

① Ⓐ

a. Which picture is the spinner most likely to stop on?

   Ⓐ 🐵   Ⓑ 🐻   Ⓒ 🦁

b. Which picture is the spinner most unlikely to stop on?

   Ⓐ 🐵   Ⓑ 🐻   Ⓒ 🦁

② Ⓑ

a. Which picture is the spinner most likely to stop on?

   Ⓐ 🐵   Ⓑ 🐻   Ⓒ 🦁

b. Which picture is the spinner most unlikely to stop on?

   Ⓐ 🐵   Ⓑ 🐻   Ⓒ 🦁

③ Ⓒ

a. Which picture is the spinner most likely to stop on?

   Ⓐ 🐵   Ⓑ 🐻   Ⓒ 🦁

b. Which picture is the spinner most unlikely to stop on?

   Ⓐ 🐵   Ⓑ 🐻   Ⓒ 🦁

④ If James wants to spin a 🦁 , which spinner should he use?

Ⓐ Spinner A   Ⓑ Spinner B   Ⓒ Spinner C

Aunt Molly has a lot of juices. Jenny is going to pick a box of juice. Help Jenny check ✔ the correct answers.

⑤ Which kind of juice is Jenny most likely to pick?

Ⓐ 　　　　　　　Ⓑ 　　　　　　　Ⓒ

⑥ Which kind of juice is Jenny most unlikely to pick?

Ⓐ 　　　　　　　Ⓑ 　　　　　　　Ⓒ

⑦ Which is the best word to describe the chance of picking a 🥤 ?

Ⓐ Never 　　　　Ⓑ Maybe 　　　　Ⓒ Likely

⑧ Is there a better chance that Jenny will pick a 🧃 , 🧃 or 🧃 ?

Ⓐ 　　　　　　　Ⓑ 　　　　　　　Ⓒ

Circle the best word for each sentence.

⑨ When you flip a coin, it is impossible / probable / likely to have the coin landing on its head.

⑩ When you toss a die, it is impossible / probable / likely to get a 7.

Mr Jenkin uses his nails to measure the lengths of the tools. Help him fill in the blanks.

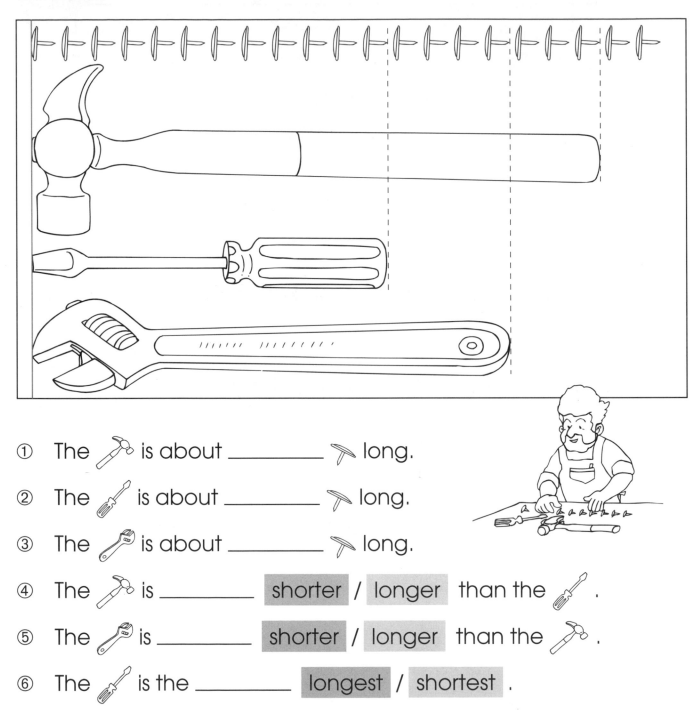

① The 🔨 is about _____ ⚒ long.

② The 🪛 is about _____ ⚒ long.

③ The 🔧 is about _____ ⚒ long.

④ The 🔨 is _____ shorter / longer than the 🪛 .

⑤ The 🔧 is _____ shorter / longer than the 🔨 .

⑥ The 🪛 is the _____ longest / shortest .

See how heavy each tool is. Write the numbers.

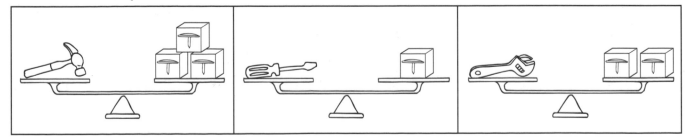

⑦ The 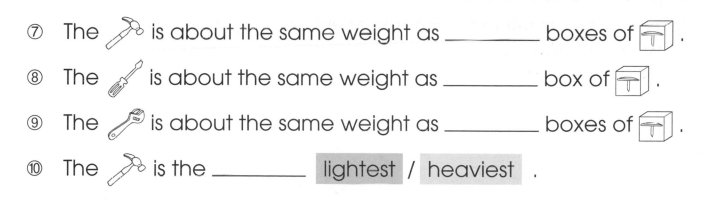 is about the same weight as _____ boxes of [cube] .

⑧ The is about the same weight as _____ box of [cube] .

⑨ The is about the same weight as _____ boxes of [cube] .

⑩ The is the _____ lightest / heaviest .

Mr Jenkin sells the tools in a garage sale. Write the price of each tool. Then answer the questions.

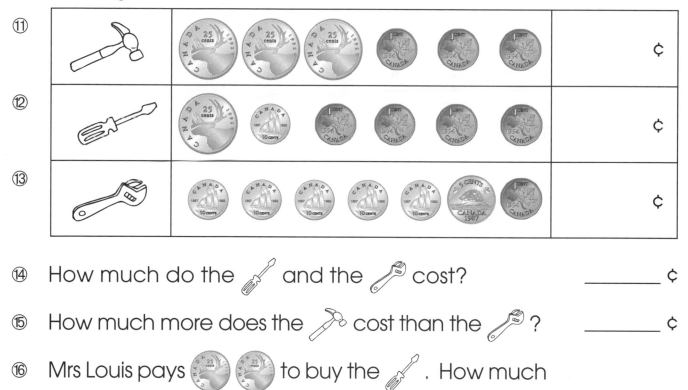

⑪ [hammer] [25 cents][25 cents][25 cents][1 cent][1 cent][1 cent] ____ ¢

⑫ [screwdriver] [25 cents][10 cents][1 cent][1 cent][1 cent][1 cent] ____ ¢

⑬ [wrench] [10 cents][10 cents][10 cents][10 cents][10 cents][5 cents][1 cent] ____ ¢

⑭ How much do the [screwdriver] and the [wrench] cost? _____ ¢

⑮ How much more does the [hammer] cost than the [wrench]? _____ ¢

⑯ Mrs Louis pays [25 cents][25 cents] to buy the [screwdriver]. How much change does she get? _____ ¢

See what time Mr Jenkin started and finished the sale. Draw the clock hands.

⑰ Start Time   10:30 a.m.

⑱ Finish Time   4:00 p.m.

Uncle Bruce puts the fruits in boxes. See how many are in each box. Then answer the questions.

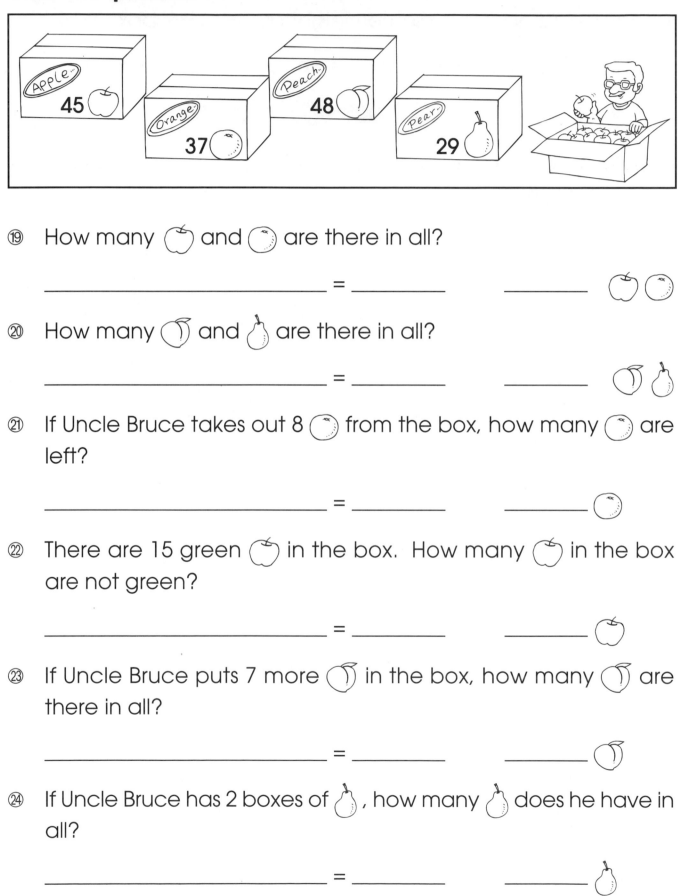

⑲ How many and are there in all?

_____ = _____   _____

⑳ How many and are there in all?

_____ = _____   _____

㉑ If Uncle Bruce takes out 8 from the box, how many are left?

_____ = _____   _____

㉒ There are 15 green in the box. How many in the box are not green?

_____ = _____   _____

㉓ If Uncle Bruce puts 7 more in the box, how many are there in all?

_____ = _____   _____

㉔ If Uncle Bruce has 2 boxes of , how many does he have in all?

_____ = _____   _____

Look at the graphs. Then answer the questions.

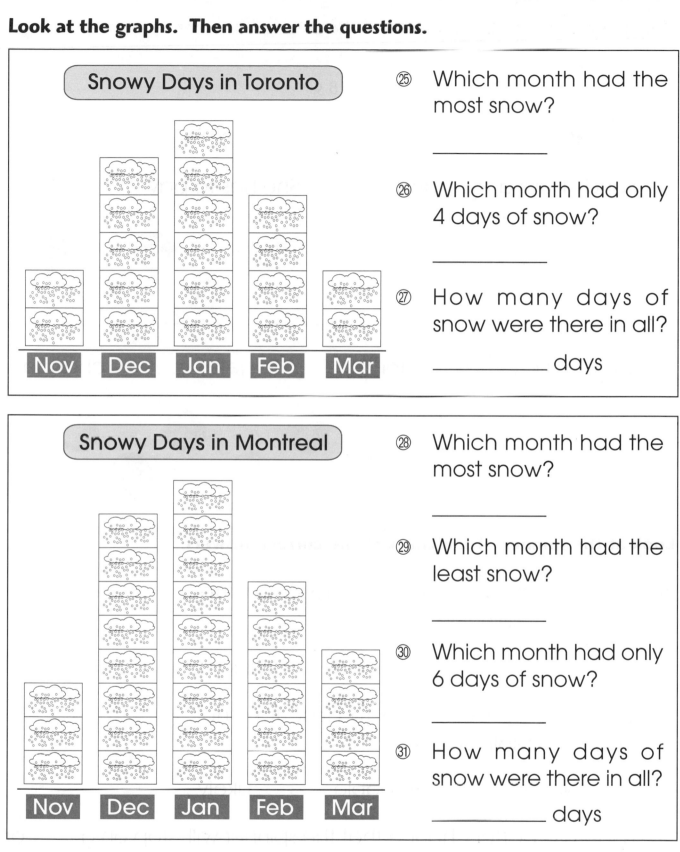

Snowy Days in Toronto

Nov Dec Jan Feb Mar

㉕ Which month had the most snow?

_____

㉖ Which month had only 4 days of snow?

_____

㉗ How many days of snow were there in all?

_____ days

Snowy Days in Montreal

Nov Dec Jan Feb Mar

㉘ Which month had the most snow?

_____

㉙ Which month had the least snow?

_____

㉚ Which month had only 6 days of snow?

_____

㉛ How many days of snow were there in all?

_____ days

㉜ Which city had more snow? _____

㉝ How many more days of snow did Montreal have than Toronto in February? _____ more days

Help the children write and check ✔ the coins to show the amount or change.

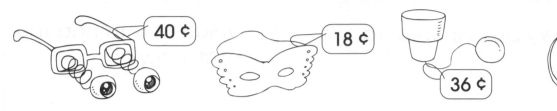

③④ Sandy buys a  and a  . She has to pay _____ ¢.

③⑤ Gordon pays 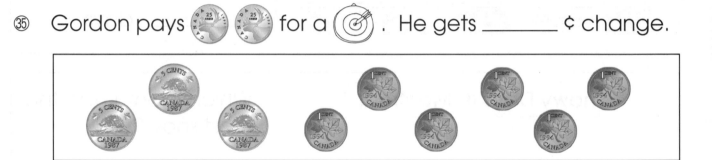 for a 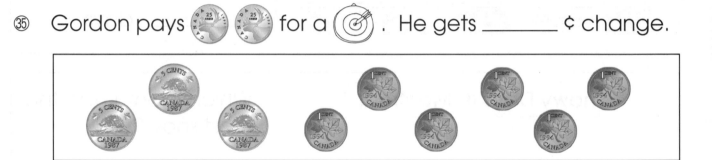 . He gets _____ ¢ change.

Look at the spinner. Then check ✔ the correct answers.

③⑥ Which is the best word to describe the chance of spinning a ✐ ?

Ⓐ Never   Ⓑ Probable   Ⓒ Likely

③⑦ Which is the best word to describe the chance of spinning a ☕ ?

Ⓐ Never   Ⓑ Probable   Ⓒ Likely

③⑧ Is there a better chance that the spinner will stop on a 〰 or a ◎ ?

Ⓐ 〰   Ⓑ ◎

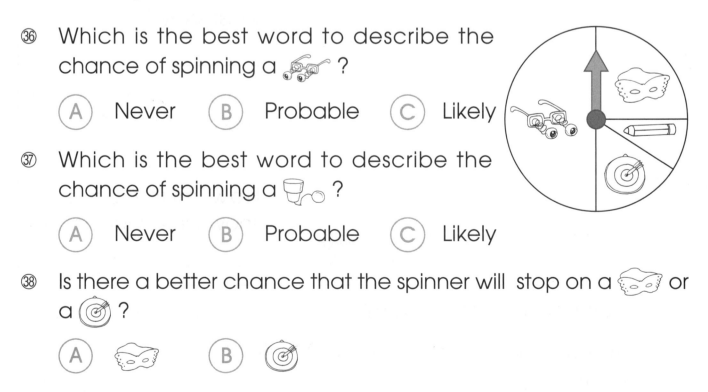

Overview

In Section I, children developed addition and subtraction skills up to 100, including money applications.

They also had opportunities to work with 2- and 3-dimensional shapes, organize and analyse data using charts, pictographs and bar graphs, and use non-standard units in measuring height, length and weight.

In this section, addition and subtraction skills are emphasized. Many exercises are provided for drill and practice with 2-digit numbers. Mastery of mental arithmetic is the goal of those exercises.

Addition and Subtraction Facts to 20

EXAMPLES

Jack has 11 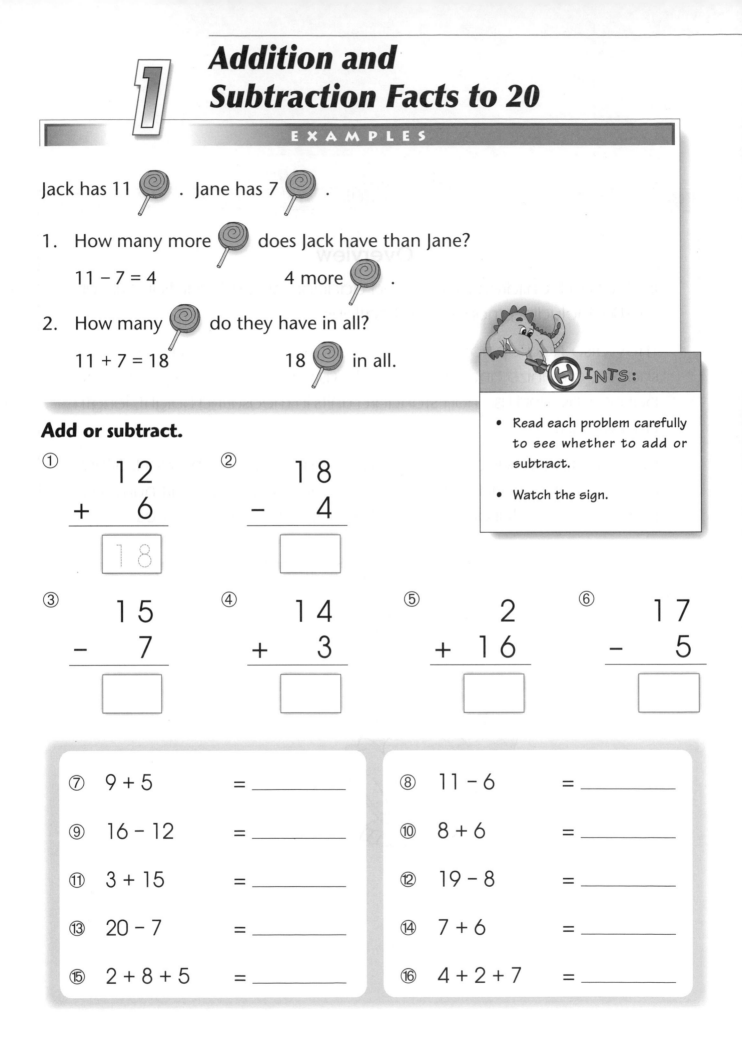 . Jane has 7 .

1. How many more does Jack have than Jane?

   11 − 7 = 4   4 more .

2. How many do they have in all?

   11 + 7 = 18   18 in all.

HINTS:
- Read each problem carefully to see whether to add or subtract.
- Watch the sign.

Add or subtract.

①
$$12 + 6 = \boxed{18}$$

②
$$18 - 4 = \boxed{}$$

③
$$15 - 7 = \boxed{}$$

④
$$14 + 3 = \boxed{}$$

⑤
$$2 + 16 = \boxed{}$$

⑥
$$17 - 5 = \boxed{}$$

⑦ 9 + 5 = _____

⑧ 11 − 6 = _____

⑨ 16 − 12 = _____

⑩ 8 + 6 = _____

⑪ 3 + 15 = _____

⑫ 19 − 8 = _____

⑬ 20 − 7 = _____

⑭ 7 + 6 = _____

⑮ 2 + 8 + 5 = _____

⑯ 4 + 2 + 7 = _____

Write the missing numbers.

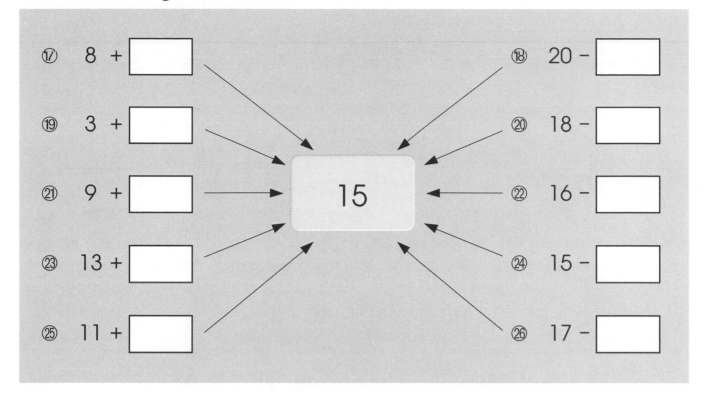

⑰ 8 + ☐

⑱ 20 − ☐

⑲ 3 + ☐

⑳ 18 − ☐

㉑ 9 + ☐

㉒ 16 − ☐

㉓ 13 + ☐

㉔ 15 − ☐

㉕ 11 + ☐

㉖ 17 − ☐

15

Fill in the ◯ with + or −.

㉗
```
  1 2
◯  7
─────
  1 9
```

㉘
```
  1 7
◯  6
─────
  1 1
```

㉙
```
  1 2
◯  8
─────
  2 0
```

㉚
```
  1 6
◯  4
─────
  1 2
```

㉛
```
  1 8
◯ 1 4
─────
    4
```

㉜
```
    9
◯  7
─────
  1 6
```

㉝
```
  1 3
◯  7
─────
    6
```

㉞
```
  1 9
◯ 1 7
─────
    2
```

㉟
```
  1 1
◯  8
─────
    3
```

㊱
```
  1 2
◯  6
─────
  1 8
```

㊲
```
  1 4
◯  6
─────
  2 0
```

㊳
```
  1 5
◯  7
─────
    8
```

Colour the bones that match each number.

(39) 8

| 12 − 6 | 18 − 10 | 6 + 2 |

(40) 13

| 6 + 7 | 16 − 3 | 17 − 5 |

(41) 17

| 12 + 5 | 20 − 4 | 9 + 8 |

(42) 12

| 6 + 5 | 15 − 3 | 17 − 5 |

(43) 10

| 19 − 8 | 3 + 7 | 16 − 6 |

Complete the related number sentences.

(44) $6 + 6 = 12$

a. $6 + 7 = $ _____

b. $6 + 8 = $ _____

c. $6 + 9 = $ _____

d. $6 + 10 = $ _____

(45) $16 − 8 = 8$

a. $16 − 7 = $ _____

b. $16 − 6 = $ _____

c. $16 − 5 = $ _____

d. $16 − 4 = $ _____

Complete.

㊻ Mom buys 12 red  and 6 green .
How many does she buy in all?

_____ = _____ _____ in all.

㊼ There are 16 in the bag. Sue eats 12 .
How many are left in the bag?

_____ = _____ _____ left.

㊽ There are 20 children in the class. 12 of them are boys.
How many girls are there in the class?

_____ = _____ _____ girls.

㊾ Sue has 10 red and 5 green .
How many does Sue have altogether?

_____ = _____ _____ altogether.

Just for Fun

Count by 5's to help Little Bunny get the carrot. Draw the path.

20	25	30	55	60	90
5	20	45	50	65	100
10	15	40	35	70	95
5	20	35	80	75	100
10	25	30	85	90	95

2 More about Addition Facts

$4 + 3 = 7$ $3 + 4 = 7$

$4 + 3 = 3 + 4 = 7$

HINTS:

- Even if the order of an addition changes, the answer is the same.

  e.g. $4 + 3 = 3 + 4 = 7$

- Different addition sentences may give the same SUM.

  e.g. $2 + 3 = 1 + 4 = 5$

Complete the related facts.

① a. $2 + 3 =$ _____ 5

  b. $3 + 2 =$ _____

  c. $2 + 3 = 3 + 2 =$ _____

② a. $5 + 3 =$ _____

  b. $3 + 5 =$ _____

  c. $5 + 3 = 3 + 5 =$ _____

③ a. $4 + 6 =$ _____

  b. $6 + 4 =$ _____

  c. $4 + 6 = 6 + 4 =$ _____

④ a. $0 + 5 =$ _____

  b. $5 + 0 =$ _____

  c. $0 + 5 = 5 + 0 =$ _____

⑤ a. $2 + 6 =$ _____

  b. $6 + 2 =$ _____

  c. $2 + 6 = 6 + 2 =$ _____

Write the missing numbers.

⑥ $3 + 8 = 8 + $ _____

⑦ $5 + 7 = $ _____ $ + 5$

⑧ $11 + 4 = $ _____ $ + 11$

⑨ $8 + 9 = 9 + $ _____

⑩ $10 + $ _____ $ = 7 + 10$

⑪ $5 + $ _____ $ = 6 + 5$

⑫ _____ $ + 12 = 12 + 6$

⑬ _____ $ + 4 = 4 + 13$

⑭ $14 + 6 = $ _____ $ + 14$

⑮ $17 + 2 = 2 + $ _____

Complete and match.

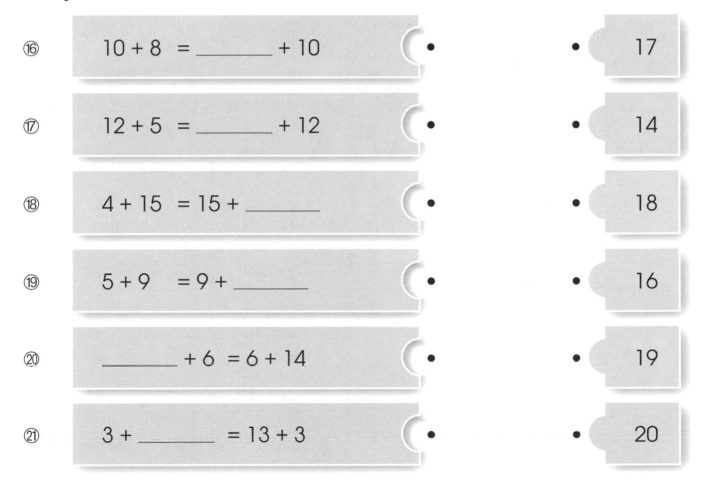

⑯ $10 + 8 = $ _____ $ + 10$ •　• 17

⑰ $12 + 5 = $ _____ $ + 12$ •　• 14

⑱ $4 + 15 = 15 + $ _____ •　• 18

⑲ $5 + 9 = 9 + $ _____ •　• 16

⑳ _____ $ + 6 = 6 + 14$ •　• 19

㉑ $3 + $ _____ $ = 13 + 3$ •　• 20

Write different addition sentences for each sum.

㉒
a. _____ + _____ = 7

b. _____ + _____ = 7

c. _____ + _____ = 7

㉓
a. _____ + _____ = 6

b. _____ + _____ = 6

c. _____ + _____ = 6

㉔
a. _____ + _____ = 8

b. _____ + _____ = 8

c. _____ + _____ = 8

d. _____ + _____ = 8

㉕
a. _____ + _____ = 9

b. _____ + _____ = 9

c. _____ + _____ = 9

d. _____ + _____ = 9

㉖
a. 4 + _____ = 14

b. 5 + _____ = 14

c. 6 + _____ = 14

d. 7 + _____ = 14

e. 8 + _____ = 14

㉗
a. 9 + _____ = 17

b. 10 + _____ = 17

c. 11 + _____ = 17

d. 12 + _____ = 17

e. 13 + _____ = 17

The children are playing darts. Look at their scores. Complete each number sentence. Find their scores in the 2nd round.

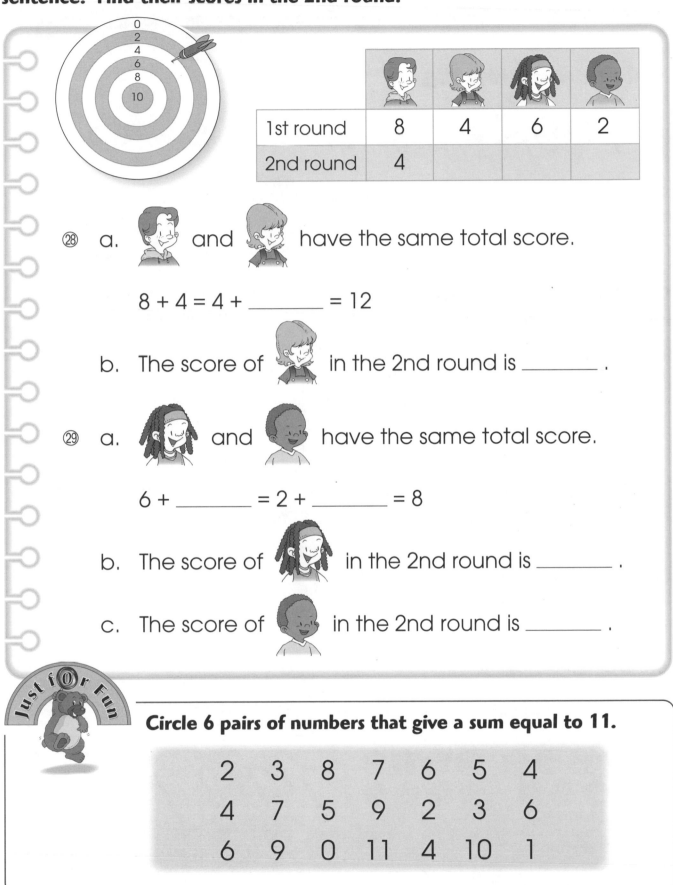

1st round	8	4	6	2
2nd round	4			

㉘ a. and have the same total score.

8 + 4 = 4 + _____ = 12

b. The score of in the 2nd round is _____ .

㉙ a. and have the same total score.

6 + _____ = 2 + _____ = 8

b. The score of in the 2nd round is _____ .

c. The score of in the 2nd round is _____ .

Circle 6 pairs of numbers that give a sum equal to 11.

2   3   8   7   6   5   4

4   7   5   9   2   3   6

6   9   0   11   4   10   1

Relating Subtraction to Addition

EXAMPLE

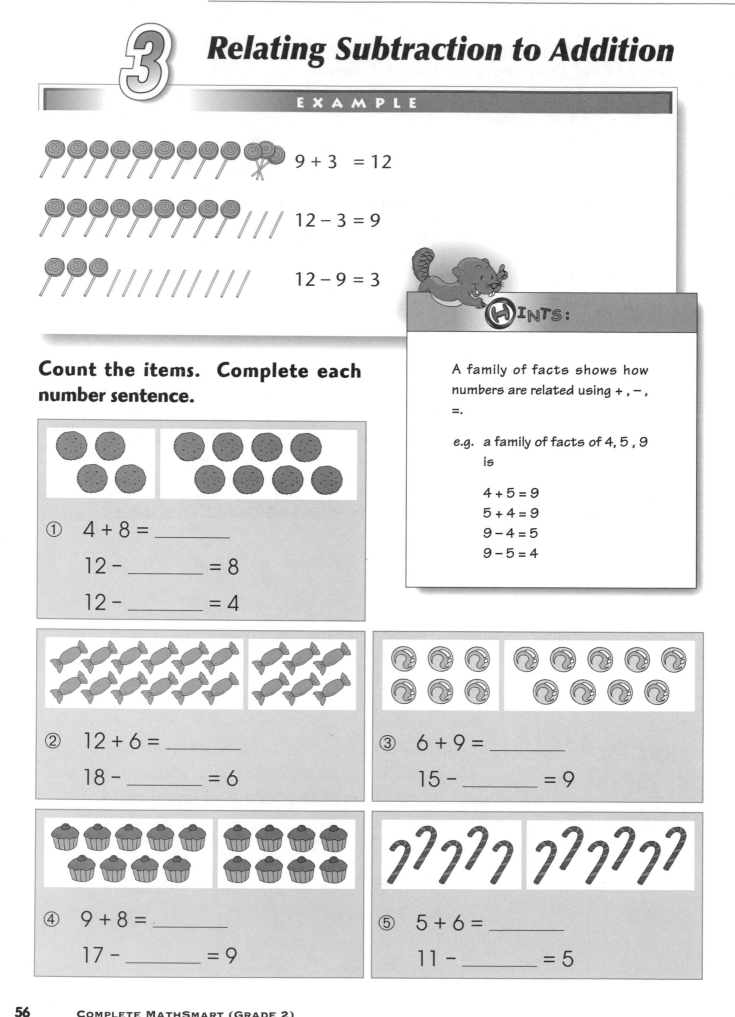

$9 + 3 = 12$

$12 - 3 = 9$

$12 - 9 = 3$

HINTS:

A family of facts shows how numbers are related using $+$, $-$, $=$.

e.g. a family of facts of 4, 5 , 9 is

$4 + 5 = 9$
$5 + 4 = 9$
$9 - 4 = 5$
$9 - 5 = 4$

Count the items. Complete each number sentence.

① $4 + 8 =$ _____

$12 -$ _____ $= 8$

$12 -$ _____ $= 4$

② $12 + 6 =$ _____

$18 -$ _____ $= 6$

③ $6 + 9 =$ _____

$15 -$ _____ $= 9$

④ $9 + 8 =$ _____

$17 -$ _____ $= 9$

⑤ $5 + 6 =$ _____

$11 -$ _____ $= 5$

Complete each family of facts.

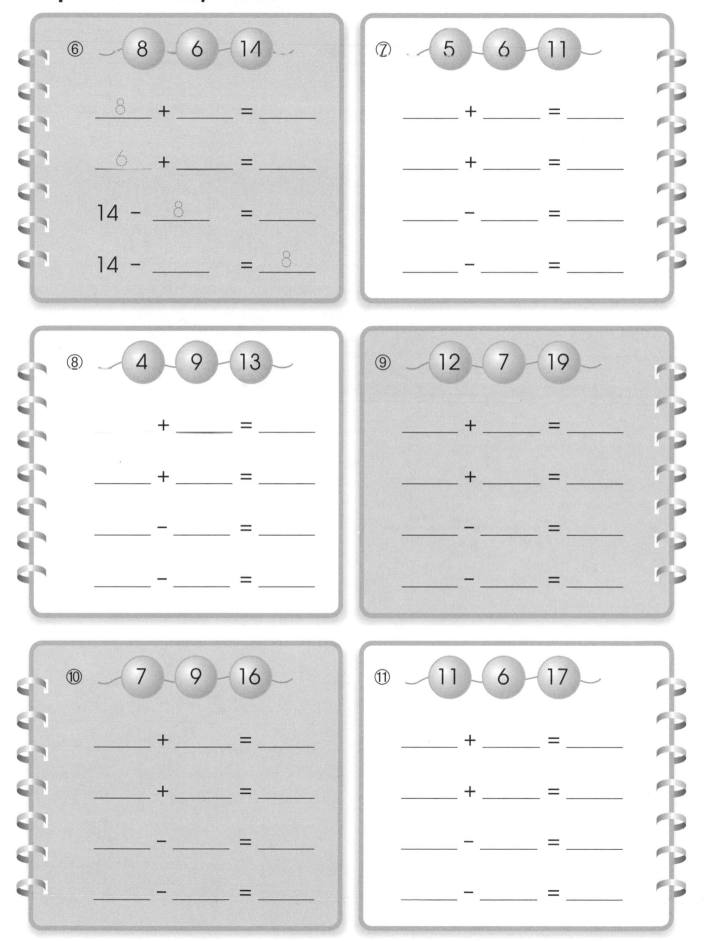

⑥   8 — 6 — 14

_8_ + _____ = _____

_6_ + _____ = _____

14 − _8_ = _____

14 − _____ = _8_

⑦   5 — 6 — 11

_____ + _____ = _____

_____ + _____ = _____

_____ − _____ = _____

_____ − _____ = _____

⑧   4 — 9 — 13

_____ + _____ = _____

_____ + _____ = _____

_____ − _____ = _____

_____ − _____ = _____

⑨   12 — 7 — 19

_____ + _____ = _____

_____ + _____ = _____

_____ − _____ = _____

_____ − _____ = _____

⑩   7 — 9 — 16

_____ + _____ = _____

_____ + _____ = _____

_____ − _____ = _____

_____ − _____ = _____

⑪   11 — 6 — 17

_____ + _____ = _____

_____ + _____ = _____

_____ − _____ = _____

_____ − _____ = _____

Write the missing numbers.

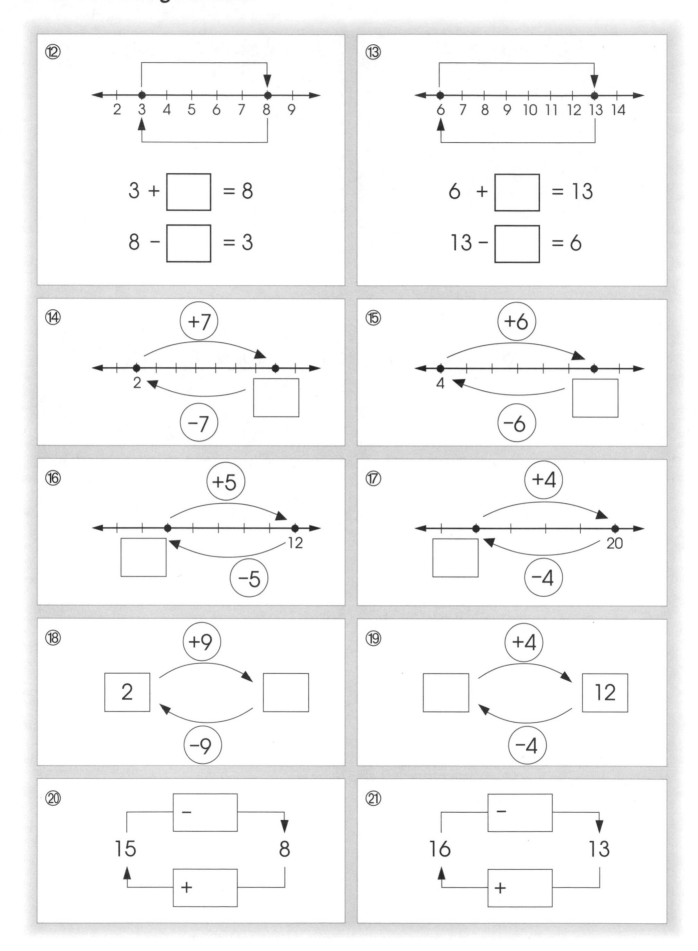

⑫

3 + ☐ = 8

8 − ☐ = 3

⑬

6 + ☐ = 13

13 − ☐ = 6

Use the family of facts. Fill in the missing numbers.

㉒ $4 + \boxed{} = 13$

$13 - \boxed{} = 4$

㉓ $9 + \boxed{} = 17$

$17 - \boxed{} = 9$

㉔ $6 + \boxed{} = 12$

$12 - 6 = \boxed{}$

㉕ $7 + \boxed{} = 11$

$11 - 7 = \boxed{}$

㉖ $7 + \boxed{} = 15$

$15 - \boxed{} = 7$

㉗ $\boxed{} + 10 = 17$

$17 - 10 = \boxed{}$

㉘
$$\begin{array}{r} 8 \\ + \boxed{} \\ \hline 13 \end{array} \qquad \begin{array}{r} 13 \\ - \boxed{} \\ \hline 8 \end{array}$$

㉙
$$\begin{array}{r} 20 \\ - \boxed{} \\ \hline 11 \end{array} \qquad \begin{array}{r} \boxed{} \\ + 11 \\ \hline 20 \end{array}$$

㉚
$$\begin{array}{r} 14 \\ - 8 \\ \hline \boxed{} \end{array} \qquad \begin{array}{r} \boxed{} \\ + 8 \\ \hline 14 \end{array}$$

㉛
$$\begin{array}{r} \boxed{} \\ + 9 \\ \hline 15 \end{array} \qquad \begin{array}{r} 15 \\ - \boxed{} \\ \hline 9 \end{array}$$

Just for Fun

Colour the squares red, the rectangles yellow, the triangles blue and the circles green.

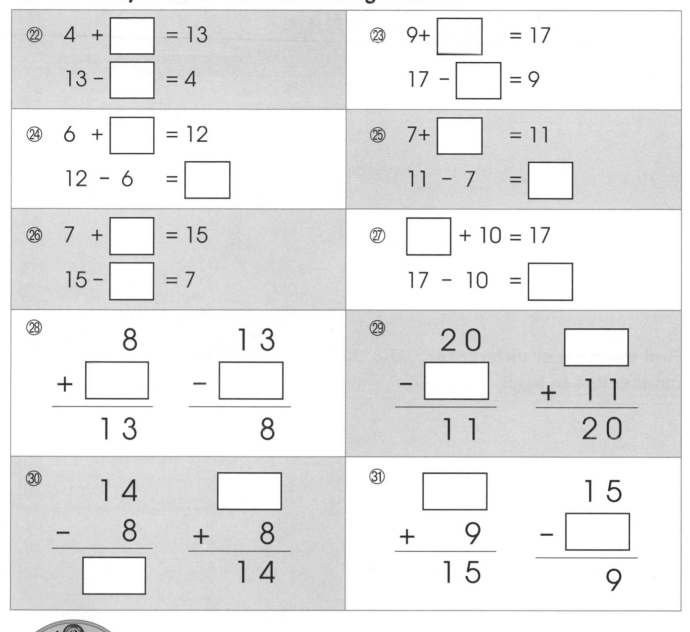

4 Adding and Subtracting Using Counting

0 1 2 3 4 5 6 7 8 9 10 11 12 13 14 15 16 17 18 19 20 21 22 23 24 25 26 27 28 29 30

1. $20 + 3 = 23$ ← counting 3 forward from 20 gives 23

2. $30 - 6 = 24$ ← counting 6 backward from 30 gives 24

HINTS:

- Count forward to find the sum of 2 numbers.

- Count backward to find the difference between 2 numbers.

- Use a number line or a number chart to help you count.

Find the sums or differences.   Use the number line to help.

① $19 + 4 = $ _____

② $18 + 6 = $ _____

③ $25 - 4 = $ _____

④ $23 - 7 = $ _____

⑤ $29 - 5 = $ _____

⑥ $18 + 9 = $ _____

⑦ $16 + 6 = $ _____

⑧ $26 - 5 = $ _____

⑨ $27 - 8 = $ _____

⑩ $20 + 8 = $ _____

⑪ $30 - 12 = $ _____

⑫ $16 + 10 = $ _____

⑬ $22 + 7 = $ _____

⑭ $28 - 6 = $ _____

⑮ $17 + 9 = $ _____

⑯ $27 - 9 = $ _____

⑰ $24 + 6 = $ _____

⑱ $22 - 8 = $ _____

Add or subtract. Use the number chart to help.

51	52	53	54	55	56	57	58	59	60
61	62	63	64	65	66	67	68	69	70
71	72	73	74	75	76	77	78	79	80
81	82	83	84	85	86	87	88	89	90

⑲ 65 − 8 = _____

⑳ 78 − 11 = _____

㉑ 52 + 6 = _____

㉒ 68 + 7 = _____

㉓ 84 − 12 = _____

㉔ 81 + 8 = _____

㉕ 77 + 9 = _____

㉖ 90 − 11 = _____

㉗ 58 + 8 = _____

㉘ 62 − 6 = _____

㉙
$$\begin{array}{r} 62 \\ -1 \\ \hline \end{array}$$

㉚
$$\begin{array}{r} 70 \\ +14 \\ \hline \end{array}$$

㉛
$$\begin{array}{r} 89 \\ -10 \\ \hline \end{array}$$

㉜
$$\begin{array}{r} 69 \\ +5 \\ \hline \end{array}$$

㉝
$$\begin{array}{r} 81 \\ +7 \\ \hline \end{array}$$

㉞
$$\begin{array}{r} 90 \\ -8 \\ \hline \end{array}$$

㉟
$$\begin{array}{r} 75 \\ -20 \\ \hline \end{array}$$

㊱
$$\begin{array}{r} 63 \\ +17 \\ \hline \end{array}$$

Count and complete the addition sentences.

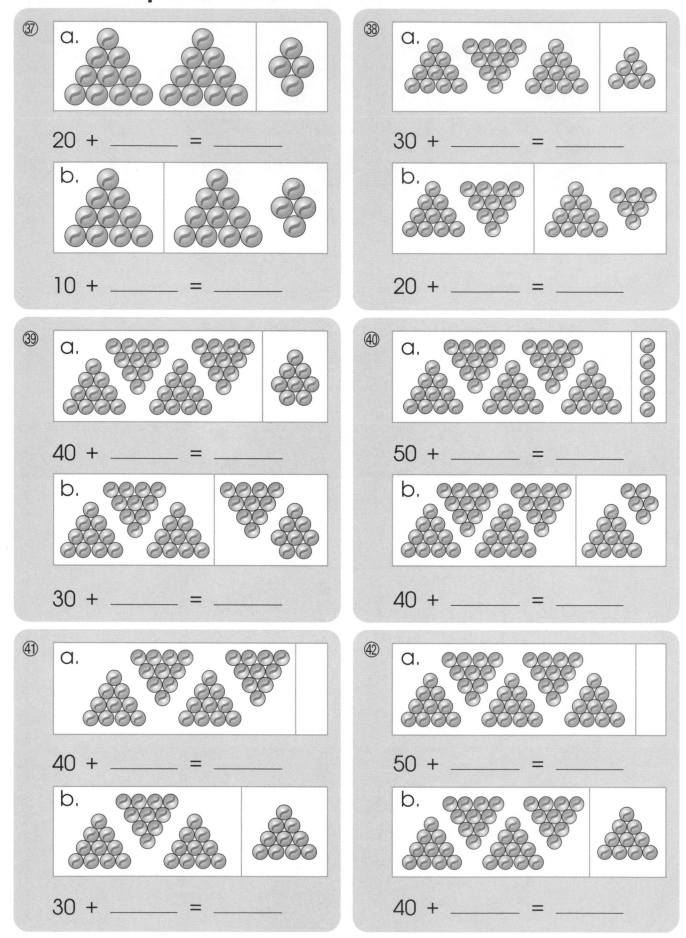

③⑦ a.

20 + _____ = _____

b.

10 + _____ = _____

③⑧ a.

30 + _____ = _____

b.

20 + _____ = _____

③⑨ a.

40 + _____ = _____

b.

30 + _____ = _____

④⓪ a.

50 + _____ = _____

b.

40 + _____ = _____

④① a.

40 + _____ = _____

b.

30 + _____ = _____

④② a.

50 + _____ = _____

b.

40 + _____ = _____

Cross out and count. Complete the subtraction sentences.

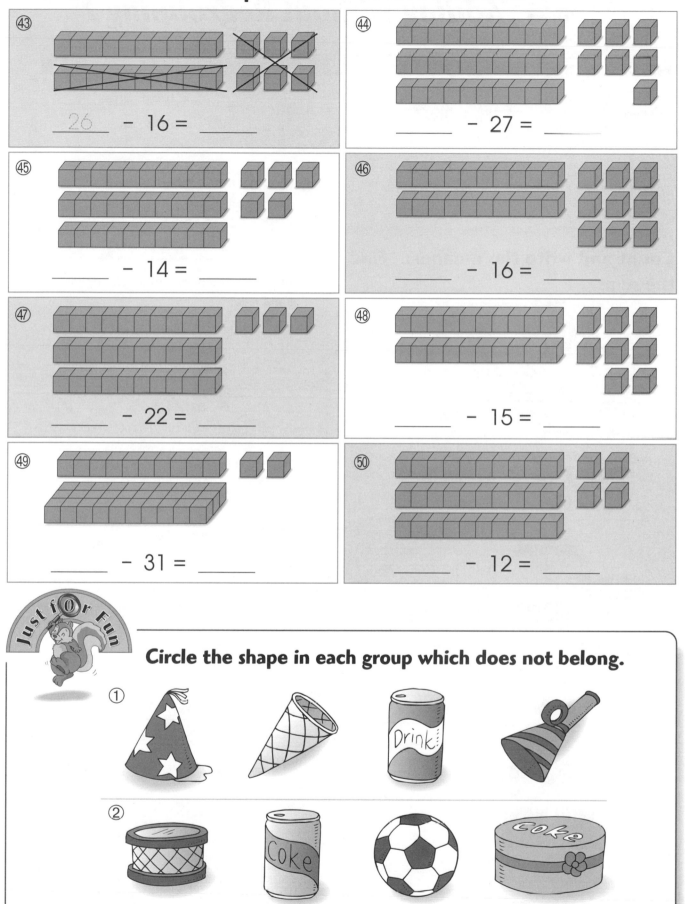

43. _26_ – 16 = _____

44. _____ – 27 = _____

45. _____ – 14 = _____

46. _____ – 16 = _____

47. _____ – 22 = _____

48. _____ – 15 = _____

49. _____ – 31 = _____

50. _____ – 12 = _____

Circle the shape in each group which does not belong.

① Drink

② Coke   Coke

Adding without Regrouping I

5

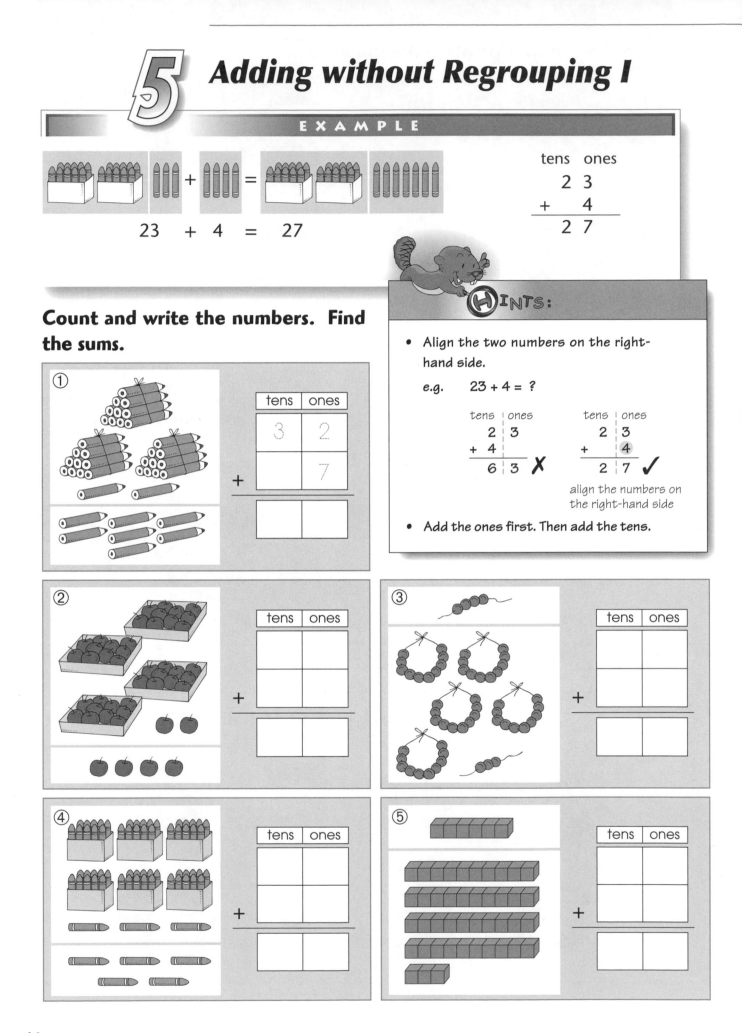

23 + 4 = 27

	tens	ones
	2	3
+		4
	2	7

Count and write the numbers. Find the sums.

HINTS:

- Align the two numbers on the right-hand side.

  e.g.   23 + 4 = ?

tens	ones
2	3
+ 4	
6	3	✗

tens	ones
2	3
+	4
2	7	✓

  align the numbers on the right-hand side

- Add the ones first. Then add the tens.

①
tens	ones
3	2
	7

②
tens	ones

③
tens	ones

④
tens	ones

⑤
tens	ones

Add.

⑥
```
  2 6
+   3
```
[ ]

⑦
```
  4 1
+   8
```
[ ]

⑧
```
    2
+ 3 6
```
[ ]

⑨
```
  6 2
+   6
```
[ ]

⑩
```
    2
+ 5 5
```
[ ]

⑪
```
  7 3
+   4
```
[ ]

⑫
```
  8 4
+   5
```
[ ]

⑬
```
  1 7
+   2
```
[ ]

⑭
```
  3 2
+   6
```
[ ]

⑮
```
    8
+ 5 1
```
[ ]

⑯
```
  6 0
+   7
```
[ ]

⑰
```
  7 5
+   3
```
[ ]

⑱
```
  4 4
+   4
```
[ ]

⑲
```
  8 0
+   6
```
[ ]

⑳
```
  2 7
+   2
```
[ ]

㉑
```
    5
+ 9 0
```
[ ]

㉒ 4 + 12 = _____

㉓ 31 + 7 = _____

㉔ 65 + 3 = _____

㉕ 42 + 6 = _____

㉖ 22 + 5 = _____

㉗ 4 + 52 = _____

㉘ 3 + 24 = _____

㉙ 15 + 3 = _____

Find the sums. Write the letters in ㊴ to solve the riddle.

㉚ i
  3 4
+   4

㉛ p
  2 2
+   6

㉝ e
  5 3
+   6

㉜ l
  6 1
+   5

㉞ m
  4 1
+   7

㉟ n
  7 0
+   5

㊱ o
  8 5
+   2

㊳ c
  9 2
+   4

㊲ a
  2 3
+   4

Riddle : Little Bear is lost. Who should he ask for help?

㊴

28	87	66	38	96	59	48	27	75

The

Complete.

㊵ Sue has 32 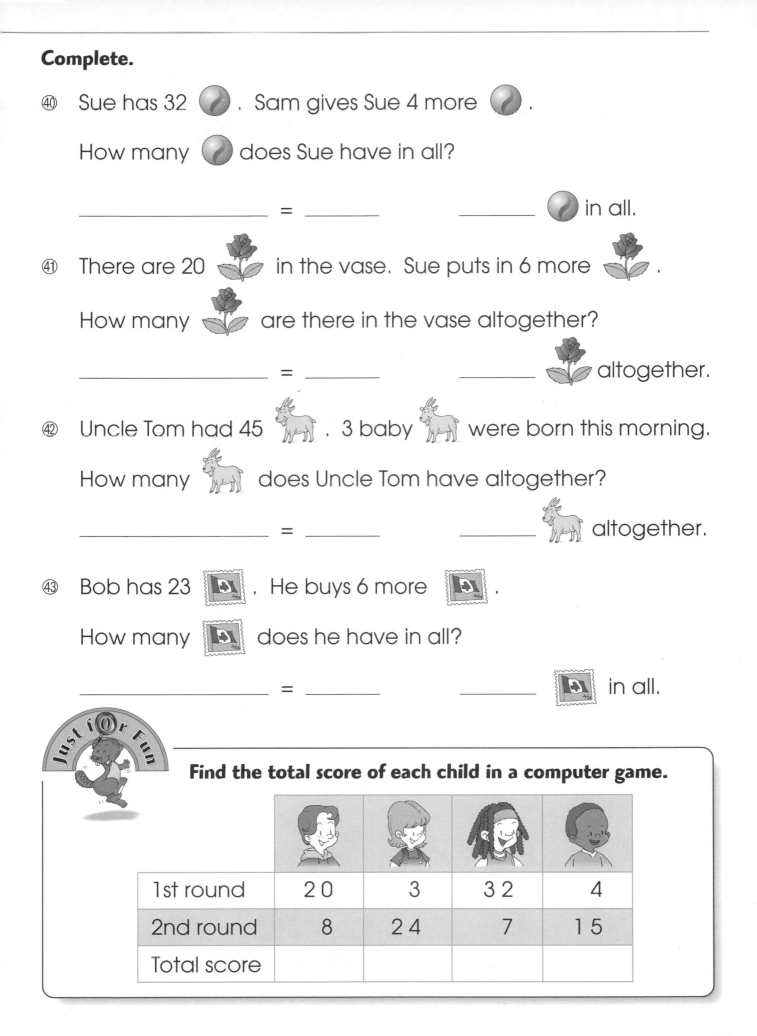 . Sam gives Sue 4 more .

How many does Sue have in all?

_____ = _____ _____ in all.

㊶ There are 20 in the vase. Sue puts in 6 more .

How many are there in the vase altogether?

_____ = _____ _____ altogether.

㊷ Uncle Tom had 45 . 3 baby were born this morning.

How many does Uncle Tom have altogether?

_____ = _____ _____ altogether.

㊸ Bob has 23 . He buys 6 more .

How many does he have in all?

_____ = _____ _____ in all.

Find the total score of each child in a computer game.

1st round	2 0	3	3 2	4
2nd round	8	2 4	7	1 5
Total score				

6 Adding without Regrouping II

EXAMPLE

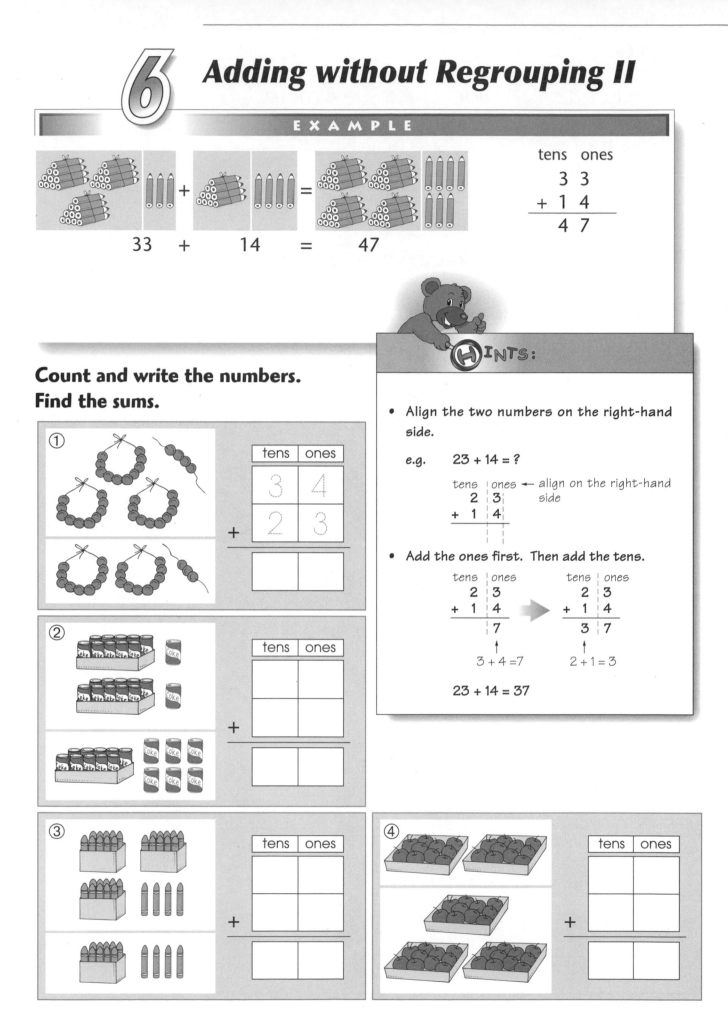

33 + 14 = 47

tens	ones
3	3
+ 1	4
4	7

Count and write the numbers.
Find the sums.

HINTS:

- Align the two numbers on the right-hand side.

  e.g.   23 + 14 = ?

tens	ones	← align on the right-hand side
2	3	
+ 1	4	

- Add the ones first. Then add the tens.

tens	ones
2	3
+ 1	4
	7

  3 + 4 = 7

tens	ones
2	3
+ 1	4
3	7

  2 + 1 = 3

  23 + 14 = 37

①
tens	ones
3	4
2	3

②
tens	ones

③
tens	ones

④
tens	ones

Add.

⑤
```
  1 2
+ 2 6
```
[ ]

⑥
```
  3 4
+ 4 3
```
[ ]

⑦
```
  5 3
+ 1 4
```
[ ]

⑧
```
  6 1
+ 1 7
```
[ ]

⑨
```
  4 5
+ 2 2
```
[ ]

⑩
```
  1 5
+ 4 3
```
[ ]

⑪
```
  7 0
+ 2 1
```
[ ]

⑫
```
  8 2
+ 1 0
```
[ ]

⑬
```
  3 1
+ 1 6
```
[ ]

⑭
```
  2 0
+ 5 3
```
[ ]

⑮
```
  4 2
+ 3 6
```
[ ]

⑯
```
  5 4
+ 2 2
```
[ ]

⑰
```
  6 3
+ 3 0
```
[ ]

⑱
```
  4 4
+ 4 4
```
[ ]

⑲
```
  1 3
+ 3 3
```
[ ]

⑳
```
  2 5
+ 1 1
```
[ ]

㉑   22 + 22 = _____

㉒   16 + 31 = _____

㉓   34 + 52 = _____

㉔   40 + 28 = _____

㉕   66 + 20 = _____

㉖   73 + 15 = _____

㉗   45 + 14 = _____

㉘   84 + 12 = _____

Find the sums. Arrange the answers in correct counting order in ㊳, starting with the smallest number.

㉙ 34 + 13

㉚ 12 + 26

㉛ 28 + 31

㉜ 26 + 43

㉝ 42 + 15

㉞ 51 + 27

㉟ 53 + 35

㊱ 38 + 30

㊲ 60 + 39

㊳

Complete the addition sentences.

㊴ Ben has 44 red 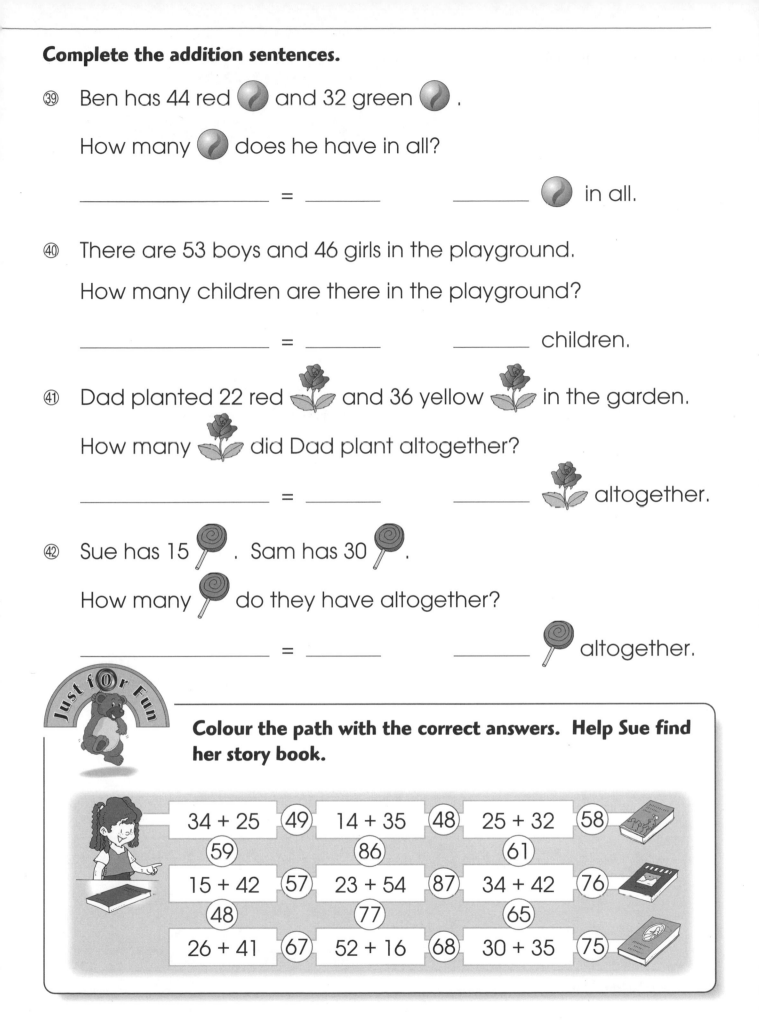 and 32 green ⬤ .

How many ⬤ does he have in all?

_____ = _____   _____ ⬤ in all.

㊵ There are 53 boys and 46 girls in the playground.

How many children are there in the playground?

_____ = _____   _____ children.

㊶ Dad planted 22 red 🌹 and 36 yellow 🌹 in the garden.

How many 🌹 did Dad plant altogether?

_____ = _____   _____ 🌹 altogether.

㊷ Sue has 15 🍭 . Sam has 30 🍭 .

How many 🍭 do they have altogether?

_____ = _____   _____ 🍭 altogether.

Just for Fun

Colour the path with the correct answers. Help Sue find her story book.

34 + 25	49	14 + 35	48	25 + 32	58
59		86		61	
15 + 42	57	23 + 54	87	34 + 42	76
48		77		65	
26 + 41	67	52 + 16	68	30 + 35	75

7 Adding with Regrouping I

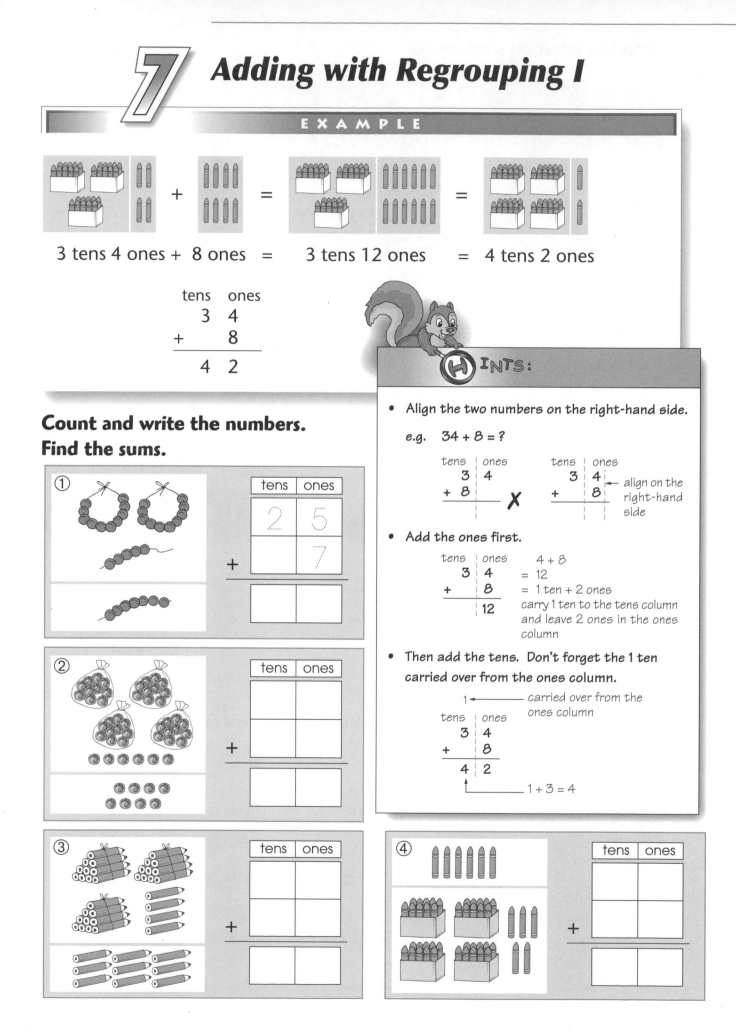

3 tens 4 ones + 8 ones = 3 tens 12 ones = 4 tens 2 ones

	tens	ones
	3	4
+		8
	4	2

Count and write the numbers. Find the sums.

HINTS:

- Align the two numbers on the right-hand side.

  e.g. 34 + 8 = ?

tens	ones
3	4
+ 8	

  ✗

tens	ones
3	4	← align on the right-hand side
+	8

- Add the ones first.

tens	ones
3	4
+	8
	12

  4 + 8
  = 12
  = 1 ten + 2 ones
  carry 1 ten to the tens column and leave 2 ones in the ones column

- Then add the tens. Don't forget the 1 ten carried over from the ones column.

  1 ← carried over from the ones column

tens	ones
3	4
+	8
4	2

  1 + 3 = 4

①
tens	ones
2	5
	7

+

②
tens	ones

+

③
tens	ones

+

④
tens	ones

+

Add. Remember to regroup.

⑤
16
+ 8
[ ]

⑥
23
+ 9
[ ]

⑦
32
+ 8
[ ]

⑧
46
+ 7
[ ]

⑨
7
+ 58
[ ]

⑩
66
+ 6
[ ]

⑪
19
+ 9
[ ]

⑫
67
+ 4
[ ]

⑬
75
+ 8
[ ]

⑭
47
+ 5
[ ]

⑮
8
+ 28
[ ]

⑯
54
+ 6
[ ]

⑰
36
+ 8
[ ]

⑱
59
+ 2
[ ]

⑲
47
+ 9
[ ]

⑳
4
+ 29
[ ]

㉑ 56 + 5 = _____

㉒ 37 + 7 = _____

㉓ 7 + 44 = _____

㉔ 26 + 9 = _____

㉕ 61 + 9 = _____

㉖ 73 + 8 = _____

㉗ 89 + 5 = _____

㉘ 3 + 37 = _____

Follow the path. Help Little Squirrel find its food.

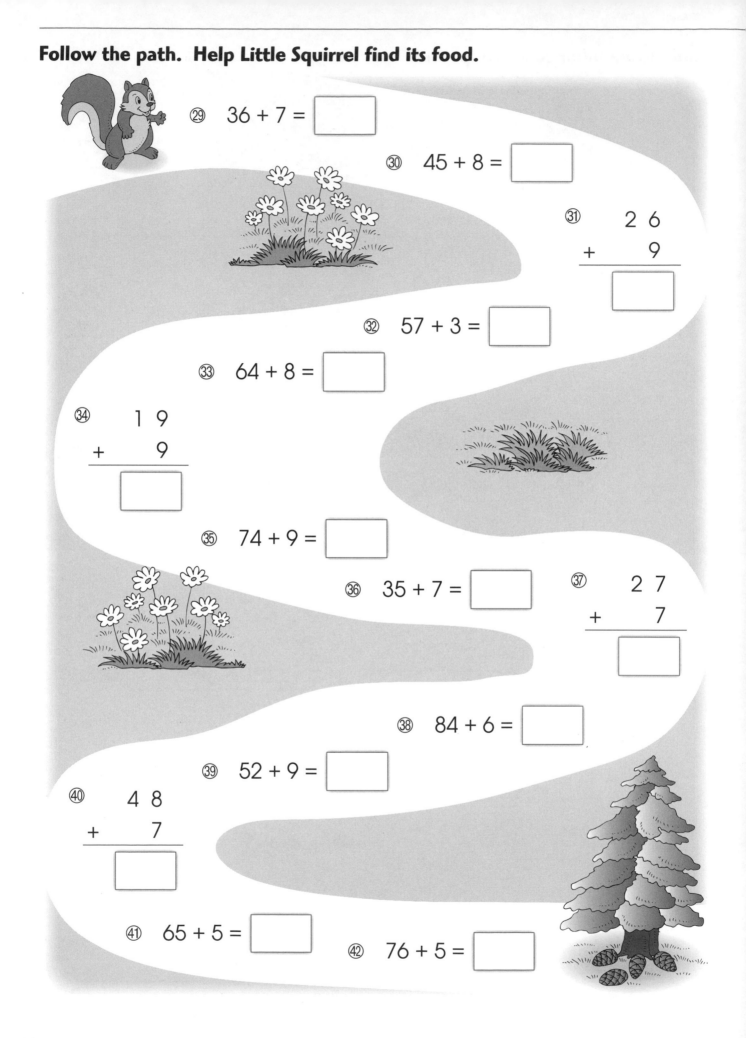

㉙ 36 + 7 = ☐

㉚ 45 + 8 = ☐

㉛
```
    2 6
 +    9
```
☐

㉜ 57 + 3 = ☐

㉝ 64 + 8 = ☐

㉞
```
  1 9
 +  9
```
☐

㉟ 74 + 9 = ☐

㊱ 35 + 7 = ☐

㊲
```
    2 7
 +    7
```
☐

㊳ 84 + 6 = ☐

㊴ 52 + 9 = ☐

㊵
```
  4 8
 +  7
```
☐

㊶ 65 + 5 = ☐

㊷ 76 + 5 = ☐

Complete.

43 Bob has 18 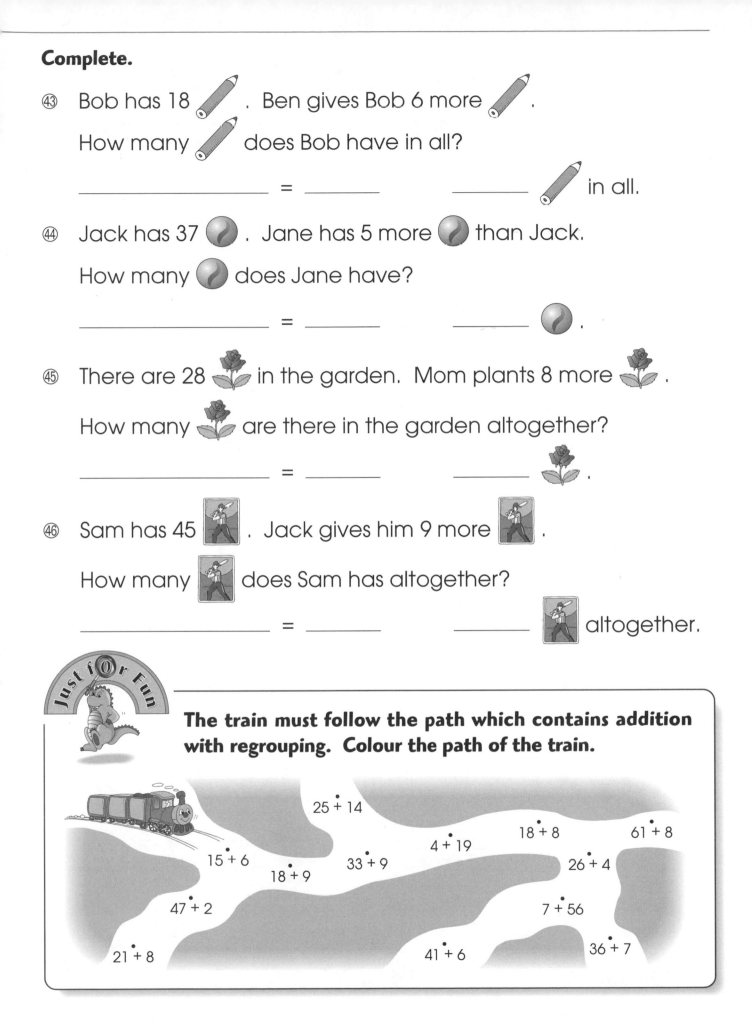 . Ben gives Bob 6 more .
How many does Bob have in all?

_____ = _____ _____ in all.

44 Jack has 37 . Jane has 5 more than Jack.
How many does Jane have?

_____ = _____ _____ .

45 There are 28 in the garden. Mom plants 8 more .
How many are there in the garden altogether?

_____ = _____ _____ .

46 Sam has 45 . Jack gives him 9 more .
How many does Sam has altogether?

_____ = _____ _____ altogether.

Just for Fun

The train must follow the path which contains addition with regrouping. Colour the path of the train.

25 + 14

18 + 8   61 + 8

4 + 19

15 + 6   33 + 9   26 + 4

18 + 9

47 + 2   7 + 56

21 + 8   41 + 6   36 + 7

Adding with Regrouping II

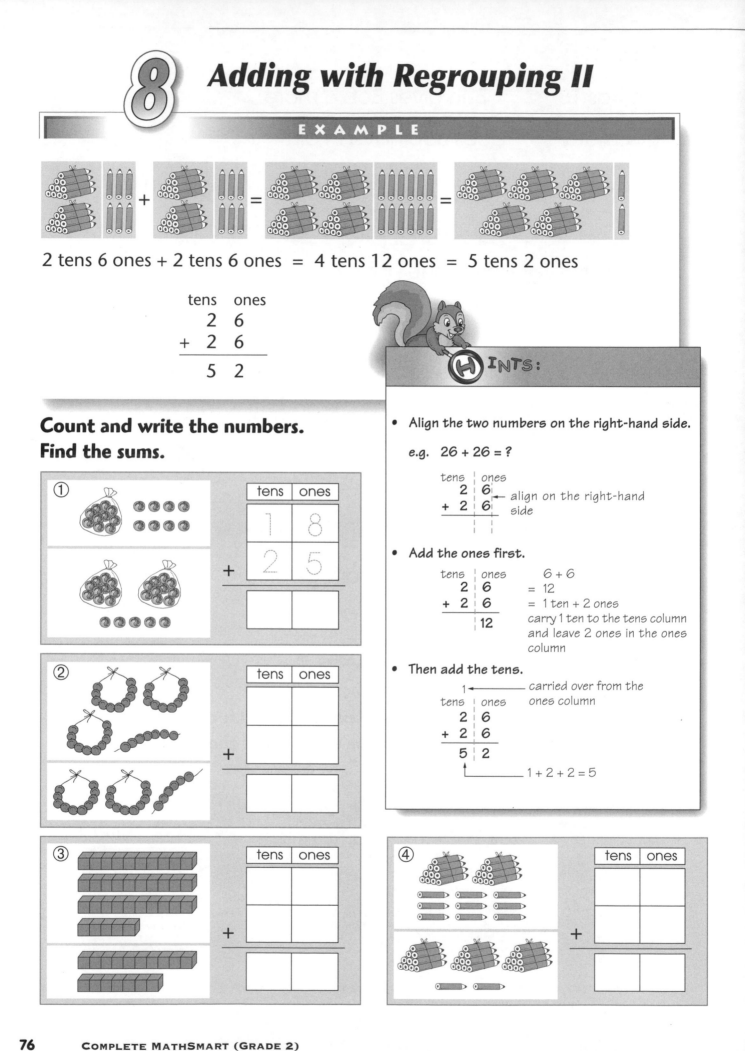

2 tens 6 ones + 2 tens 6 ones = 4 tens 12 ones = 5 tens 2 ones

tens	ones
2	6
+ 2	6
5	2

Count and write the numbers.
Find the sums.

①

tens	ones
1	8
2	5

②

tens	ones

③

tens	ones

④

tens	ones

HINTS:

- Align the two numbers on the right-hand side.

  e.g.   26 + 26 = ?

tens	ones
2	6
+ 2	6

  ← align on the right-hand side

- Add the ones first.

tens	ones
2	6
+ 2	6
	12

  6 + 6
  = 12
  = 1 ten + 2 ones
  carry 1 ten to the tens column and leave 2 ones in the ones column

- Then add the tens.

  1 ← carried over from the ones column

tens	ones
2	6
+ 2	6
5	2

  1 + 2 + 2 = 5

Add. Remember to regroup.

⑤
```
   3 7
+  1 9
```
[ ]

⑥
```
   2 6
+  3 8
```
[ ]

⑦
```
   4 3
+  2 7
```
[ ]

⑧
```
   4 4
+  3 8
```
[ ]

⑨
```
   6 4
+  1 6
```
[ ]

⑩
```
   5 7
+  2 6
```
[ ]

⑪
```
   3 2
+  5 9
```
[ ]

⑫
```
   1 9
+  4 4
```
[ ]

⑬
```
   2 7
+  5 8
```
[ ]

⑭
```
   3 8
+  4 6
```
[ ]

⑮
```
   5 6
+  1 5
```
[ ]

⑯
```
   4 8
+  4 8
```
[ ]

⑰
```
   6 3
+  2 9
```
[ ]

⑱
```
   5 6
+  3 9
```
[ ]

⑲
```
   1 5
+  4 5
```
[ ]

⑳
```
   2 2
+  4 8
```
[ ]

㉑ 18 + 65 = _____

㉒ 49 + 36 = _____

㉓ 43 + 38 = _____

㉔ 56 + 28 = _____

㉕ 24 + 69 = _____

㉖ 47 + 17 = _____

㉗ 55 + 27 = _____

㉘ 37 + 54 = _____

Colour the bookmarks that match each number.

㉙ **44** | 18 + 26 | 27 + 15 | 27 + 17

㉚ **65** | 32 + 33 | 36 + 29 | 22 + 33

㉛ **52** | 26 + 16 | 15 + 37 | 17 + 35

㉜ **63** | 25 + 38 | 34 + 27 | 27 + 36

㉝ **81** | 54 + 27 | 63 + 28 | 45 + 36

㉞ **74** | 36 + 38 | 29 + 45 | 27 + 37

㉟ **91** | 46 + 45 | 33 + 59 | 62 + 29

㊱ **46** | 23 + 13 | 19 + 27 | 36 + 10

Complete.

㊲ There are 15 girls and 9 boys in the class.

How many children are there in the class altogether?

_____ = _____   _____ children altogether.

㊳ Bob has 36 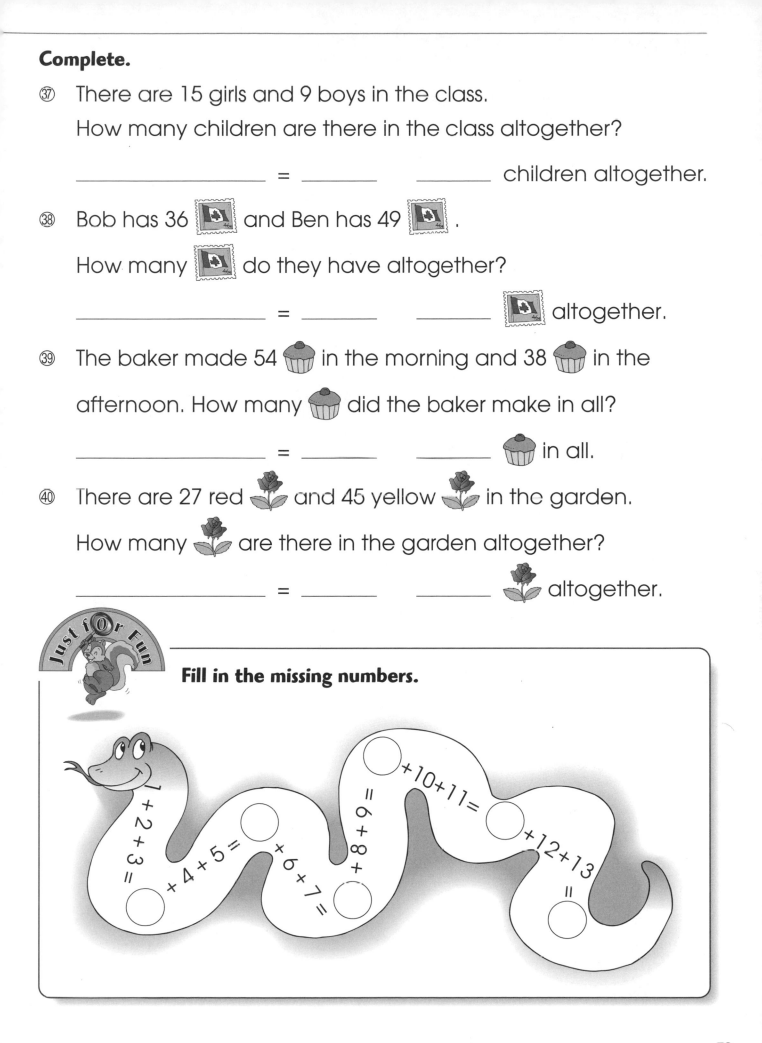 and Ben has 49 .

How many do they have altogether?

_____ = _____   _____ altogether.

㊴ The baker made 54 in the morning and 38 in the

afternoon. How many did the baker make in all?

_____ = _____   _____ in all.

㊵ There are 27 red and 45 yellow in the garden.

How many are there in the garden altogether?

_____ = _____   _____ altogether.

Just for Fun

Fill in the missing numbers.

1 + 2 + 3 =

+ 4 + 5 =

+ 6 + 7 =

+ 8 + 9 =

+ 10 + 11 =

+ 12 + 13 =

Complete the number sentences to show the related facts.

① 6 + 7 = _____ + 6 = _____   ② _____ + 6 = 6 + 5 = _____

③ 9 + 8 = 8 + _____ = _____   ④ 4 + 9 = _____ + 4 = _____

⑤ _____ + 5 = 5 + 7 = _____   ⑥ 3 + _____ = _____ + 3 = 11

⑦ 4 + _____ = 8 + 4 = _____   ⑧ 7 + _____ = _____ + 7 = 18

Write different addition sentences for each sum.

⑨
a. _____ + _____ = 10

b. _____ + _____ = 10

c. _____ + _____ = 10

d. _____ + _____ = 10

e. _____ + _____ = 10

⑩
a. 2 + _____ = 12

b. 3 + _____ = 12

c. 4 + _____ = 12

d. 5 + _____ = 12

e. 6 + _____ = 12

Complete each family of facts.

⑪
8   7   15

_8_ + _____ = _____

_7_ + _____ = _____

15 − _8_ = _____

15 − _____ = _8_

⑫
3   10   13

_____ + _____ = _____

_____ + _____ = _____

_____ − _____ = _____

_____ − _____ = _____

Write the missing numbers. Use the family of facts.

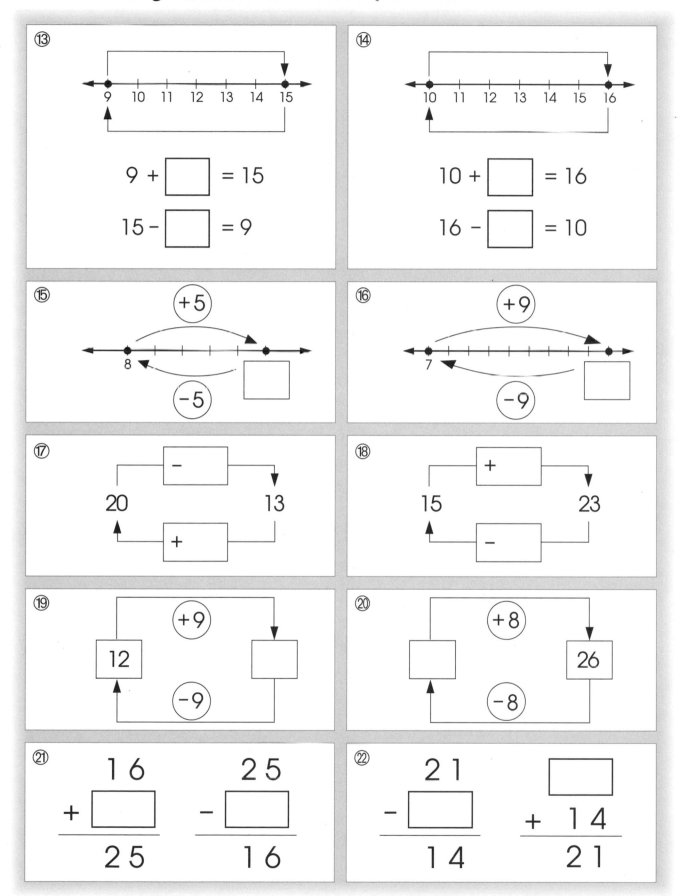

⑬
$9 + \boxed{} = 15$

$15 - \boxed{} = 9$

⑭
$10 + \boxed{} = 16$

$16 - \boxed{} = 10$

⑮ +5 −5

⑯ +9 −9

⑰ 20 − 13 +

⑱ 15 + 23 −

⑲ +9 12 −9

⑳ +8 26 −8

㉑
$\begin{array}{r} 16 \\ + \boxed{} \\ \hline 25 \end{array}$

$\begin{array}{r} 25 \\ - \boxed{} \\ \hline 16 \end{array}$

㉒
$\begin{array}{r} 21 \\ - \boxed{} \\ \hline 14 \end{array}$

$\begin{array}{r} \boxed{} \\ + 14 \\ \hline 21 \end{array}$

Add or subtract.

㉓
```
   1 6
+    8
─────
```
☐

㉔
```
   3 4
+    7
─────
```
☐

㉕
```
   2 2
+  1 8
─────
```
☐

㉖
```
   4 3
+  1 5
─────
```
☐

㉗
```
   1 9
-    8
─────
```
☐

㉘
```
   5 2
+  1 1
─────
```
☐

㉙
```
   6 4
+  2 9
─────
```
☐

㉚
```
   2 0
-  1 4
─────
```
☐

㉛
```
   3 1
+  1 9
─────
```
☐

㉜
```
   2 8
+  4 6
─────
```
☐

㉝
```
   3 5
+  5 5
─────
```
☐

㉞
```
   6 2
+  2 7
─────
```
☐

㉟
```
     9
     6
+  1 3
─────
```
☐

㊱
```
     7
     4
+  1 1
─────
```
☐

㊲
```
     6
     8
+  1 6
─────
```
☐

㊳
```
     8
     7
+  1 5
─────
```
☐

㊴ 64 + 15 = _____

㊵ 47 + 28 = _____

㊶ 39 + 23 = _____

㊷ 72 + 9 = _____

㊸ 8 + 41 = _____

㊹ 26 + 59 = _____

㊺ 13 + 43 = _____

㊻ 18 − 11 = _____

Count Sue and Sam's cards, and answer the questions.

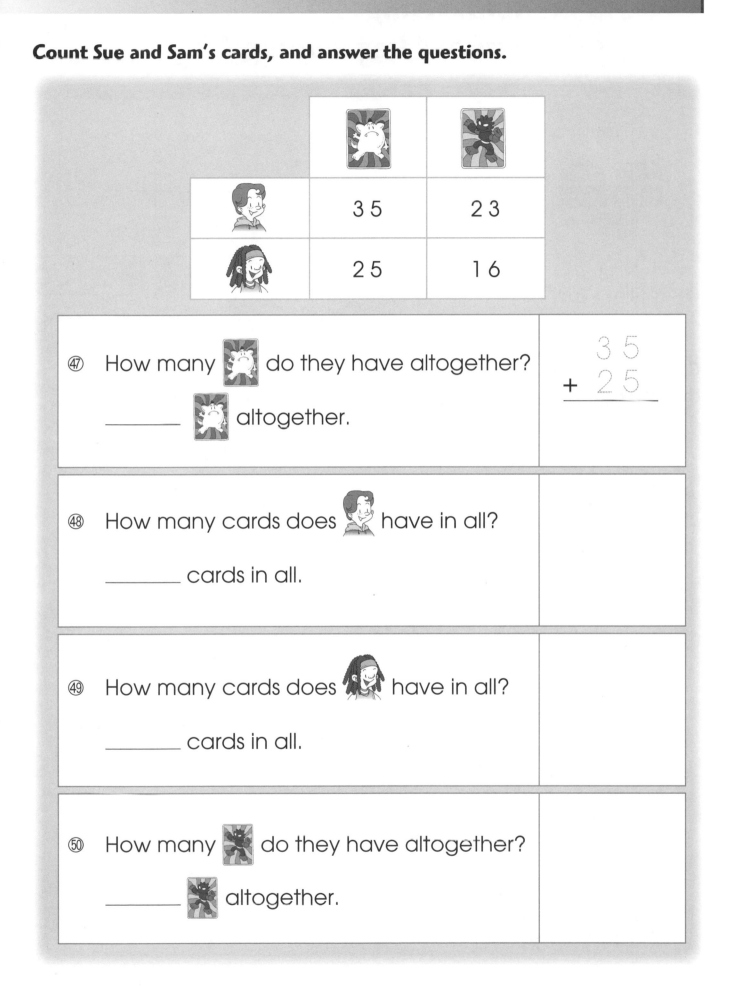

	3 5	2 3
	2 5	1 6

㊼ How many 🐮 do they have altogether?

_____ 🐮 altogether.

$$\begin{array}{r} 3\ 5 \\ +\ 2\ 5 \\ \hline \end{array}$$

㊽ How many cards does 👦 have in all?

_____ cards in all.

㊾ How many cards does 👧 have in all?

_____ cards in all.

㊿ How many 👹 do they have altogether?

_____ 👹 altogether.

9 Subtracting without Regrouping I

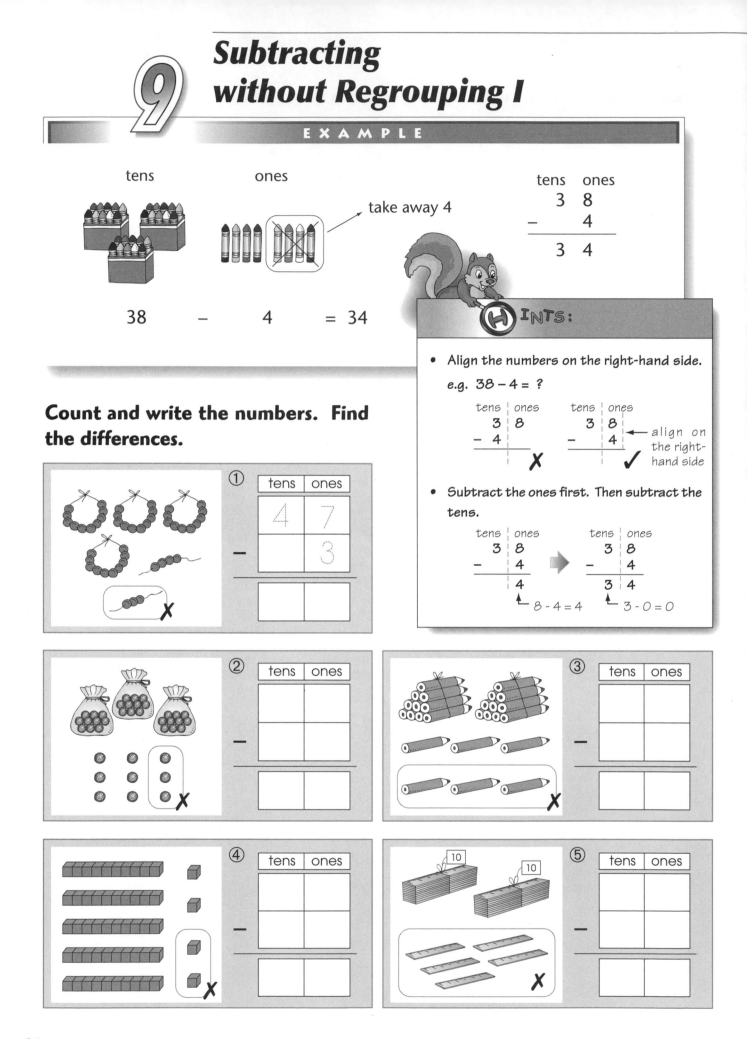

tens   ones

take away 4

tens	ones
3	8
−	4
3	4

38 − 4 = 34

HINTS:

- Align the numbers on the right-hand side.

  e.g. 38 − 4 = ?

tens	ones		tens	ones
3	8		3	8
− 4			−	4

  X   ✓ ← align on the right-hand side

- Subtract the ones first. Then subtract the tens.

tens	ones
3	8
−	4
	4

  ➡

tens	ones
3	8
−	4
3	4

  ↳ 8 − 4 = 4   ↳ 3 − 0 = 0

Count and write the numbers. Find the differences.

①
tens	ones
4	7
−	3

②
tens	ones
−	

③
tens	ones
−	

④
tens	ones
−	

⑤
tens	ones
−	

Subtract.

⑥
$$36 - 5 = \boxed{}$$

⑦
$$27 - 6 = \boxed{}$$

⑧
$$48 - 5 = \boxed{}$$

⑨
$$96 - 4 = \boxed{}$$

⑩
$$55 - 3 = \boxed{}$$

⑪
$$72 - 2 = \boxed{}$$

⑫
$$89 - 7 = \boxed{}$$

⑬
$$46 - 3 = \boxed{}$$

⑭
$$69 - 3 = \boxed{}$$

⑮
$$24 - 3 = \boxed{}$$

⑯
$$57 - 2 = \boxed{}$$

⑰
$$38 - 7 = \boxed{}$$

⑱
$$77 - 5 = \boxed{}$$

⑲
$$18 - 6 = \boxed{}$$

⑳
$$98 - 5 = \boxed{}$$

㉑
$$43 - 3 = \boxed{}$$

㉒ $58 - 8 = \boxed{}$

㉓ $29 - 5 = \boxed{}$

㉔ $34 - 2 = \boxed{}$

㉕ $66 - 4 = \boxed{}$

㉖ $75 - 4 = \boxed{}$

㉗ $87 - 3 = \boxed{}$

㉘ $93 - 2 = \boxed{}$

㉙ $41 - 1 = \boxed{}$

Follow the path. Help Little Monkey get the coconuts.

30) 49
    − 5
    ☐

31) 36
    − 2
    ☐

32) 57
    − 4
    ☐

33) 65
    − 3
    ☐

34) 55
    − 5
    ☐

35) 39
    − 4
    ☐

36) 84
    − 3
    ☐

37) 93
    − 3
    ☐

38) 22
    − 1
    ☐

39) 49
    − 8
    ☐

40) 84
    − 3
    ☐

41) 37
    − 6
    ☐

42) 65
    − 2
    ☐

43) 66
    − 3
    ☐

44) 58
    − 6
    ☐

Complete.

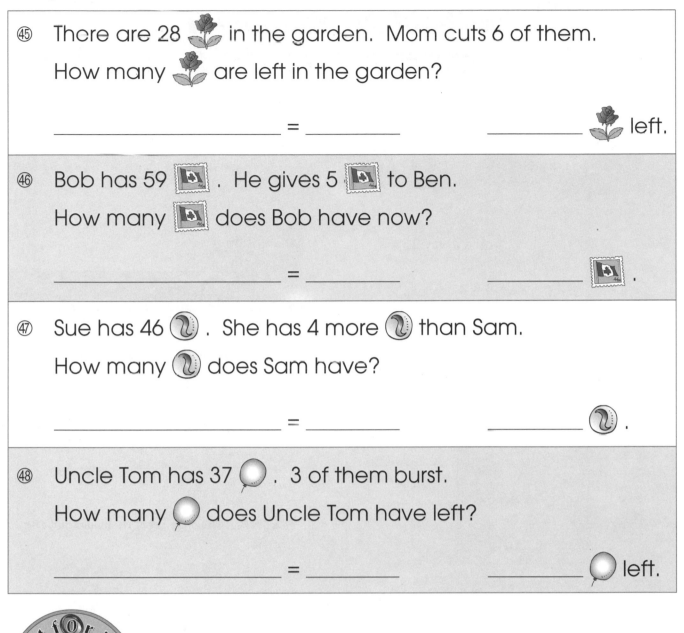

45. There are 28 🌹 in the garden. Mom cuts 6 of them.
How many 🌹 are left in the garden?

_____ = _____   _____ 🌹 left.

46. Bob has 59 🏴. He gives 5 🏴 to Ben.
How many 🏴 does Bob have now?

_____ = _____   _____ 🏴 .

47. Sue has 46 🫘. She has 4 more 🫘 than Sam.
How many 🫘 does Sam have?

_____ = _____   _____ 🫘 .

48. Uncle Tom has 37 🎈. 3 of them burst.
How many 🎈 does Uncle Tom have left?

_____ = _____   _____ 🎈 left.

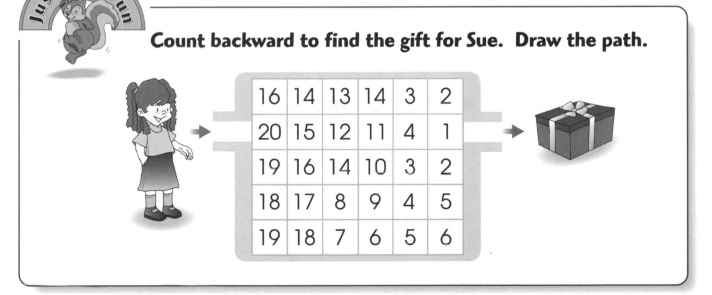

Just for Fun

Count backward to find the gift for Sue. Draw the path.

16	14	13	14	3	2
20	15	12	11	4	1
19	16	14	10	3	2
18	17	8	9	4	5
19	18	7	6	5	6

10 Subtracting without Regrouping II

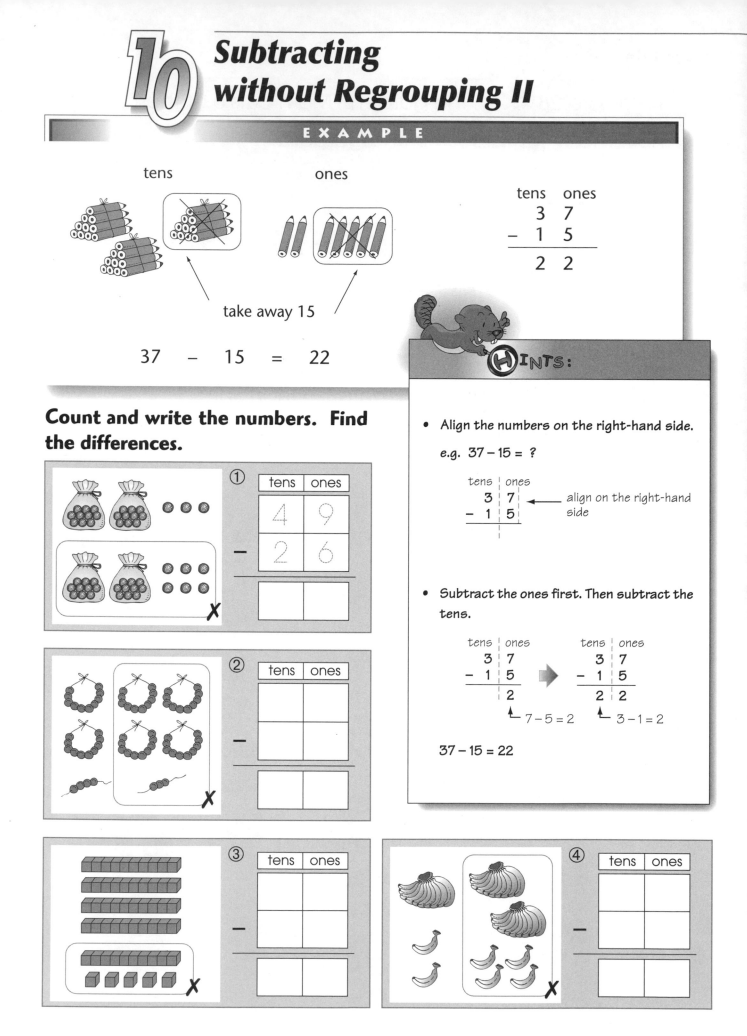

tens   ones

take away 15

37 – 15 = 22

	tens	ones
	3	7
–	1	5
	2	2

HINTS:

- Align the numbers on the right-hand side.

  e.g. 37 – 15 = ?

tens	ones
3	7	← align on the right-hand side
– 1	5

- Subtract the ones first. Then subtract the tens.

tens	ones		tens	ones
3	7		3	7
– 1	5		– 1	5
	2		2	2

  7 – 5 = 2   3 – 1 = 2

  37 – 15 = 22

Count and write the numbers. Find the differences.

①

tens	ones
4	9
2	6

②

tens	ones

③

tens	ones

④

tens	ones

Subtract.

⑤
```
   3 6
 - 1 2
 _____
```
[ ]

⑥
```
   4 8
 - 2 5
 _____
```
[ ]

⑦
```
   5 7
 - 3 3
 _____
```
[ ]

⑧
```
   6 5
 - 2 4
 _____
```
[ ]

⑨
```
   8 6
 - 5 4
 _____
```
[ ]

⑩
```
   7 4
 - 4 4
 _____
```
[ ]

⑪
```
   9 6
 - 6 5
 _____
```
[ ]

⑫
```
   2 9
 - 2 5
 _____
```
[ ]

⑬
```
   5 8
 - 3 7
 _____
```
[ ]

⑭
```
   6 6
 - 4 4
 _____
```
[ ]

⑮
```
   4 3
 - 3 1
 _____
```
[ ]

⑯
```
   8 4
 - 3 0
 _____
```
[ ]

⑰
```
   2 7
 - 1 2
 _____
```
[ ]

⑱
```
   3 3
 - 2 3
 _____
```
[ ]

⑲
```
   1 9
 - 1 5
 _____
```
[ ]

⑳
```
   7 8
 - 4 6
 _____
```
[ ]

㉑ 45 - 22 = [ ]

㉒ 99 - 77 = [ ]

㉓ 76 - 30 = [ ]

㉔ 54 - 14 = [ ]

㉕ 69 - 58 = [ ]

㉖ 25 - 11 = [ ]

㉗ 37 - 21 = [ ]

㉘ 83 - 70 = [ ]

Find the differences. In each group, colour the balloons with the same answers.

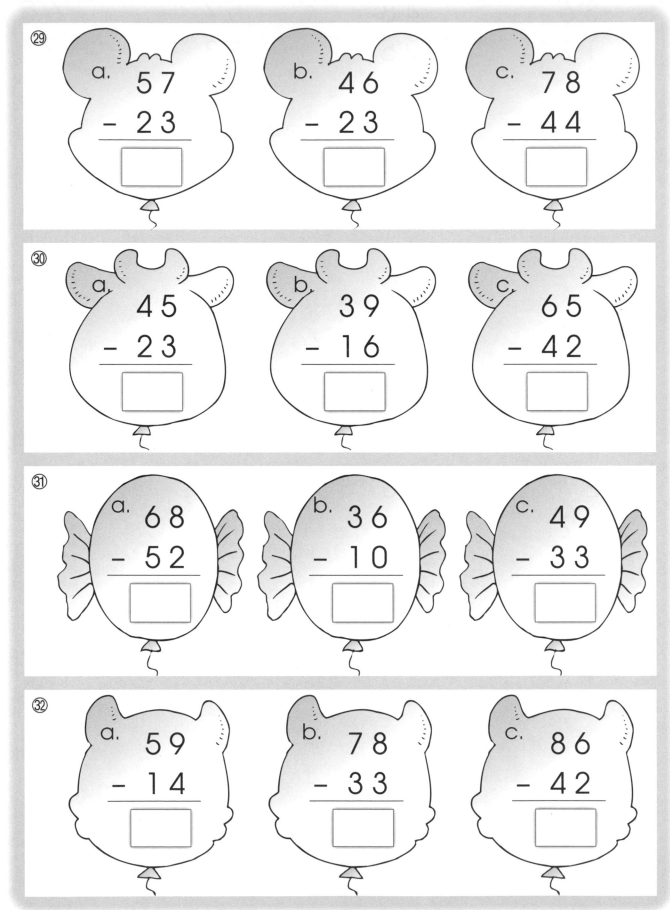

㉙ a. 57 − 23 = ▢ b. 46 − 23 = ▢ c. 78 − 44 = ▢

㉚ a. 45 − 23 = ▢ b. 39 − 16 = ▢ c. 65 − 42 = ▢

㉛ a. 68 − 52 = ▢ b. 36 − 10 = ▢ c. 49 − 33 = ▢

㉜ a. 59 − 14 = ▢ b. 78 − 33 = ▢ c. 86 − 42 = ▢

Complete.

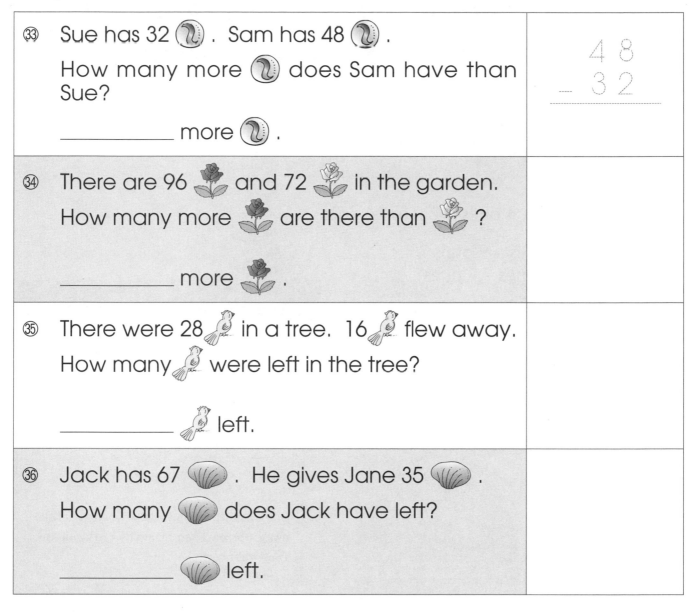

㉝ Sue has 32 🪙 . Sam has 48 🪙 . How many more 🪙 does Sam have than Sue?

_____ more 🪙 .

$$\begin{array}{r} 4\,8 \\ -\ 3\,2 \\ \hline \end{array}$$

㉞ There are 96 🌹 and 72 🌹 in the garden. How many more 🌹 are there than 🌹 ?

_____ more 🌹 .

㉟ There were 28 🐦 in a tree. 16 🐦 flew away. How many 🐦 were left in the tree?

_____ 🐦 left.

㊱ Jack has 67 🐚 . He gives Jane 35 🐚 . How many 🐚 does Jack have left?

_____ 🐚 left.

Just for Fun

Write the answers in the puzzle with one digit in each square.

Across
1. 84 – 23
3. 66 – 13
4. 57 – 20
5. 38 – 10
7. 26 – 16

Down
1. 98 – 34
2. 79 – 56
3. 89 – 32
4. 49 – 11
5. 56 – 32
6. 42 – 22

Subtracting with Regrouping I

EXAMPLE

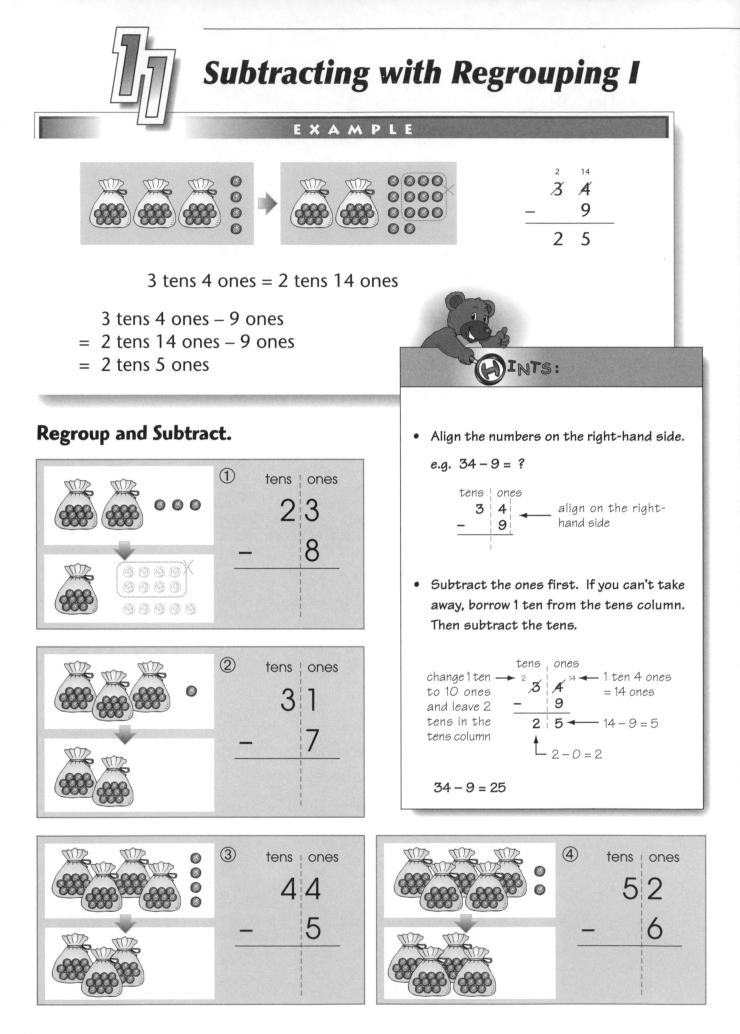

3 tens 4 ones = 2 tens 14 ones

3 tens 4 ones − 9 ones
= 2 tens 14 ones − 9 ones
= 2 tens 5 ones

$$\begin{array}{r} \overset{2}{\cancel{3}}\ \overset{14}{\cancel{4}} \\ -\quad\ \ 9 \\ \hline 2\ \ 5 \end{array}$$

Regroup and Subtract.

① tens ones
$$\begin{array}{c} 2\ |\ 3 \\ -\ \ |\ 8 \\ \hline \end{array}$$

② tens ones
$$\begin{array}{c} 3\ |\ 1 \\ -\ \ |\ 7 \\ \hline \end{array}$$

③ tens ones
$$\begin{array}{c} 4\ |\ 4 \\ -\ \ |\ 5 \\ \hline \end{array}$$

④ tens ones
$$\begin{array}{c} 5\ |\ 2 \\ -\ \ |\ 6 \\ \hline \end{array}$$

HINTS:

- Align the numbers on the right-hand side.

  e.g. 34 − 9 = ?

  tens | ones
  3 | 4   ← align on the right-hand side
  − | 9

- Subtract the ones first. If you can't take away, borrow 1 ten from the tens column. Then subtract the tens.

  change 1 ten to 10 ones and leave 2 tens in the tens column

  tens | ones
  $\overset{2}{\cancel{3}}$ | $\overset{14}{\cancel{4}}$ ← 1 ten 4 ones = 14 ones
  − | 9
  2 | 5   ← 14 − 9 = 5
  └ 2 − 0 = 2

  34 − 9 = 25

Subtract. Remember to regroup.

⑤
```
   6 3
 -   6
 ─────
```

⑥
```
   4 5
 -   8
 ─────
```

⑦
```
   3 4
 -   7
 ─────
```

⑧
```
   7 1
 -   9
 ─────
```

⑨
```
   2 7
 -   8
 ─────
```

⑩
```
   8 4
 -   9
 ─────
```

⑪
```
   5 6
 -   8
 ─────
```

⑫
```
   4 7
 -   9
 ─────
```

⑬
```
   9 0
 -   6
 ─────
```

⑭
```
   3 5
 -   9
 ─────
```

⑮
```
   7 2
 -   4
 ─────
```

⑯
```
   6 6
 -   8
 ─────
```

⑰
```
   4 3
 -   7
 ─────
```

⑱
```
   2 8
 -   9
 ─────
```

⑲
```
   8 1
 -   4
 ─────
```

⑳
```
   5 4
 -   6
 ─────
```

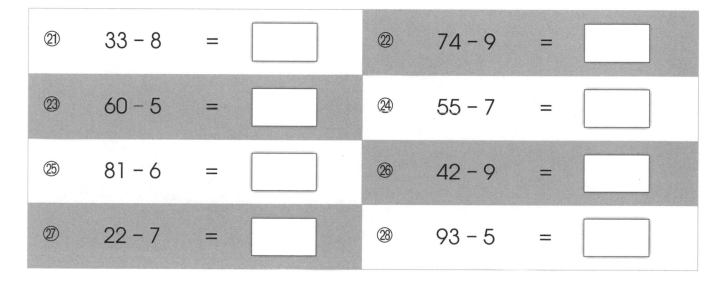

㉑ 33 – 8 = ☐	㉒ 74 – 9 = ☐
㉓ 60 – 5 = ☐	㉔ 55 – 7 = ☐
㉕ 81 – 6 = ☐	㉖ 42 – 9 = ☐
㉗ 22 – 7 = ☐	㉘ 93 – 5 = ☐

Subtract. Colour the lily pads if the answers are odd numbers. Help Little Frog find its Mom.

29)
$$\begin{array}{r} 32 \\ -9 \\ \hline \end{array}$$

30)
$$\begin{array}{r} 53 \\ -8 \\ \hline \end{array}$$

33)
$$\begin{array}{r} 25 \\ -7 \\ \hline \end{array}$$

32)
$$\begin{array}{r} 23 \\ -6 \\ \hline \end{array}$$

31)
$$\begin{array}{r} 46 \\ -9 \\ \hline \end{array}$$

34)
$$\begin{array}{r} 64 \\ -9 \\ \hline \end{array}$$

35)
$$\begin{array}{r} 71 \\ -8 \\ \hline \end{array}$$

36)
$$\begin{array}{r} 61 \\ -7 \\ \hline \end{array}$$

38)
$$\begin{array}{r} 37 \\ -9 \\ \hline \end{array}$$

37)
$$\begin{array}{r} 35 \\ -6 \\ \hline \end{array}$$

39)
$$\begin{array}{r} 40 \\ -7 \\ \hline \end{array}$$

Complete.

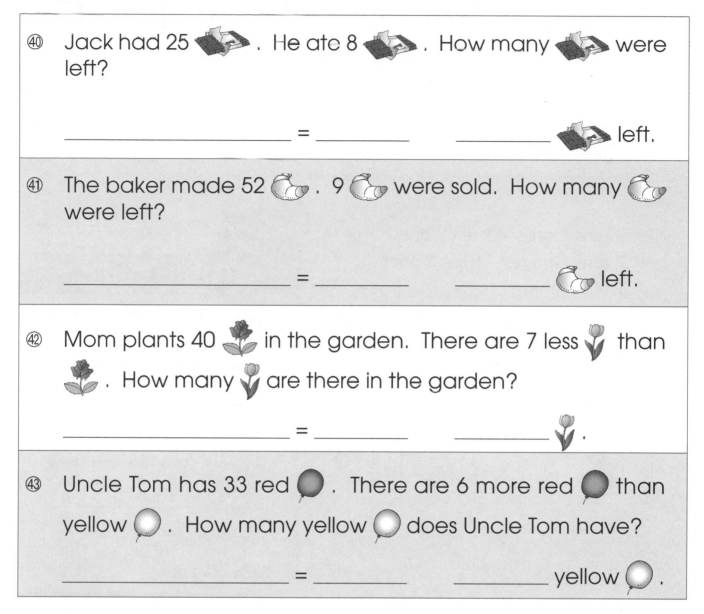

40 Jack had 25 🍫. He ate 8 🍫. How many 🍫 were left?

_____ = _____   _____ 🍫 left.

41 The baker made 52 🥐. 9 🥐 were sold. How many 🥐 were left?

_____ = _____   _____ 🥐 left.

42 Mom plants 40 🌹 in the garden. There are 7 less 🌷 than 🌹. How many 🌷 are there in the garden?

_____ = _____   _____ 🌷.

43 Uncle Tom has 33 red 🎈. There are 6 more red 🎈 than yellow 🎈. How many yellow 🎈 does Uncle Tom have?

_____ = _____   _____ yellow 🎈.

Just for Fun

Subtract. Fill in the missing numbers.

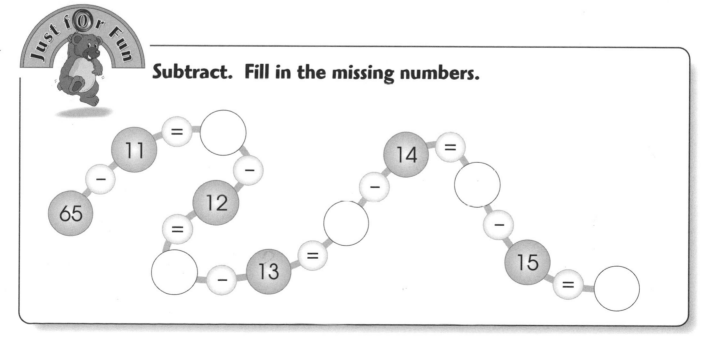

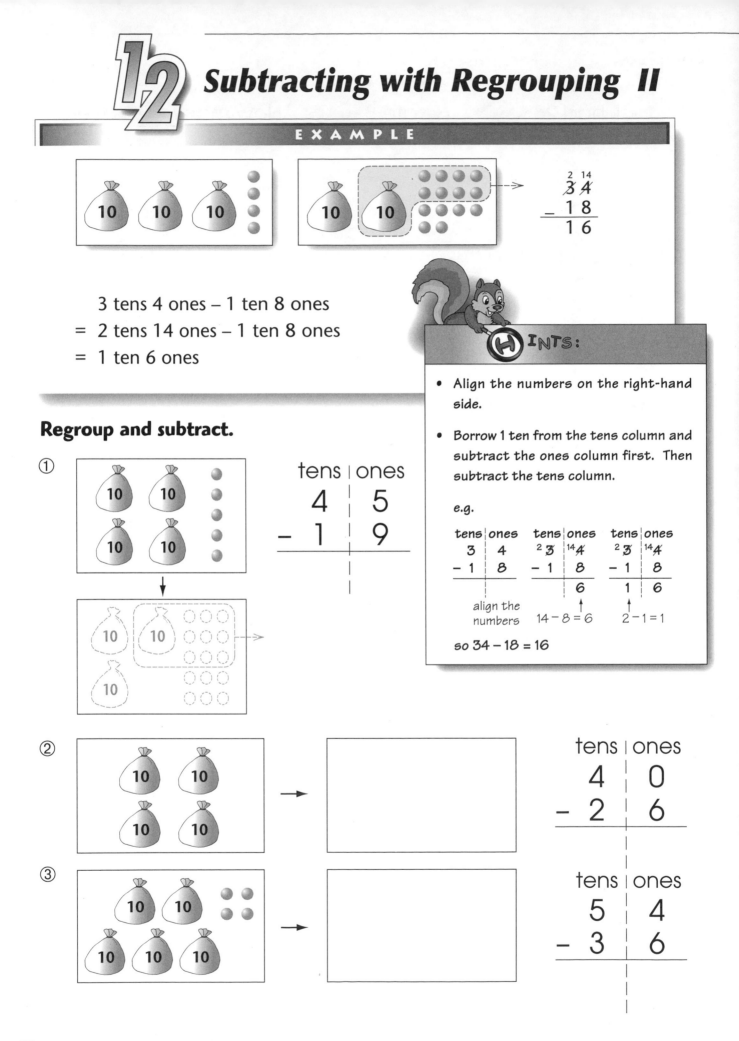

12 Subtracting with Regrouping II

$$\begin{array}{r} \overset{2}{\cancel{3}}\ \overset{14}{\cancel{4}} \\ -\ 1\ 8 \\ \hline 1\ 6 \end{array}$$

3 tens 4 ones – 1 ten 8 ones

= 2 tens 14 ones – 1 ten 8 ones

= 1 ten 6 ones

HINTS:

- Align the numbers on the right-hand side.

- Borrow 1 ten from the tens column and subtract the ones column first. Then subtract the tens column.

e.g.

tens	ones
3	4
– 1	8

align the numbers

tens	ones
$\overset{2}{\cancel{3}}$	$\overset{14}{\cancel{4}}$
– 1	8
	6

↑
14 – 8 = 6

tens	ones
$\overset{2}{\cancel{3}}$	$\overset{14}{\cancel{4}}$
– 1	8
1	6

↑
2 – 1 = 1

so 34 – 18 = 16

Regroup and subtract.

①

tens	ones
4	5
– 1	9

②

tens	ones
4	0
– 2	6

③

tens	ones
5	4
– 3	6

Subtract. Remember to regroup.

④
```
   4 3
 - 2 7
```

⑤
```
   5 6
 - 1 8
```

⑥
```
   3 5
 - 1 9
```

⑦
```
   7 0
 - 2 5
```

⑧
```
   6 1
 - 4 3
```

⑨
```
   8 4
 - 5 6
```

⑩
```
   2 7
 - 1 9
```

⑪
```
   4 6
 - 1 7
```

⑫
```
   7 2
 - 5 5
```

⑬
```
   3 3
 - 1 4
```

⑭
```
   8 5
 - 4 8
```

⑮
```
   9 6
 - 6 9
```

⑯
```
   5 4
 - 3 8
```

⑰
```
   4 0
 - 2 7
```

⑱
```
   2 5
 - 1 6
```

⑲
```
   6 5
 - 3 7
```

⑳ 31 – 14 = _____

㉑ 53 – 25 = _____

㉒ 64 – 39 = _____

㉓ 81 – 44 = _____

㉔ 93 – 46 = _____

㉕ 41 – 18 = _____

㉖ 71 – 59 = _____

㉗ 62 – 36 = _____

Subtract. Colour the eggs that match each number.

㉘ 36

a.
$$\begin{array}{r} 63 \\ -\ 27 \\ \hline \end{array}$$

b.
$$\begin{array}{r} 52 \\ -\ 29 \\ \hline \end{array}$$

c.
$$\begin{array}{r} 52 \\ -\ 16 \\ \hline \end{array}$$

㉙ 37

a.
$$\begin{array}{r} 63 \\ -\ 36 \\ \hline \end{array}$$

b.
$$\begin{array}{r} 74 \\ -\ 37 \\ \hline \end{array}$$

c.
$$\begin{array}{r} 96 \\ -\ 59 \\ \hline \end{array}$$

㉚ 14

a.
$$\begin{array}{r} 41 \\ -\ 27 \\ \hline \end{array}$$

b.
$$\begin{array}{r} 60 \\ -\ 46 \\ \hline \end{array}$$

c.
$$\begin{array}{r} 53 \\ -\ 38 \\ \hline \end{array}$$

㉛ 25

a.
$$\begin{array}{r} 83 \\ -\ 57 \\ \hline \end{array}$$

b.
$$\begin{array}{r} 43 \\ -\ 18 \\ \hline \end{array}$$

c.
$$\begin{array}{r} 62 \\ -\ 37 \\ \hline \end{array}$$

㉜ 44

a.
$$\begin{array}{r} 72 \\ -\ 28 \\ \hline \end{array}$$

b.
$$\begin{array}{r} 63 \\ -\ 29 \\ \hline \end{array}$$

c.
$$\begin{array}{r} 80 \\ -\ 36 \\ \hline \end{array}$$

Complete.

③③ There are 92 children in the gym. 37 of them are boys. How many girls are there in the gym?

_____ = _____   _____ girls.

③④ At Sea World, Sue saw 43 🦭 on the rocks and 27 🦭 in the water. How many more 🦭 were there on the rocks than in the water?

_____ = _____   _____ more 🦭.

③⑤ The baker made 55 🧁 in the morning and 39 🧁 in the afternoon. How many more 🧁 did he make in the morning than in the afternoon?

_____ = _____   _____ more 🧁.

③⑥ There were 61 🌭 in the snack bar. 46 🌭 were sold. How many 🌭 were left?

_____ = _____   _____ 🌭 left.

Just for Fun

Add or subtract. Write the letters to find what Sue wants to be.

19 + 27 = [I]   73 − 48   = [E]

52 − 36 = [R]   25 + 46   = [S]

44 − 27 = [G]   4 + 9 + 26 = [N]

A | 71 | 46 | 39 | 17 | 25 | 16 | .

13 Estimating Sums and Differences

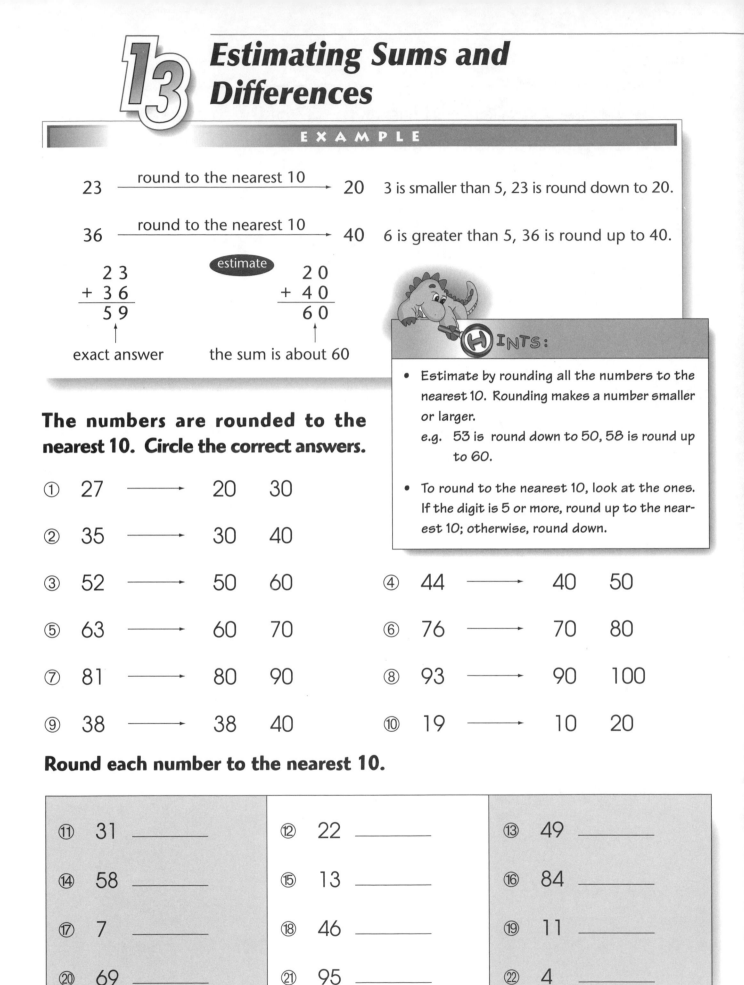

23 — round to the nearest 10 → 20   3 is smaller than 5, 23 is round down to 20.

36 — round to the nearest 10 → 40   6 is greater than 5, 36 is round up to 40.

```
    2 3              2 0
  + 3 6            + 4 0
    5 9              6 0
```

↑ exact answer   ↑ the sum is about 60

estimate

HINTS:

- Estimate by rounding all the numbers to the nearest 10. Rounding makes a number smaller or larger.
  e.g. 53 is round down to 50, 58 is round up to 60.

- To round to the nearest 10, look at the ones. If the digit is 5 or more, round up to the nearest 10; otherwise, round down.

The numbers are rounded to the nearest 10. Circle the correct answers.

① 27 ⟶ 20   30

② 35 ⟶ 30   40

③ 52 ⟶ 50   60   ④ 44 ⟶ 40   50

⑤ 63 ⟶ 60   70   ⑥ 76 ⟶ 70   80

⑦ 81 ⟶ 80   90   ⑧ 93 ⟶ 90   100

⑨ 38 ⟶ 38   40   ⑩ 19 ⟶ 10   20

Round each number to the nearest 10.

⑪ 31 _____   ⑫ 22 _____   ⑬ 49 _____

⑭ 58 _____   ⑮ 13 _____   ⑯ 84 _____

⑰ 7 _____   ⑱ 46 _____   ⑲ 11 _____

⑳ 69 _____   ㉑ 95 _____   ㉒ 4 _____

Estimate the sums. Compare the estimates with the exact answers.

㉓
a.
```
  3 9
+ 2 7
```
b. estimate
```
  4 0
+ 3 0
```

㉔
a.
```
  1 6
+ 2 8
```
b. estimate

㉕
a.
```
    8
+ 4 5
```
b. estimate

㉖
a.
```
  5 1
+ 1 4
```
b. estimate

㉗
a.
```
  2 6
+   7
```
b. estimate

㉘
a.
```
  3 4
+ 5 5
```
b. estimate

㉙ a. 73 + 19 = _____

estimate

b. _____ + _____ = _____

㉚ a. 22 + 66 = _____

estimate

b. _____ + _____ = _____

㉛ a. 33 + 46 = _____

estimate

b. _____ + _____ = _____

㉜ a. 51 + 44 = _____

estimate

b. _____ + _____ = _____

㉝ a. 64 + 27 = _____

estimate

b. _____ + _____ = _____

㉞ a. 13 + 45 = _____

estimate

b. _____ + _____ = _____

Estimate the differences. Compare the estimates with the exact answers.

㉟
a.
$$\begin{array}{r} 4\,2 \\ -\ 1\,8 \\ \hline \end{array}$$

b. **estimate**
$$\begin{array}{r} 4\,0 \\ -\ 2\,0 \\ \hline \end{array}$$

㊱
a.
$$\begin{array}{r} 3\,8 \\ -\ 2\,3 \\ \hline \end{array}$$

b. **estimate**

㊲
a.
$$\begin{array}{r} 6\,9 \\ -\ 3\,7 \\ \hline \end{array}$$

b. **estimate**

㊳
a.
$$\begin{array}{r} 7\,2 \\ -\ 4\,6 \\ \hline \end{array}$$

b. **estimate**

㊴
a.
$$\begin{array}{r} 5\,5 \\ -\ 1\,4 \\ \hline \end{array}$$

b. **estimate**

㊵
a.
$$\begin{array}{r} 8\,7 \\ -\ 5\,1 \\ \hline \end{array}$$

b. **estimate**

㊶ a. 93 – 46 = _____

estimate

b. _____ – _____ = _____

㊷ a. 46 – 13 = _____

estimate

b. _____ – _____ = _____

㊸ a. 75 – 27 = _____

estimate

b. _____ – _____ = _____

㊹ a. 64 – 19 = _____

estimate

b. _____ – _____ = _____

㊺ a. 82 – 34 = _____

estimate

b. _____ – _____ = _____

㊻ a. 36 – 8 = _____

estimate

b. _____ – _____ = _____

Estimate the sums or differences. Circle the correct descriptions.

㊼ 43 − 9

more than 20	less than 20

㊽ 25 + 47

more than 90	less than 90

㊾ 33 + 58

more than 80	less than 80

㊿ 62 − 44

more than 30	less than 30

(51) 95 − 57

more than 50	less than 50

(52) 19 + 54

more than 60	less than 60

Just for Fun

Join the numbers.

13
54
41
①
28
7

① Join 2 numbers that give a sum of about 40.

② Join 2 numbers that give a difference of about 30.

③ Join 2 numbers that give a sum of about 60.

④ Join 2 numbers that give a difference of about 20.

⑤ Join 2 numbers that give a sum of about 80.

⑥ Join 2 numbers that give a difference of about 40.

14 Checking Subtraction by Using Addition

Farmer Joe had 89 🍎 . 52 🍎 were sold. How many 🍎 were left?

```
   8 9
 – 5 2
 ─────
   3 7
```

check
```
   3 7
 + 5 2
 ─────
   8 9
```

37 🍎 were left.

HINTS:

- Recall the family of facts,

  e.g.
  $5 + 4 = 9$
  $4 + 5 = 9$
  $9 - 5 = 4$
  $9 - 4 = 5$

- Check your subtraction by using addition.

  e.g.
  ```
     4 1          2 6
   – 1 5  same  + 1 5
   ─────        ─────
     2 6          4 1
  ```
  The answer is right.

  ```
     4 1   not the   3 6
   – 1 5    same    + 1 5
   ─────            ─────
     3 6              5 1
  ```
  The answer is wrong.

Do the subtraction and check the answers .

① a.
```
   2 8
 – 1 6
 ─────
 [    ]
```
b. **check** [   ]
```
 + 1 6
 ─────
 [    ]
```

② a.
```
   6 3
 – 3 7
 ─────
 [    ]
```
b. **check** [   ]
```
 + 3 7
 ─────
 [    ]
```

③ a.
```
   4 8
 – 2 6
 ─────
 [    ]
```
b. **check** [   ]
```
 + 2 6
 ─────
 [    ]
```

④ a.
```
   5 1
 – 3 3
 ─────
 [    ]
```
b. **check** [   ]
```
 + 3 3
 ─────
 [    ]
```

⑤ a.
```
   7 7
 – 4 2
 ─────
 [    ]
```
b. **check** [   ]
```
 + 4 2
 ─────
 [    ]
```

⑥ a.
```
   8 2
 – 5 9
 ─────
 [    ]
```
b. **check** [   ]
```
 + 5 9
 ─────
 [    ]
```

Subtract and check your answers.

⑦ a. 52 − 8 = _____

    check

    b. _____ + _____ = _____

⑧ a. 39 − 17 = _____

    check

    b. _____ + _____ = _____

⑨ a. 45 − 23 = _____

    check

    b. _____ + _____ = _____

⑩ a. 66 − 39 = _____

    check

    b. _____ + _____ = _____

⑪ a. 87 − 45 = _____

    check

    b. _____ + _____ = _____

⑫ a. 23 − 16 = _____

    check

    b. _____ + _____ = _____

⑬ a. 71 − 33 = _____

    check

    b. _____ + _____ = _____

⑭ a. 98 − 63 = _____

    check

    b. _____ + _____ = _____

⑮ a. 32 − 14 = _____

    check

    b. _____ + _____ = _____

⑯ a. 27 − 6 = _____

    check

    b. _____ + _____ = _____

⑰ a. 56 − 31 = _____

    check

    b. _____ + _____ = _____

⑱ a. 45 − 29 = _____

    check

    b. _____ + _____ = _____

Subtract. Complete 1 addition sentence and 1 subtraction sentence to check each answer.

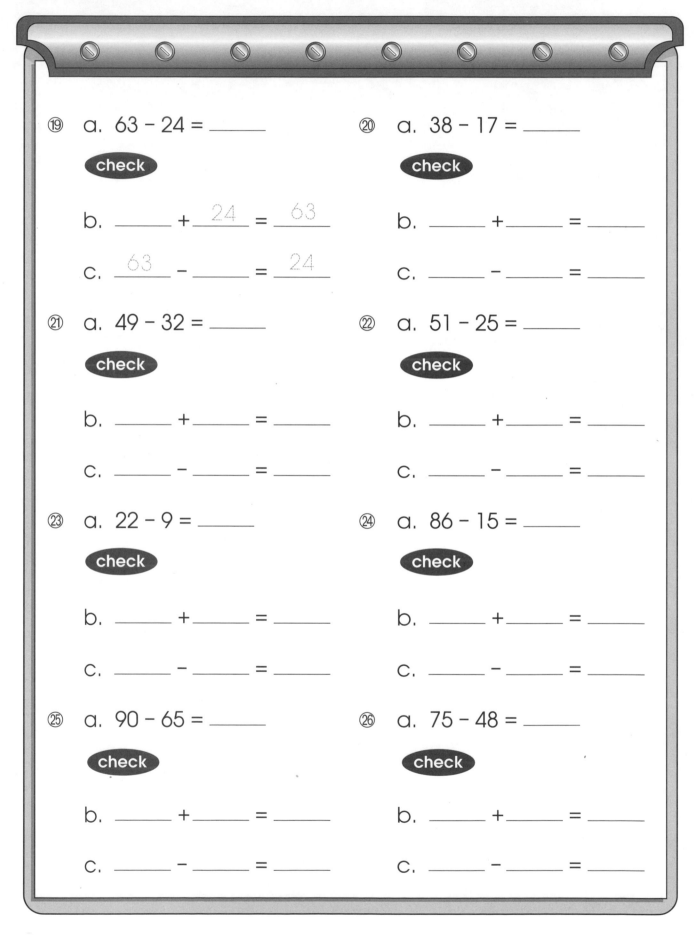

⑲ a. 63 – 24 = _____

    check

    b. _____ + _24_ = _63_

    c. _63_ – _____ = _24_

⑳ a. 38 – 17 = _____

    check

    b. _____ + _____ = _____

    c. _____ – _____ = _____

㉑ a. 49 – 32 = _____

    check

    b. _____ + _____ = _____

    c. _____ – _____ = _____

㉒ a. 51 – 25 = _____

    check

    b. _____ + _____ = _____

    c. _____ – _____ = _____

㉓ a. 22 – 9 = _____

    check

    b. _____ + _____ = _____

    c. _____ – _____ = _____

㉔ a. 86 – 15 = _____

    check

    b. _____ + _____ = _____

    c. _____ – _____ = _____

㉕ a. 90 – 65 = _____

    check

    b. _____ + _____ = _____

    c. _____ – _____ = _____

㉖ a. 75 – 48 = _____

    check

    b. _____ + _____ = _____

    c. _____ – _____ = _____

Complete and check.

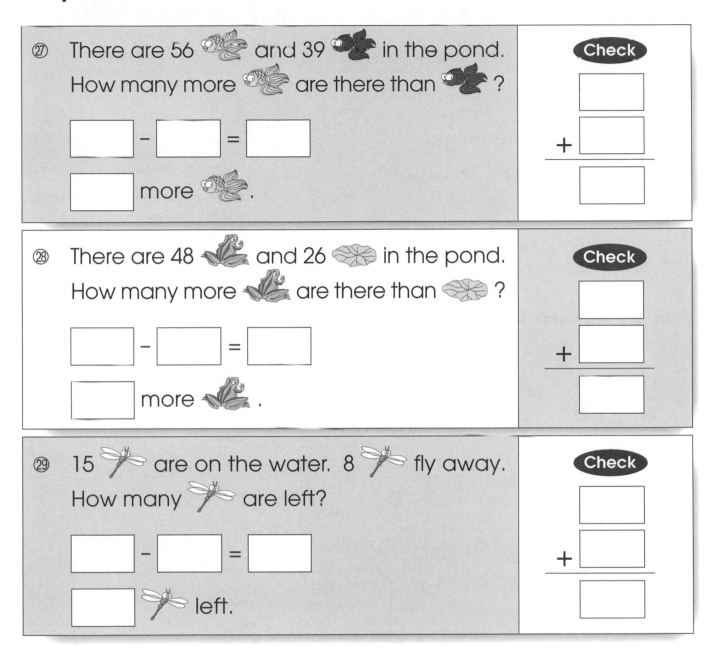

㉗ There are 56 🐟 and 39 🐟 in the pond. How many more 🐟 are there than 🐟 ?

☐ − ☐ = ☐

☐ more 🐟 .

Check

☐
+ ☐
___
☐

㉘ There are 48 🐸 and 26 🪷 in the pond. How many more 🐸 are there than 🪷 ?

☐ − ☐ = ☐

☐ more 🐸 .

Check

☐
+ ☐
___
☐

㉙ 15 🪰 are on the water. 8 🪰 fly away. How many 🪰 are left?

☐ − ☐ = ☐

☐ 🪰 left.

Check

☐
+ ☐
___
☐

Just for Fun

Fill in the missing numbers.

① 15 _____ 25 30 _____ 40 _____

② 36 38 _____ 42 _____ _____ 48

③ 30 _____ _____ 60 70 _____ 90

15 More Addition and Subtraction

1. $17 + 9 - 16 = 26 - 16 = 10$
    └─── do the addition first

2. $33 - 19 + 27 = 14 + 27 = 41$
    └─── do the subtraction first

HINTS:

- To solve a problem with addition and subtraction, follow the order of the + and − signs in the problem to do the addition and subtraction.

- Knowing the patterns may help you find the sums or differences faster.

Find the answers. Be careful with the signs.

①
$$
\begin{array}{r} 4 \\ + \ 5 \\ \hline \boxed{} \\ - \ 3 \\ \hline \boxed{} \end{array}
$$

②
$$
\begin{array}{r} 7 \\ - \ 5 \\ \hline \boxed{} \\ + \ 8 \\ \hline \boxed{} \end{array}
$$

③
$$
\begin{array}{r} 8 \\ + \ 6 \\ \hline \boxed{} \\ - \ 9 \\ \hline \boxed{} \end{array}
$$

④
$$
\begin{array}{r} 14 \\ - \ 8 \\ \hline \boxed{} \\ + \ 6 \\ \hline \boxed{} \end{array}
$$

⑤
$$
\begin{array}{r} 32 \\ - \ 16 \\ \hline \boxed{} \\ - \ 14 \\ \hline \boxed{} \end{array}
$$

⑥
$$
\begin{array}{r} 23 \\ + \ 12 \\ \hline \boxed{} \\ - \ 6 \\ \hline \boxed{} \end{array}
$$

⑦
$$
\begin{array}{r} 54 \\ + \ 28 \\ \hline \boxed{} \\ - \ 2 \\ \hline \boxed{} \end{array}
$$

⑧
$$
\begin{array}{r} 56 \\ - \ 27 \\ \hline \boxed{} \\ + \ 7 \\ \hline \boxed{} \end{array}
$$

⑨ $45 + 25 - 18$

     = _____ − 18

     = _____

⑩ $27 + 53 - 46$

     = _____ − 46

     = _____

Add.

⑪ 10 + 30 = _40_ ⑫ 40 + 20 = _____

⑬ 16 + 20 = _____ ⑭ 20 + 26 = _____

⑮ 16 + 10 + 10 = _____ ⑯ 10 + 10 + 26 = _____

⑰ 9 + 4 = 10 + _3_

= _____

⑱ 19 + 25 = 20 + _____ = _____

⑲ 29 + 33 = 30 + _____ = _____

⑳ 18 + 35 = 20 + _____ = _____

㉑ 38 + 16 = 40 + _____ = _____

㉒ 4 + 8 = _____ + 10

= _____

㉓ 22 + 18 = _____ + 20 = _____

㉔ 21 + 19 = _____ + 20 = _____

㉕ 16 + 28 = _____ + 30 = _____

㉖ 13 + 29 = _____ + 30 = _____

Subtract.

㉗ 50 − 20 = _____   ㉘ 36 − 26 = _____

㉙ 64 − 20 = _____   ㉚ 53 − 13 = _____

㉛ 73 − 30 = _____   ㉜ 48 − 28 = _____

㉝ 60 − 30 = _____   ㉞ 76 − 50 = _____

㉟ 87 − 57 = _____   ㊱ 38 − 20 = _____

㊲ 49 − 29 = _____   ㊳ 96 − 66 = _____

㊴ a. 8 − 5 = _____   ㊵ a. 14 − 8 = _____

b. 18 − 5 = _____   b. 24 − 8 = _____

c. 28 − 5 = _____   c. 34 − 8 = _____

d. 38 − 5 = _____   d. 44 − 8 = _____

e. 48 − 5 = _____   e. 54 − 8 = _____

㊶ a. 72 − 8 = _____   ㊷ a. 67 − 9 = _____

b. 72 − 18 = _____   b. 67 − 19 = _____

c. 72 − 28 = _____   c. 67 − 29 = _____

d. 72 − 38 = _____   d. 67 − 39 = _____

e. 72 − 48 = _____   e. 67 − 49 = _____

The children are playing with the spinner. Look at the children's scores in 3 rounds of the game. Find their final scores.

	1st round	2nd round	3rd round
	Add 8	Add 4	Subtract 5
	Add 9	Subtract 3	Add 5
	Add 7	Add 6	Subtract 4

means add 5

-1 -2 5 -3
7   8
-2   1
6   -4
-6   9
    2 -5 4

means subtract 5

㊸ The final score of 👦 is :

_____ = _____

㊹ The final score of 👵 is :

_____ = _____

㊺ The final score of 👧 is :

_____ = _____

Just for Fun

Colour the correct answers to help Sue find her gift.

8 + 3 + 5
4 + 7 – 6
9 – 3 + 5
7 + 9 – 8
8 – 6 + 7
7 – 2 – 4

6	12	10	2
16	7	9	1
5	11	8	3

16 Addition and Subtraction with Money

How many cents does Sam have?

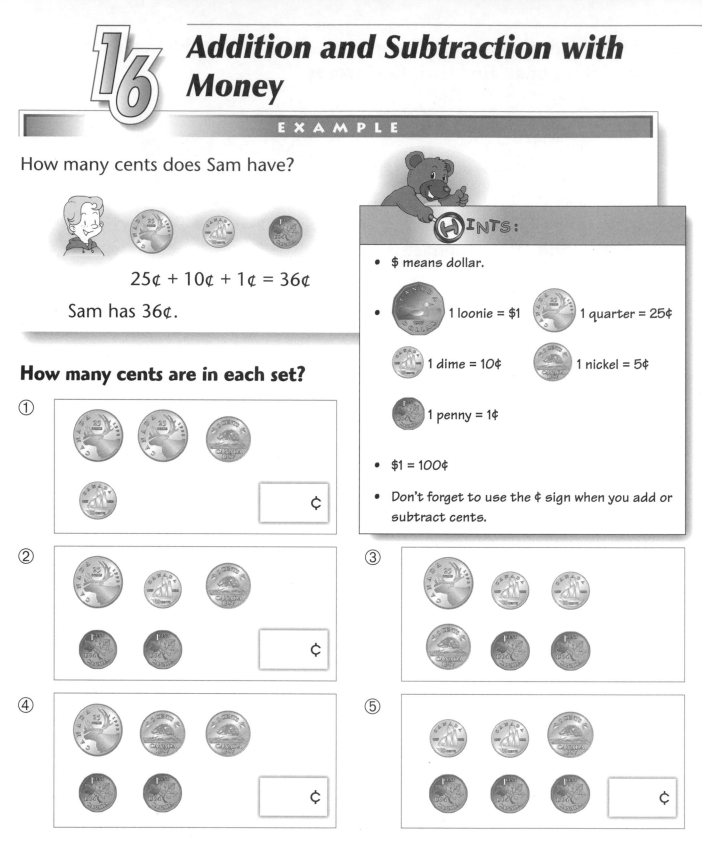

$25¢ + 10¢ + 1¢ = 36¢$

Sam has 36¢.

HINTS:

- $ means dollar.

- 1 loonie = $1   1 quarter = 25¢

- 1 dime = 10¢   1 nickel = 5¢

- 1 penny = 1¢

- $1 = 100¢

- Don't forget to use the $ sign when you add or subtract cents.

How many cents are in each set?

① [   ] ¢

② [   ] ¢

③

④ [   ] ¢

⑤ [   ] ¢

Which set gives a total of 100¢? Put a ✓ in the box.

⑥  [ ]

⑦  [ ]

How much change does Sue get?

Sue has	Sue buys	Change Sue gets
⑧	49¢	_____ ¢ – _____ ¢ = _____ ¢
⑨	85¢	_____ ¢ – _____ ¢ = _____ ¢
⑩	36¢	_____ ¢ – _____ ¢ = _____ ¢
⑪	Drink 56¢	_____ ¢ – _____ ¢ = _____ ¢

How much more does Sam need?

Sam has	Sam wants to buy	Extra amount Sam needs
⑫	67¢	_____ ¢ – _____ ¢ = _____ ¢
⑬	milk 76¢	_____ ¢ – _____ ¢ = _____ ¢
⑭	72¢	_____ ¢ – _____ ¢ = _____ ¢
⑮	28¢	_____ ¢ – _____ ¢ = _____ ¢

Pay with the least number of coins. Write the number of each coin needed.

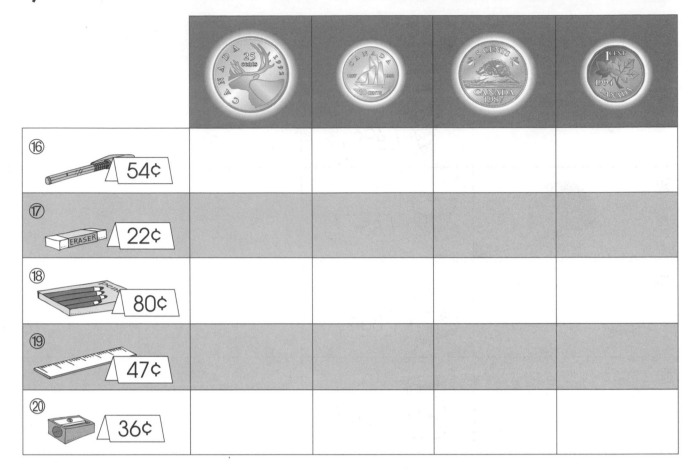

	25¢	10¢	5¢	1¢
⑯ 54¢				
⑰ 22¢				
⑱ 80¢				
⑲ 47¢				
⑳ 36¢				

Write each price. Then solve the problems.

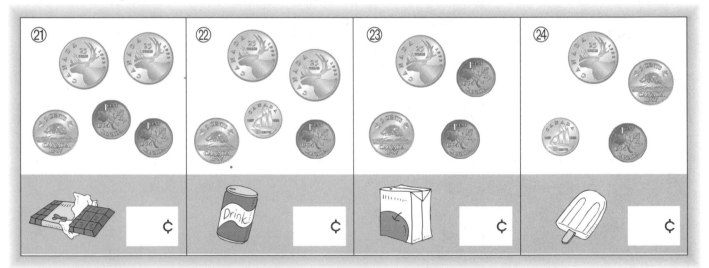

㉑	㉒	㉓	㉔
_____ ¢	_____ ¢	_____ ¢	_____ ¢

㉕ Sue has 100¢. She buys a [Drink]. How much does Sue have left?

$$\begin{array}{r} 100 \\ -66 \\ \hline \end{array}$$

_____ ¢ left.

㉖ Sam buys a ▨ and a 🍦. How much does Sam pay in all?

_____ ¢ in all.

㉗ Jack buys a ▨ and a 📦. How much does Jack pay in all?

_____ ¢ in all.

㉘ Ben buys a 🥤. Bob buys a 📦. How much more does Ben pay than Bob?

_____ ¢ more.

㉙ Sue buys a 🥤. Jane buys a 🍦. How much less does Jane pay than Sue?

_____ ¢ less.

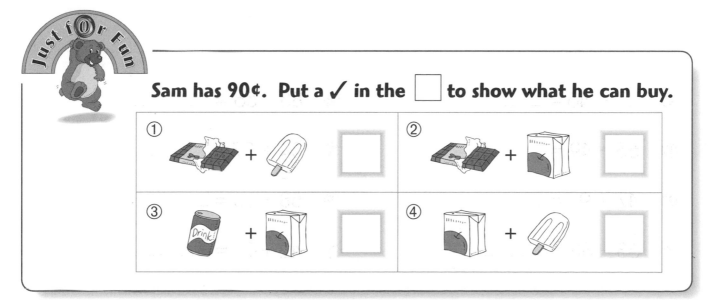

Sam has 90¢. Put a ✓ in the ☐ to show what he can buy.

① ▨ + 🍦 ☐   ② ▨ + 📦 ☐

③ 🥤 + 📦 ☐   ④ 📦 + 🍦 ☐

Final Review

Add or subtract.

①
```
  3 2
+   9
```

②
```
  2 8
+ 1 7
```

③
```
  3 6
-   4
```

④
```
  5 2
-   9
```

⑤
```
  7 9
- 5 1
```

⑥
```
  8 4
- 6 6
```

⑦
```
  4 9
+   8
```

⑧
```
  2 1
+ 4 5
```

⑨
```
  4 6
+ 2 5
```

⑩
```
  9 2
- 3 7
```

⑪
```
  1 8
+ 6 2
```

⑫
```
  6 0
- 4 1
```

⑬
```
  5 8
- 2 2
```

⑭
```
  1 4
+ 5 5
```

⑮
```
  7 3
- 3 0
```

⑯
```
  2 3
+ 4 7
```

⑰ $27 + 46 =$ _____

⑱ $83 - 56 =$ _____

⑲ $65 - 49 =$ _____

⑳ $34 + 57 =$ _____

㉑ $47 + 9 \ =$ _____

㉒ $58 - 16 =$ _____

㉓ $63 - 38 =$ _____

㉔ $42 + 7 \ =$ _____

Estimate the sums or differences by rounding the numbers to the nearest 10. Compare the estimates with the exact answers.

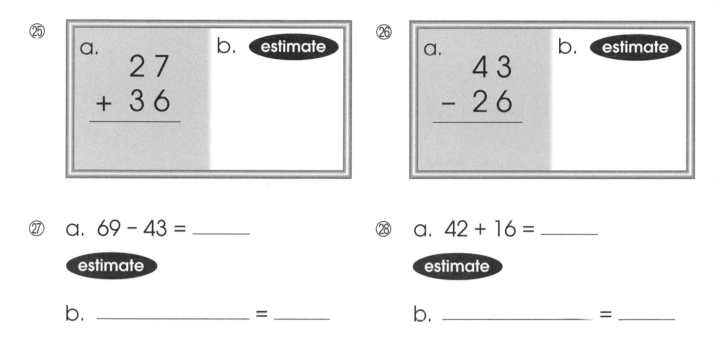

㉕
a.
$$\begin{array}{r} 2\,7 \\ +\ 3\,6 \\ \hline \end{array}$$
b. estimate

㉖
a.
$$\begin{array}{r} 4\,3 \\ -\ 2\,6 \\ \hline \end{array}$$
b. estimate

㉗ a. 69 − 43 = _____

estimate

b. _____ = _____

㉘ a. 42 + 16 = _____

estimate

b. _____ = _____

Subtract. Check the answers using addition.

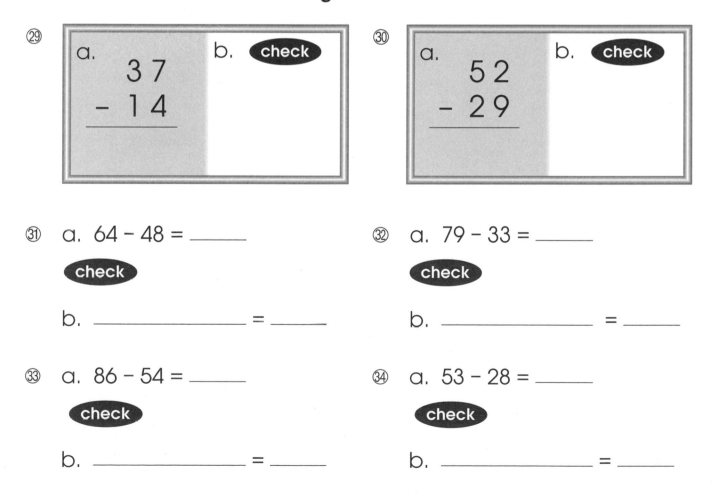

㉙
a.
$$\begin{array}{r} 3\,7 \\ -\ 1\,4 \\ \hline \end{array}$$
b. check

㉚
a.
$$\begin{array}{r} 5\,2 \\ -\ 2\,9 \\ \hline \end{array}$$
b. check

㉛ a. 64 − 48 = _____

check

b. _____ = _____

㉜ a. 79 − 33 = _____

check

b. _____ = _____

㉝ a. 86 − 54 = _____

check

b. _____ = _____

㉞ a. 53 − 28 = _____

check

b. _____ = _____

Complete.

③⑤ $8 + 3 = 10 +$ _____ = _____

③⑥ $19 + 26 = 20 +$ _____ = _____

③⑦ $13 + 29 =$ _____ $+ 30 =$ _____

③⑧ $25 + 38 =$ _____ $+ 40 =$ _____

③⑨ a. $9 - 6 =$ _____   ④⓪ a. $62 - 9 =$ _____

　 b. $19 - 6 =$ _____   　 b. $62 - 19 =$ _____

　 c. $29 - 6 =$ _____   　 c. $62 - 29 =$ _____

　 d. $39 - 6 =$ _____   　 d. $62 - 39 =$ _____

Fill in the numbers.

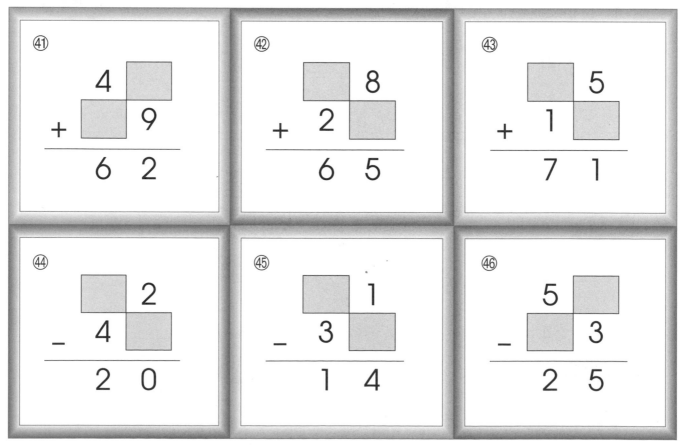

Find the answers.

47 9 + 7 − 6 = _____

48 5 + 7 + 8 = _____

49 8 − 3 + 6 = _____

50 7 + 2 − 4 = _____

51 69 − 23 + 17

= _____ + 17

= _____

52 14 + 35 − 26

= _____ − 26

= _____

53 22 + 36 − 49

= _____ − 49

= _____

54 72 − 58 + 13

= _____ + 13

= _____

The children are shopping. Put a ✓ in the ⬡ to show what they buy.

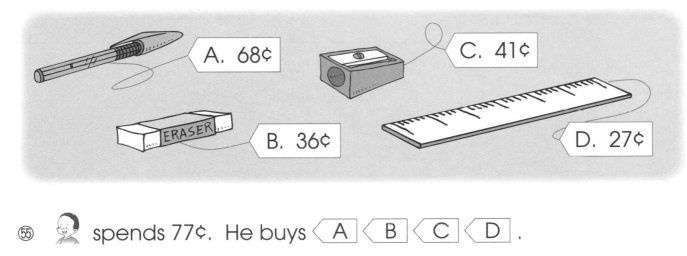

A. 68¢   C. 41¢   B. 36¢   D. 27¢

55 spends 77¢. He buys ⟨A ⟨B ⟨C ⟨D .

56 spends 63¢. He buys ⟨A ⟨B ⟨C ⟨D .

57 gets 32¢ change from 100¢. She buys ⟨A ⟨B ⟨C ⟨D .

Complete.

58. Mom buys 8 red 🌹 and 25 yellow 🌹 . How many 🌹 does she buy in all?

    $$\begin{array}{r} 8 \\ + 2\,5 \\ \hline \end{array}$$

    _____ 🌹 in all.

59. There are 23 girls and 19 boys on the school bus. How many children are there on the school bus altogether?

    _____ children altogether.

60. Sue has 92¢. She spends 57¢ for a 🥤 . How many ¢ does she have left?

    _____ ¢ left.

61. There are 26 children in a class. 17 children are reading. How many children are not reading?

    _____ children.

62. Jack buys a 🍫 for 69¢. Jane buys a 🍭 for 35¢. How many more ¢ does Jack spend than Jane?

    _____ ¢ more.

63. There are 38 🧁 and 45 🍪 in a cake shop. How many 🧁 🍪 are there altogether in the cake shop?

    _____ 🧁 🍪 altogether.

Section III

Overview

In Section II, addition and subtraction skills were practised. In this section, children are expected to be able to apply the skills in other areas, such as measurement, patterning and graphs.

In addition, real-life situations are provided for them to develop other skills, including multiplication and division, fractions and decimals, transformations, graphing and measurement.

Through practice in naming and stating the value of different coins, children are able to put coins in sets up to $1 in value.

3-digit Numbers

Hi, I'm Nicky. I've collected many baseball cards.

Look at the cards of my favourite baseball players' uniforms. I have laid them out in order.

Write the missing numbers on the 👕 .

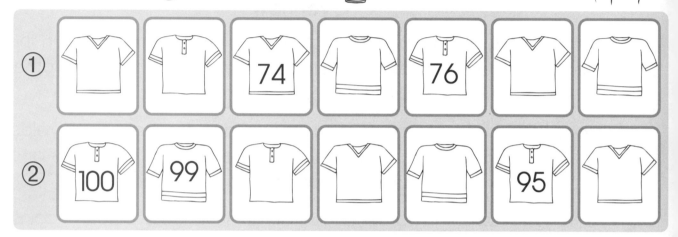

① ___ ___ 74 ___ 76 ___ ___

② 100 99 ___ ___ ___ ___ 95

Nicky has put his cards in piles of 10. Help him count and write the numbers.

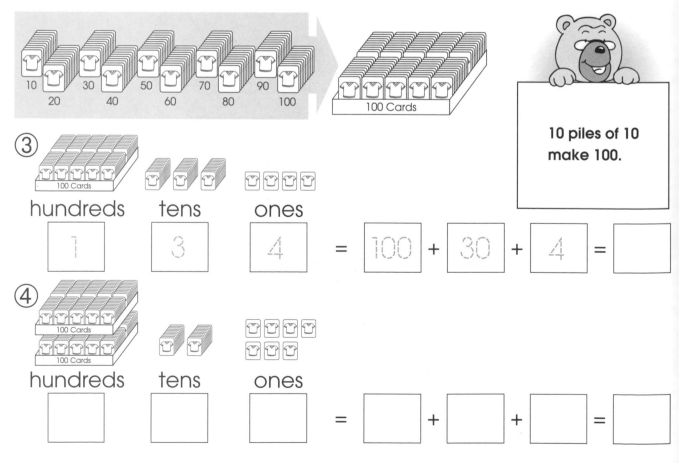

10 20 30 40 50 60 70 80 90 100

100 Cards

10 piles of 10 make 100.

③

100 Cards

hundreds   tens   ones

| 1 | 3 | 4 | = | 100 | + | 30 | + | 4 | = | |

④

100 Cards
100 Cards

hundreds   tens   ones

| | | | = | | + | | + | | = | |

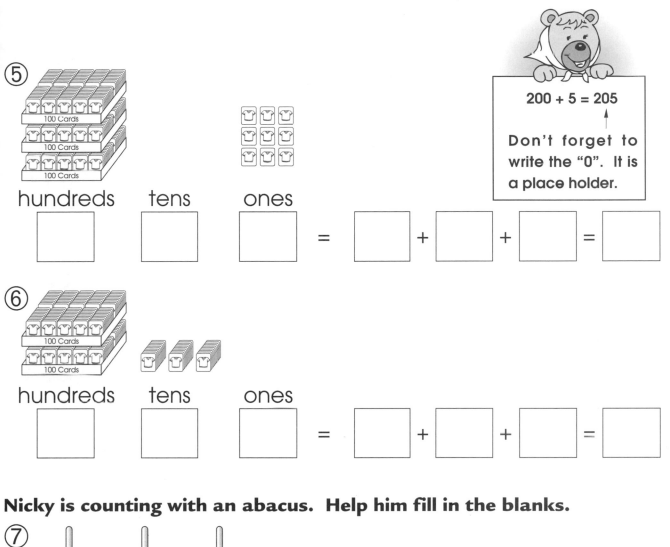

⑤

hundreds   tens   ones

[ ]   [ ]   [ ]   =   [ ]   +   [ ]   +   [ ]   =   [ ]

200 + 5 = 205

Don't forget to write the "0". It is a place holder.

⑥

hundreds   tens   ones

[ ]   [ ]   [ ]   =   [ ]   +   [ ]   +   [ ]   =   [ ]

Nicky is counting with an abacus. Help him fill in the blanks.

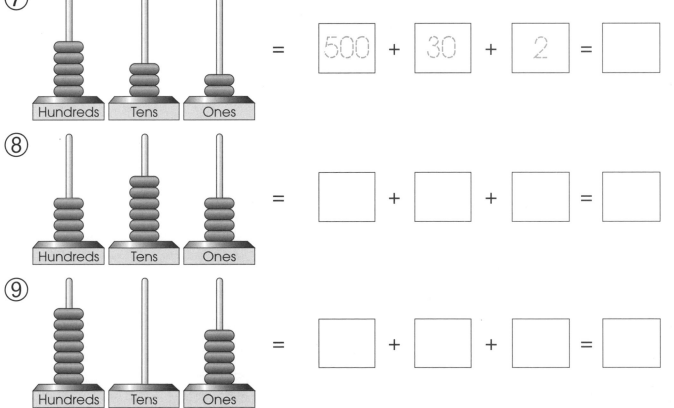

⑦   =   500   +   30   +   2   =   [ ]

⑧   =   [ ]   +   [ ]   +   [ ]   =   [ ]

⑨   =   [ ]   +   [ ]   +   [ ]   =   [ ]

Match the bats with the gloves.

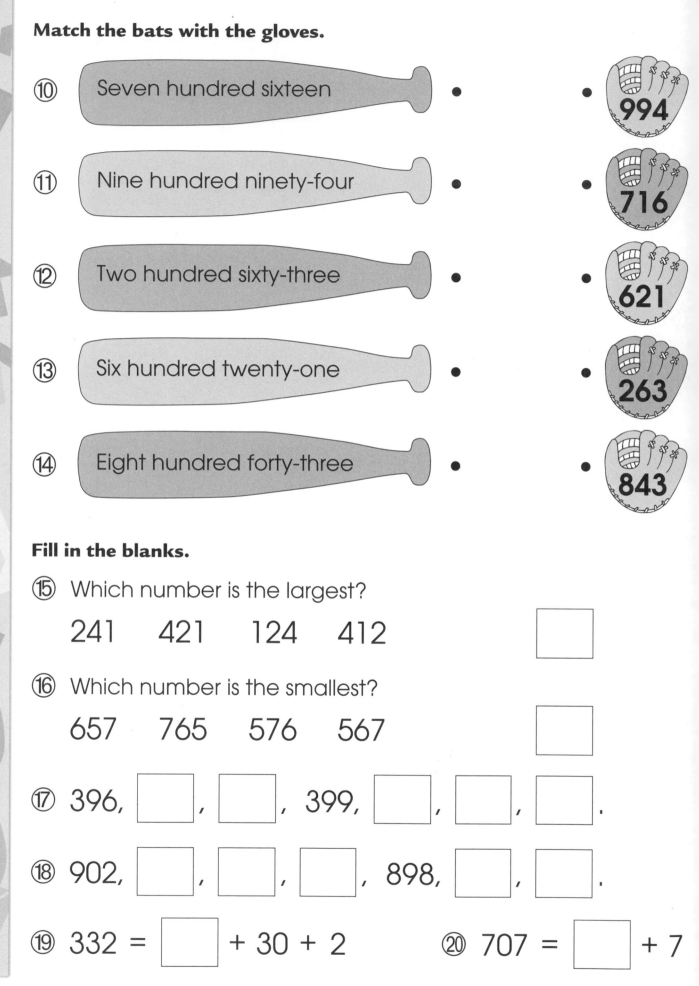

⑩ Seven hundred sixteen

⑪ Nine hundred ninety-four

⑫ Two hundred sixty-three

⑬ Six hundred twenty-one

⑭ Eight hundred forty-three

994
716
621
263
843

Fill in the blanks.

⑮ Which number is the largest?

241   421   124   412

⑯ Which number is the smallest?

657   765   576   567

⑰ 396, ☐ , ☐ , 399, ☐ , ☐ , ☐ .

⑱ 902, ☐ , ☐ , ☐ , 898, ☐ , ☐ .

⑲ 332 = ☐ + 30 + 2   ⑳ 707 = ☐ + 7

Look at Nicky's baseball cards. Circle the right answers.

㉑ How many cards are there in all?   30   31   32

㉒ How many  are there?   10   11   12

㉓ How many  are there?   12   13   14

㉔ Which is the 21st?

㉕ Which is the 29th?

ACTIVITY

Answer the questions.

1. These numbers follow a pattern.

   What comes next?

   123   234   345   _____   _____

2. How many 3-digit numbers can be made

   with 0, 4 and 7? _____ .

   They are _____ .

2 Addition and Subtraction

Nicky and Tim are counting their cards. Write the numbers.

	16	14	49
	36	27	12

Remember to carry groups of 10 to the tens column.

① How many cards do they have in all?

a.
```
  1 6
+ 3 6
------
```

b.
```
+ 
------
```

c.
```
+ 
------
```

② How many does have more than ?

□ – □ = □

```
-
------
```

has □ more than .

③ How many does have more than ?

□ – □ = □

```
-
------
```

has □ more than .

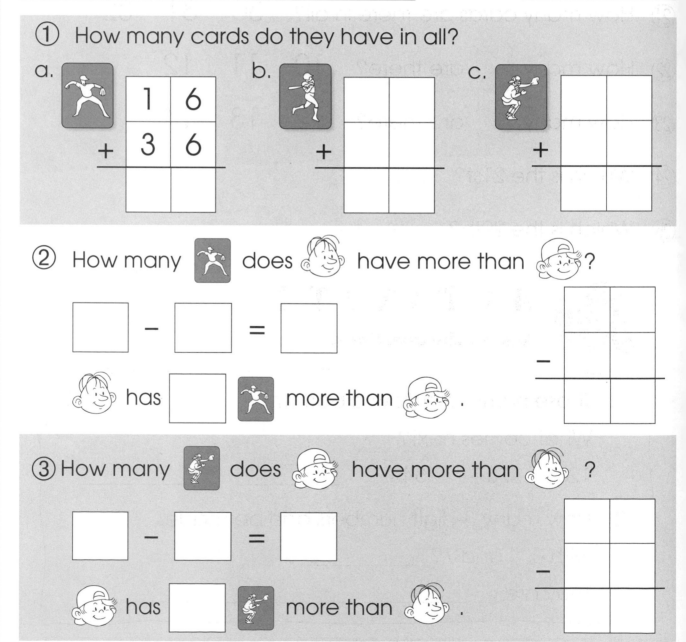

$$5 - 3 = 2 \qquad 2 + 3 = 5$$

How many cards does Nicky have?

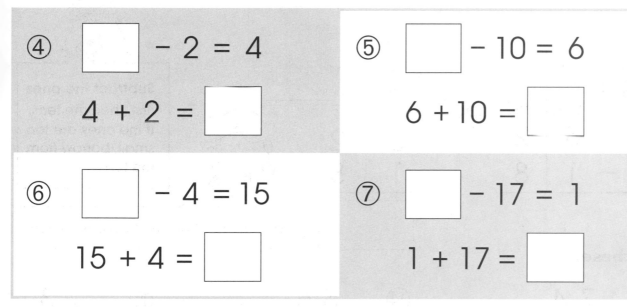

④ $\boxed{} - 2 = 4$

$4 + 2 = \boxed{}$

⑤ $\boxed{} - 10 = 6$

$6 + 10 = \boxed{}$

⑥ $\boxed{} - 4 = 15$

$15 + 4 = \boxed{}$

⑦ $\boxed{} - 17 = 1$

$1 + 17 = \boxed{}$

Put the sign + or - in the ○ .

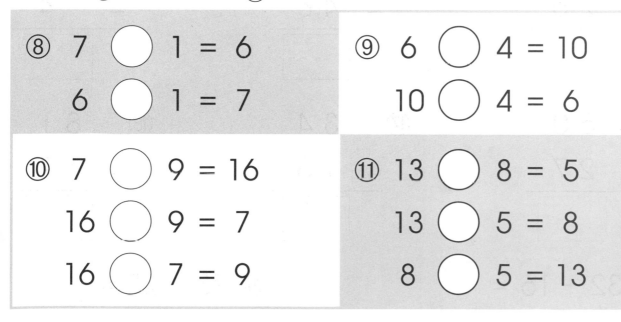

⑧ $7 \bigcirc 1 = 6$

$6 \bigcirc 1 = 7$

⑨ $6 \bigcirc 4 = 10$

$10 \bigcirc 4 = 6$

⑩ $7 \bigcirc 9 = 16$

$16 \bigcirc 9 = 7$

$16 \bigcirc 7 = 9$

⑪ $13 \bigcirc 8 = 5$

$13 \bigcirc 5 = 8$

$8 \bigcirc 5 = 13$

Find how many cards Nicky will have.

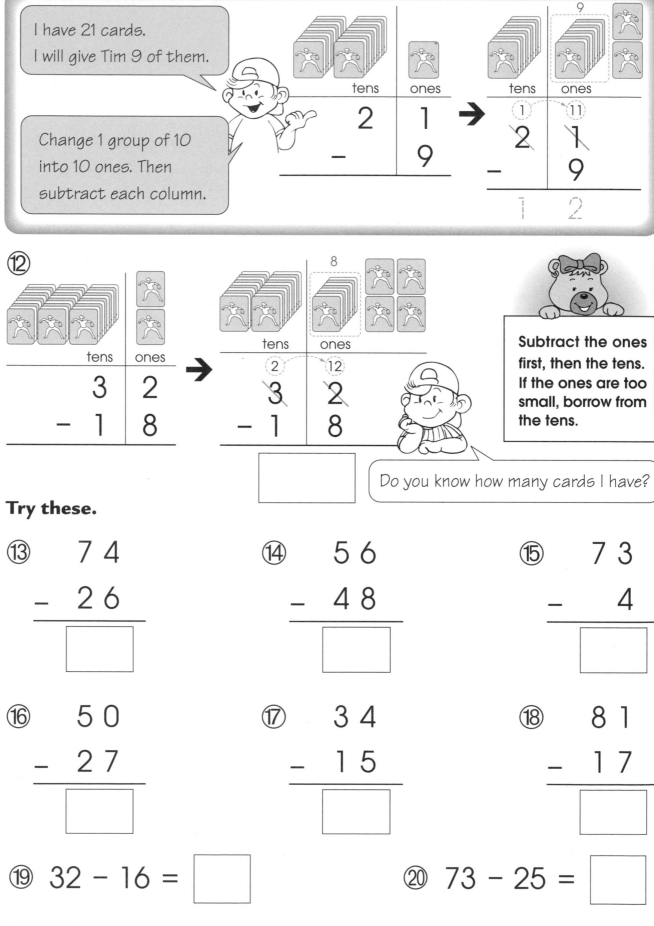

I have 21 cards.
I will give Tim 9 of them.

Change 1 group of 10 into 10 ones. Then subtract each column.

tens	ones
2	1
–	9

tens	ones
2	1
–	9
1	2

⑫

tens	ones
3	2
– 1	8

tens	ones
3	2
– 1	8

Subtract the ones first, then the tens. If the ones are too small, borrow from the tens.

Do you know how many cards I have?

Try these.

⑬
```
  7 4
- 2 6
```

⑭
```
  5 6
- 4 8
```

⑮
```
  7 3
-   4
```

⑯
```
  5 0
- 2 7
```

⑰
```
  3 4
- 1 5
```

⑱
```
  8 1
- 1 7
```

⑲ 32 – 16 =

⑳ 73 – 25 =

Help Nicky count the food and drinks for his uncle.

1st	Add the ones.
2nd	Add the tens.
3rd	Add the hundreds.

㉑

```
    2  1  3
+   3  7  1
_____
```

㉒

```
    3  2  5
+   2  7  3
_____
```

㉓

```
    1  2  6
+   3  6  2
_____
```

㉔

```
    5  3  6
+   1  0  2
_____
```

```
    4  1  6
+   1  2  9
_____
    5  4  5
```

Carry groups of 10 from the ones column to the tens column.

㉕

```
    3  5  7
+   1  3  7
_____
```

㉖

```
    2  6  3
+   1  1  9
_____
```

㉗

```
    1  3  8
+   3  2  6
_____
```

㉘

```
    2  3  7
+   2  0  8
_____
```

㉙

```
       3  4
+   1  2  8
_____
```

㉚

```
    1  0  9
+      7  5
_____
```

Find the points Nicky got in the game.

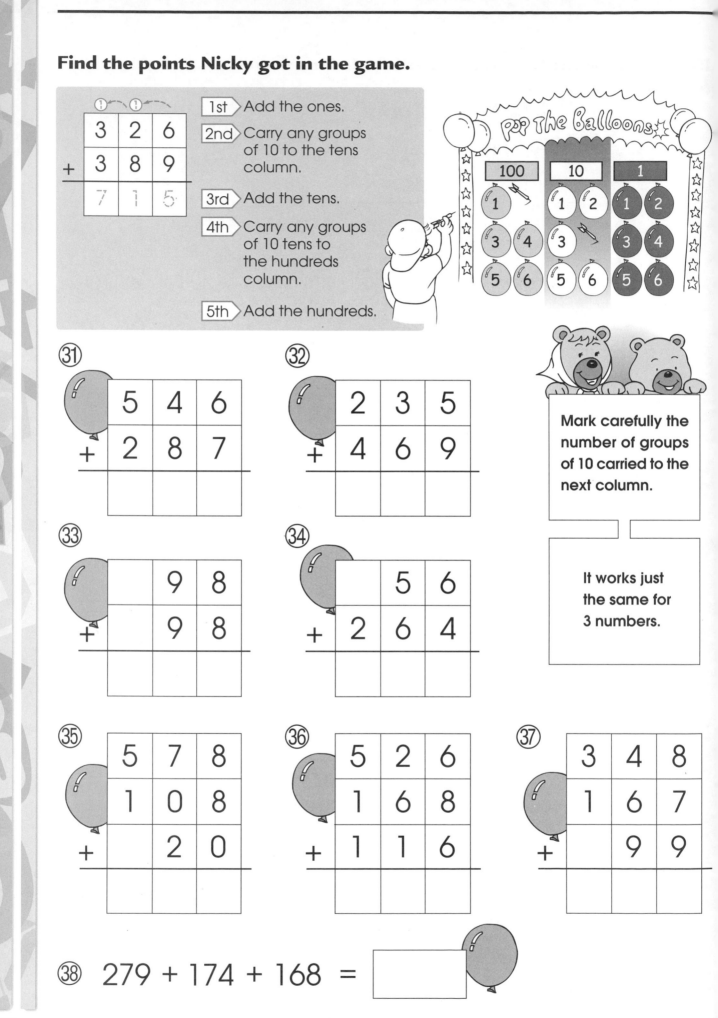

	3	2	6
+	3	8	9
	7	1	5

1st ▷ Add the ones.

2nd ▷ Carry any groups of 10 to the tens column.

3rd ▷ Add the tens.

4th ▷ Carry any groups of 10 tens to the hundreds column.

5th ▷ Add the hundreds.

pop the balloons

100	10	1

Mark carefully the number of groups of 10 carried to the next column.

It works just the same for 3 numbers.

31

	5	4	6
+	2	8	7

32

	2	3	5
+	4	6	9

33

		9	8
+		9	8

34

		5	6
+	2	6	4

35

	5	7	8
	1	0	8
+		2	0

36

	5	2	6
	1	6	8
+	1	1	6

37

	3	4	8
	1	6	7
+		9	9

38 279 + 174 + 168 = ☐

Nicky has traded some cards with his friends. How many cards does he have now? Write the numbers.

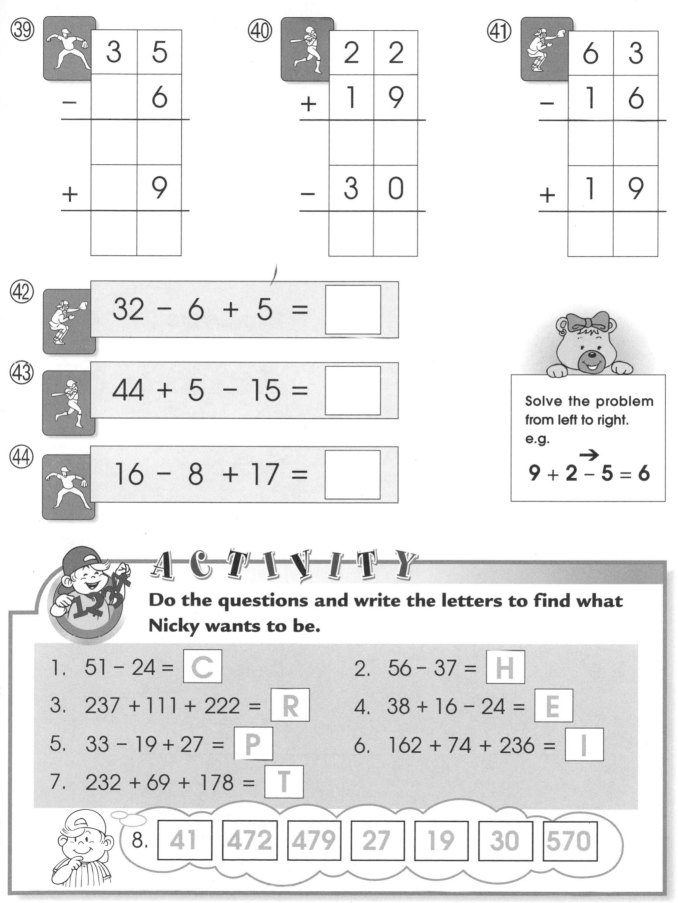

39)

	3	5
−		6
+		9

40)

	2	2
+	1	9
−	3	0

41)

	6	3
−	1	6
+	1	9

42) 32 − 6 + 5 = ☐

43) 44 + 5 − 15 = ☐

44) 16 − 8 + 17 = ☐

Solve the problem from left to right.
e.g.

→
9 + 2 − 5 = 6

ACTIVITY

Do the questions and write the letters to find what Nicky wants to be.

1. 51 − 24 = **C**

2. 56 − 37 = **H**

3. 237 + 111 + 222 = **R**

4. 38 + 16 − 24 = **E**

5. 33 − 19 + 27 = **P**

6. 162 + 74 + 236 = **I**

7. 232 + 69 + 178 = **T**

8. | 41 | 472 | 479 | 27 | 19 | 30 | 570 |

3 Multiplication

Adding groups of the same size is the same as multiplying.

2 + 2 + 2 = 3 twos
= 6

6 = 3 times 2
= 3 x 2

Help Nicky count the stickers he has. Write the numbers.

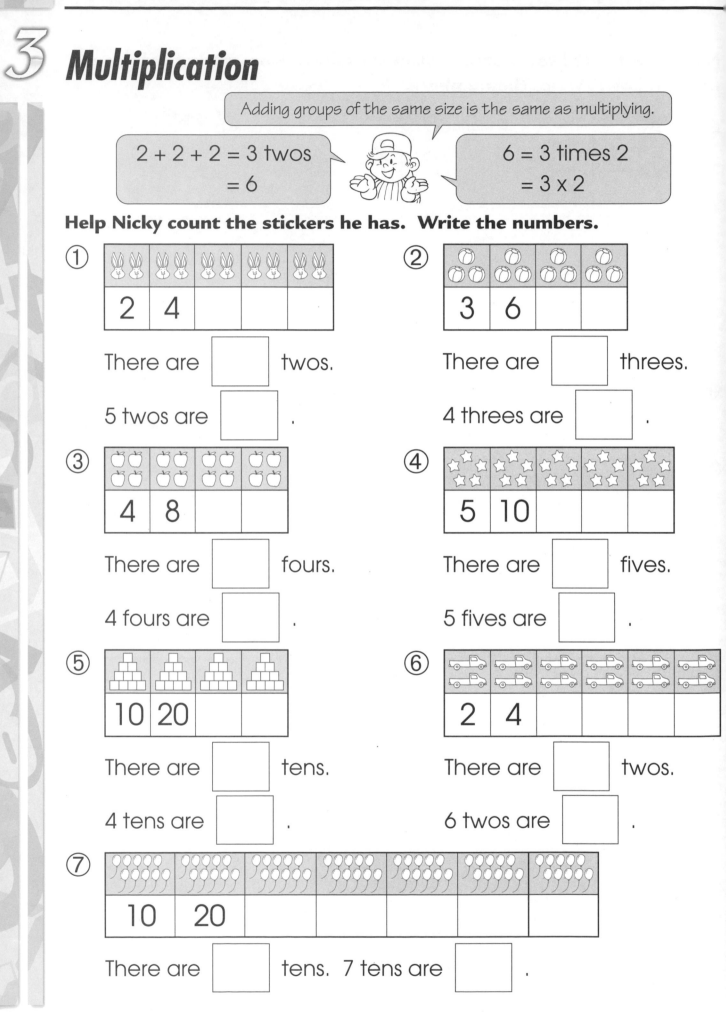

①

| 2 | 4 | | | |

There are ☐ twos.

5 twos are ☐ .

②

| 3 | 6 | | |

There are ☐ threes.

4 threes are ☐ .

③

| 4 | 8 | | |

There are ☐ fours.

4 fours are ☐ .

④

| 5 | 10 | | | |

There are ☐ fives.

5 fives are ☐ .

⑤

| 10 | 20 | | |

There are ☐ tens.

4 tens are ☐ .

⑥

| 2 | 4 | | | | |

There are ☐ twos.

6 twos are ☐ .

⑦

| 10 | 20 | | | | | |

There are ☐ tens. 7 tens are ☐ .

Nicky and his family had a barbecue yesterday. Count and write the amount of food they ate.

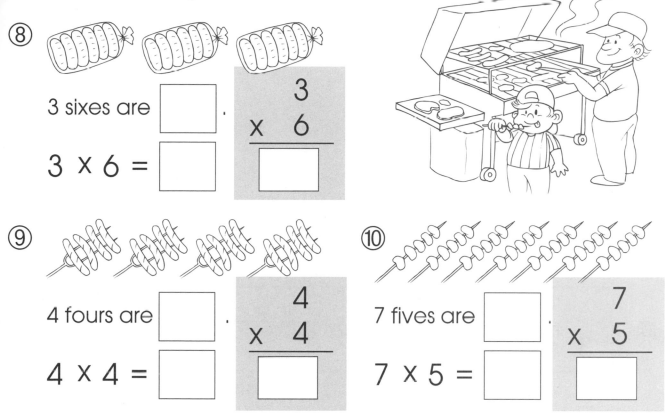

⑧

3 sixes are ☐ .

3 × 6 = ☐

$$\begin{array}{r} 3 \\ \times\ 6 \\ \hline \square \end{array}$$

⑨

4 fours are ☐ .

4 × 4 = ☐

$$\begin{array}{r} 4 \\ \times\ 4 \\ \hline \square \end{array}$$

⑩

7 fives are ☐ .

7 × 5 = ☐

$$\begin{array}{r} 7 \\ \times\ 5 \\ \hline \square \end{array}$$

Find out the number of bugs in Nicky's backyard.

3 twos = 3 times 2
= 3 × 2 = 6

⑪ 4 times 3 = 4 × ☐ = ☐

⑫ 4 times ☐ = ☐ × ☐ = ☐

⑬ 2 times ☐ = ☐ × ☐ = ☐

⑭ 7 times ☐ = ☐ × ☐ = ☐

Colour the first 3 red, the second 3 yellow and the third 3 green. Follow the pattern to 30. Then complete the table.

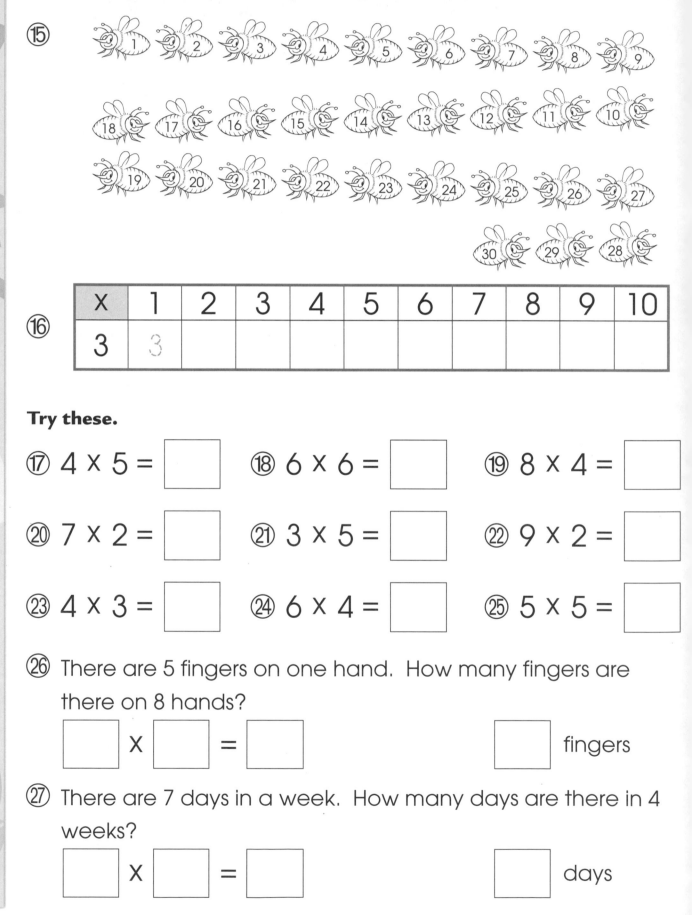

⑮

X	1	2	3	4	5	6	7	8	9	10
3	3									

⑯

Try these.

⑰ 4 X 5 = ☐

⑱ 6 X 6 = ☐

⑲ 8 X 4 = ☐

⑳ 7 X 2 = ☐

㉑ 3 X 5 = ☐

㉒ 9 X 2 = ☐

㉓ 4 X 3 = ☐

㉔ 6 X 4 = ☐

㉕ 5 X 5 = ☐

㉖ There are 5 fingers on one hand. How many fingers are there on 8 hands?

☐ X ☐ = ☐   ☐ fingers

㉗ There are 7 days in a week. How many days are there in 4 weeks?

☐ X ☐ = ☐   ☐ days

Read what Nicky and Tim say. Write the numbers.

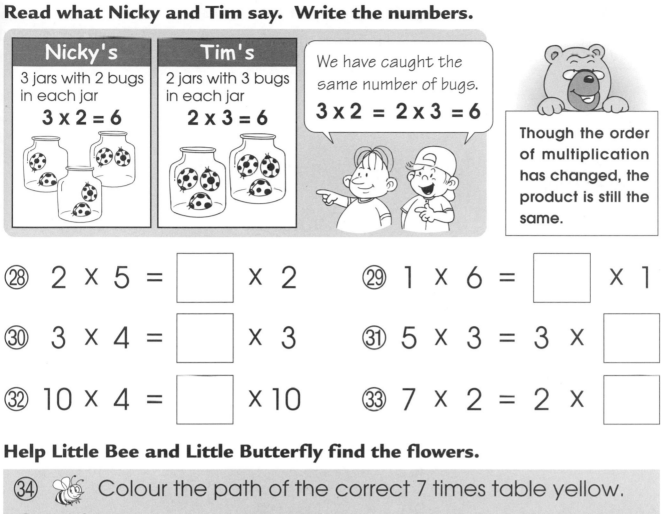

Nicky's	Tim's
3 jars with 2 bugs in each jar	2 jars with 3 bugs in each jar
3 x 2 = 6	2 x 3 = 6

We have caught the same number of bugs.
3 x 2 = 2 x 3 = 6

Though the order of multiplication has changed, the product is still the same.

㉘ 2 X 5 = ☐ X 2

㉙ 1 X 6 = ☐ X 1

㉚ 3 X 4 = ☐ X 3

㉛ 5 X 3 = 3 X ☐

㉜ 10 X 4 = ☐ X 10

㉝ 7 X 2 = 2 X ☐

Help Little Bee and Little Butterfly find the flowers.

㉞ Colour the path of the correct 7 times table yellow.

㉟ Colour the path of the correct 6 times table orange.

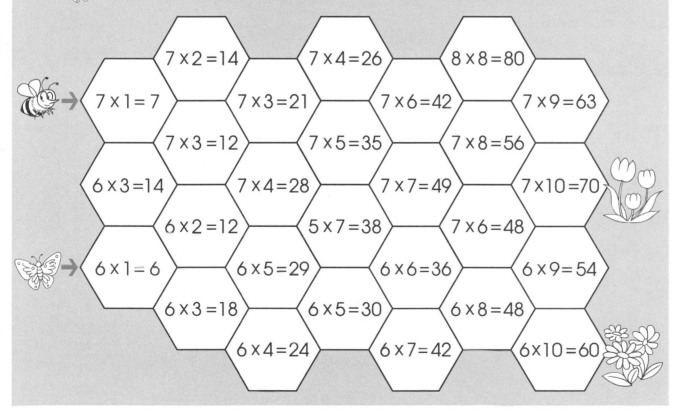

7 x 2 = 14
7 x 4 = 26
8 x 8 = 80
7 x 1 = 7
7 x 3 = 21
7 x 6 = 42
7 x 9 = 63
7 x 3 = 12
7 x 5 = 35
7 x 8 = 56
6 x 3 = 14
7 x 4 = 28
7 x 7 = 49
7 x 10 = 70
6 x 2 = 12
5 x 7 = 38
7 x 6 = 48
6 x 1 = 6
6 x 5 = 29
6 x 6 = 36
6 x 9 = 54
6 x 3 = 18
6 x 5 = 30
6 x 8 = 48
6 x 4 = 24
6 x 7 = 42
6 x 10 = 60

Complete the spider webs with the right numbers.

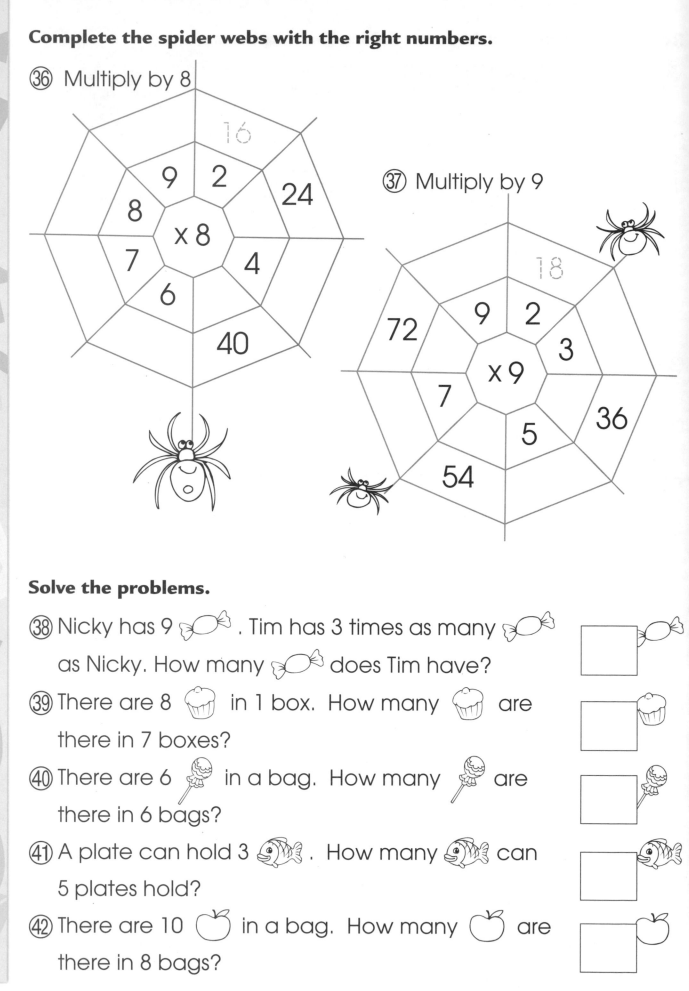

㊱ Multiply by 8

16

9   2   24

8

× 8   4

7

6

40

㊲ Multiply by 9

18

72   9   2

3

7   × 9

5   36

54

Solve the problems.

㊳ Nicky has 9 🍬 . Tim has 3 times as many 🍬 as Nicky. How many 🍬 does Tim have?

㊴ There are 8 🧁 in 1 box. How many 🧁 are there in 7 boxes?

㊵ There are 6 🍭 in a bag. How many 🍭 are there in 6 bags?

㊶ A plate can hold 3 🐟 . How many 🐟 can 5 plates hold?

㊷ There are 10 🍎 in a bag. How many 🍎 are there in 8 bags?

Count and write how many bugs Nicky and Tim have caught.

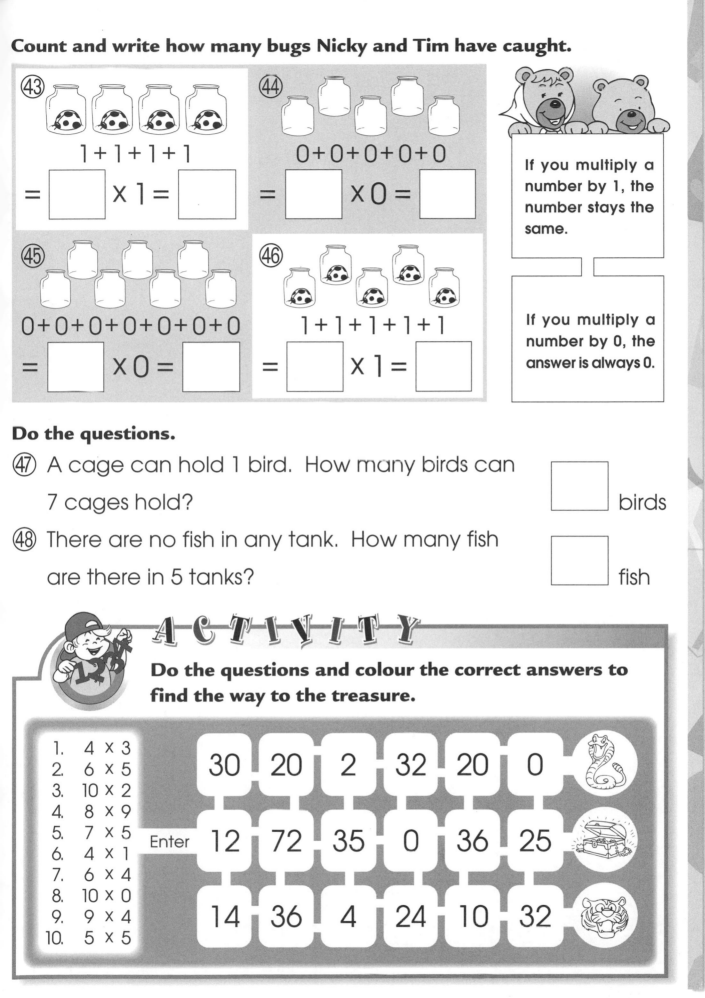

43) 1 + 1 + 1 + 1

= ☐ X 1 = ☐

44) 0 + 0 + 0 + 0 + 0

= ☐ X 0 = ☐

45) 0 + 0 + 0 + 0 + 0 + 0 + 0

= ☐ X 0 = ☐

46) 1 + 1 + 1 + 1 + 1

= ☐ X 1 = ☐

If you multiply a number by 1, the number stays the same.

If you multiply a number by 0, the answer is always 0.

Do the questions.

47) A cage can hold 1 bird. How many birds can 7 cages hold?

☐ birds

48) There are no fish in any tank. How many fish are there in 5 tanks?

☐ fish

ACTIVITY

Do the questions and colour the correct answers to find the way to the treasure.

1. 4 X 3
2. 6 X 5
3. 10 X 2
4. 8 X 9
5. 7 X 5
6. 4 X 1
7. 6 X 4
8. 10 X 0
9. 9 X 4
10. 5 X 5

| 30 | 20 | 2 | 32 | 20 | 0 |

Enter | 12 | 72 | 35 | 0 | 36 | 25 |

| 14 | 36 | 4 | 24 | 10 | 32 |

4 Length

Measure or draw the shapes.

① Write the length of the sides.

☐ cm

☐ cm

☐ cm

② Draw a square with sides of 6 cm.

1cm

1cm

Nicky has measured the things below with a metre ruler. Tick ✔ the right answers.

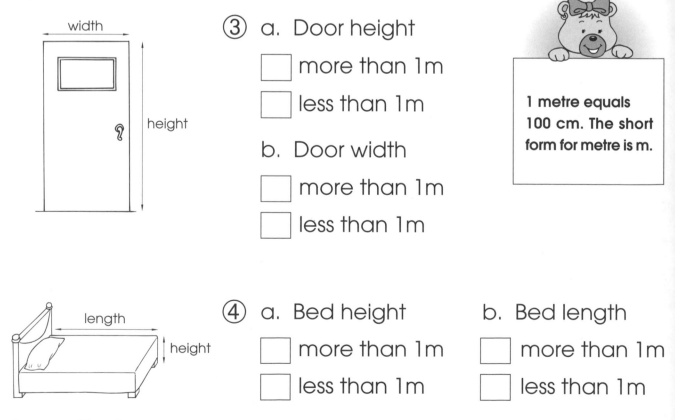

width

height

③ a. Door height

☐ more than 1m

☐ less than 1m

b. Door width

☐ more than 1m

☐ less than 1m

1 metre equals 100 cm. The short form for metre is m.

length

height

④ a. Bed height

☐ more than 1m

☐ less than 1m

b. Bed length

☐ more than 1m

☐ less than 1m

The children have measured their bedrooms. Help them write the perimeters.

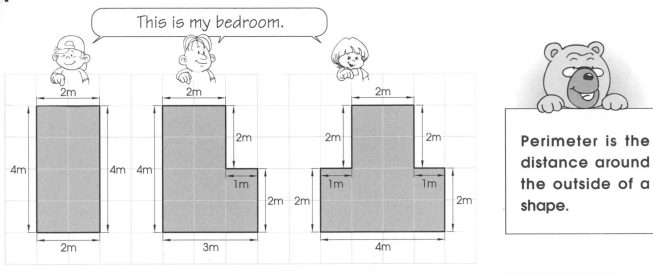

This is my bedroom.

Perimeter is the distance around the outside of a shape.

		Perimeter of bedroom		
⑤		$2 + 4 + 2 + 4$	=	m
⑥			=	m
⑦			=	m

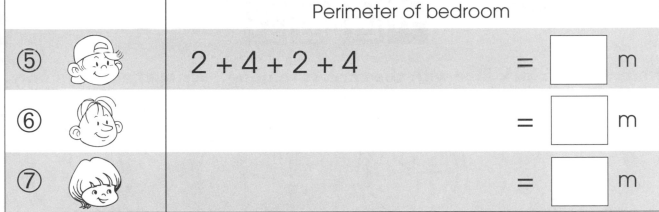

ACTIVITY

Do the question.

We want to cover our bedrooms with this carpet. How many pieces does each of us need? Use the pictures at the top of the page to help you.

Number of	Nicky's bedroom	Tim's bedroom	Jill's bedroom

2m

1m

Time and Temperature

to

Here is 5 minutes. When the minute hand goes from one digit to the next, 5 minutes has passed. When the hour hand goes from one digit to the next, 1 hour has passed.   (1 hour = 60 minutes)

minute hand

hour hand

In a digital clock, the hour is always shown on the left of :, and minutes on the right.

past

Match each clock face with the correct reading. Write the letters only.

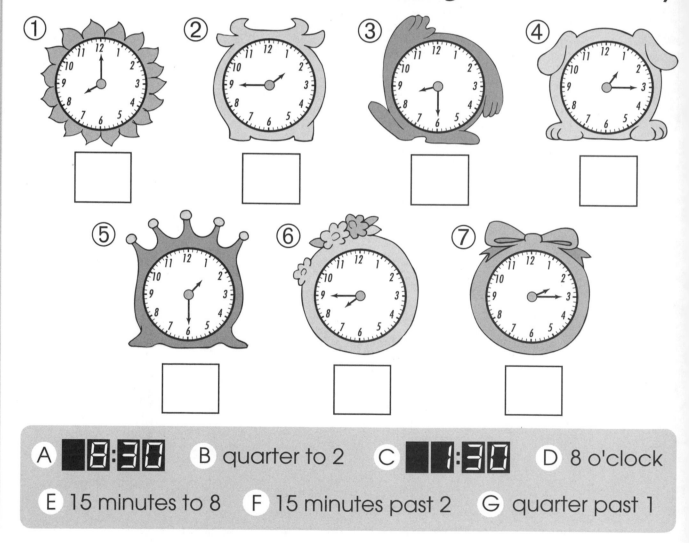

① ② ③ ④

⑤ ⑥ ⑦

A 8:30   B quarter to 2   C 1:30   D 8 o'clock

E 15 minutes to 8   F 15 minutes past 2   G quarter past 1

Write the times.

⑧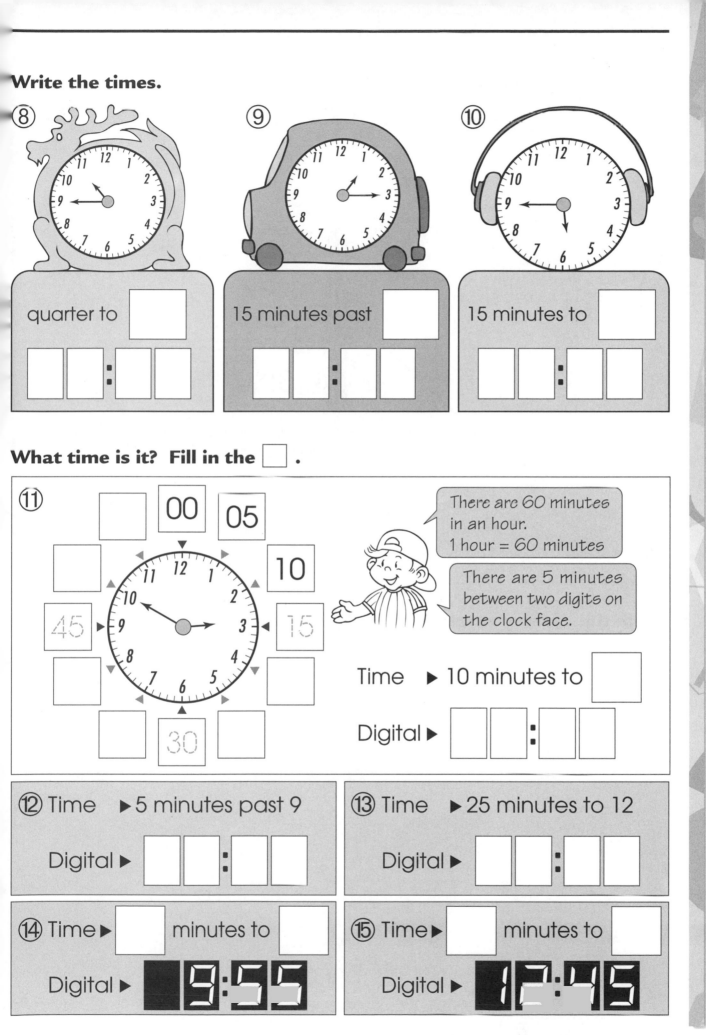

quarter to ☐

☐ ☐ : ☐ ☐

⑨

15 minutes past ☐

☐ ☐ : ☐ ☐

⑩

15 minutes to ☐

☐ ☐ : ☐ ☐

What time is it? Fill in the ☐ .

⑪

☐ 00 05

☐   10

45 ►   ⟨15⟩

☐   ☐

☐ 30 ☐

There are 60 minutes in an hour.
1 hour = 60 minutes

There are 5 minutes between two digits on the clock face.

Time ► 10 minutes to ☐

Digital ► ☐ ☐ : ☐ ☐

⑫ Time ► 5 minutes past 9

Digital ► ☐ ☐ : ☐ ☐

⑬ Time ► 25 minutes to 12

Digital ► ☐ ☐ : ☐ ☐

⑭ Time ► ☐ minutes to ☐

Digital ► **9:55**

⑮ Time ► ☐ minutes to ☐

Digital ► **12:45**

Look at the pictures. Write a.m. or p.m.

a.m. The period from midnight to noon.

p.m. The period from noon to midnight.

There are 24 hours in a day.

⑯ 10:00

10:00

⑰ 1:00

1:00

⑱ 8:30

8:30

Write the missing numbers on Nicky's calendar.

There are 7 days in a week.
The first day of a week is Sunday.

⑲ **JULY**

SUN	MON	TUE	WED	THU	FRI	SAT
			1	2	3	4
			8		10	
	13	14			17	18
19			22	23		
26			29	30	31	

Look at Nicky's calendar and help him find the answers.

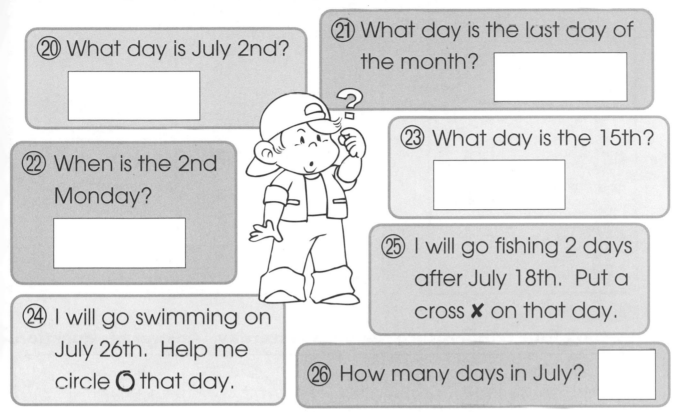

⑳ What day is July 2nd?

㉑ What day is the last day of the month?

㉒ When is the 2nd Monday?

㉓ What day is the 15th?

㉔ I will go swimming on July 26th. Help me circle ⓞ that day.

㉕ I will go fishing 2 days after July 18th. Put a cross ✖ on that day.

㉖ How many days in July?

Tim shows the number of days in each month with his fists. Answer the questions.

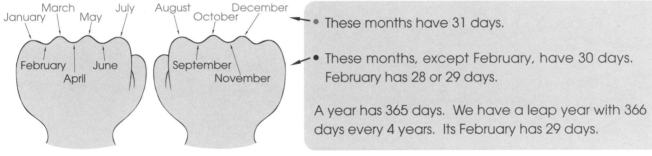

January March May July August October December
February April June September November

• These months have 31 days.

• These months, except February, have 30 days. February has 28 or 29 days.

A year has 365 days. We have a leap year with 366 days every 4 years. Its February has 29 days.

㉗ How many months have 30 days?

㉘ How many months have 31 days?

㉙ Which month has the fewest days?

㉚ How many months are there in a year?

㉛ The year 2000 is a leap year. How many days are there in its February?

Write the temperatures. Then tick ✔ the right answers.

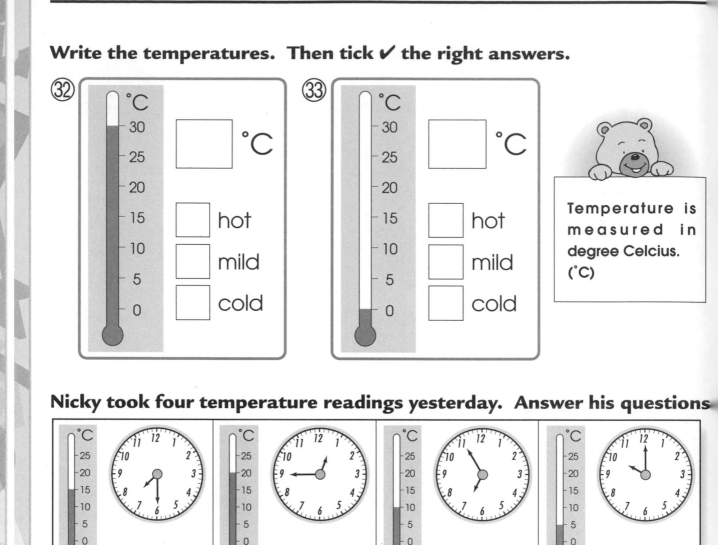

32 °C [ ] °C

hot
mild
cold

33 °C [ ] °C

hot
mild
cold

Temperature is measured in degree Celcius. (°C)

Nicky took four temperature readings yesterday. Answer his questions

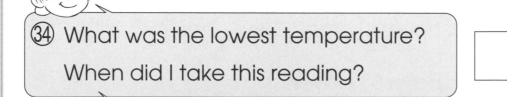

34 What was the lowest temperature?
When did I take this reading?

[ ] °C, [ ] :

35 What was the highest temperature?
When did I take this reading?

[ ] °C, [ ] :

36 How many °C higher was the morning
temperature than the night temperature?

[ ] °C

Tick ✔ **the right** ☐ **.**

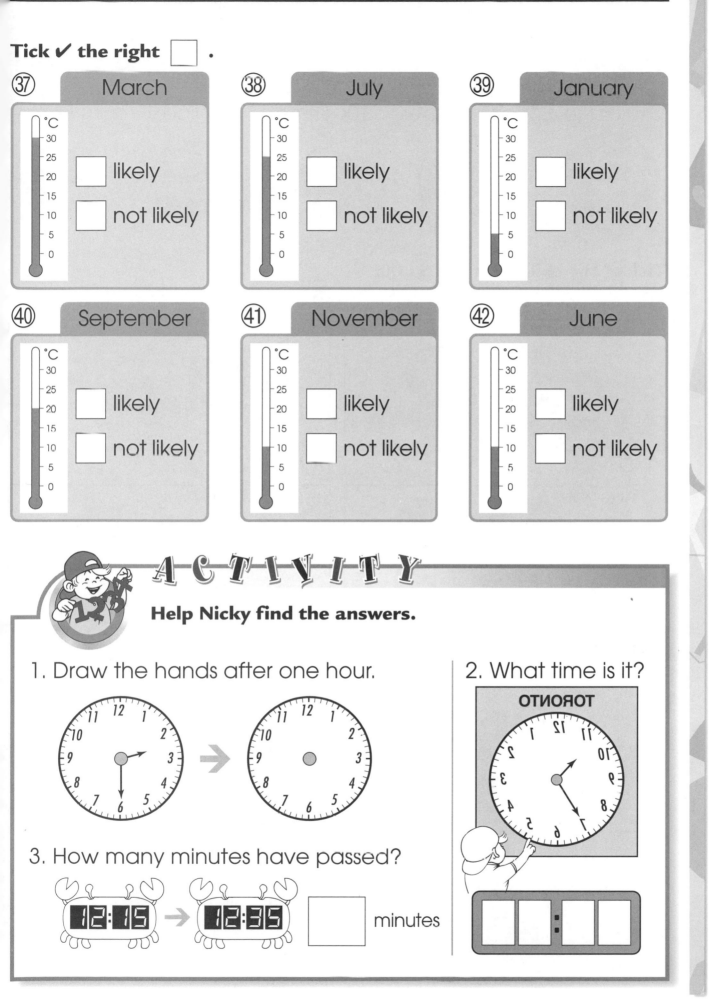

37 **March**
- ☐ likely
- ☐ not likely

38 **July**
- ☐ likely
- ☐ not likely

39 **January**
- ☐ likely
- ☐ not likely

40 **September**
- ☐ likely
- ☐ not likely

41 **November**
- ☐ likely
- ☐ not likely

42 **June**
- ☐ likely
- ☐ not likely

ACTIVITY

Help Nicky find the answers.

1. Draw the hands after one hour.

2. What time is it?

TORONTO

3. How many minutes have passed?

12:15 → 12:35   ☐ minutes

6 *Money*

$1 Loonie   25¢ Quarter   10¢ Dime   5¢ Nickel   1¢ Penny

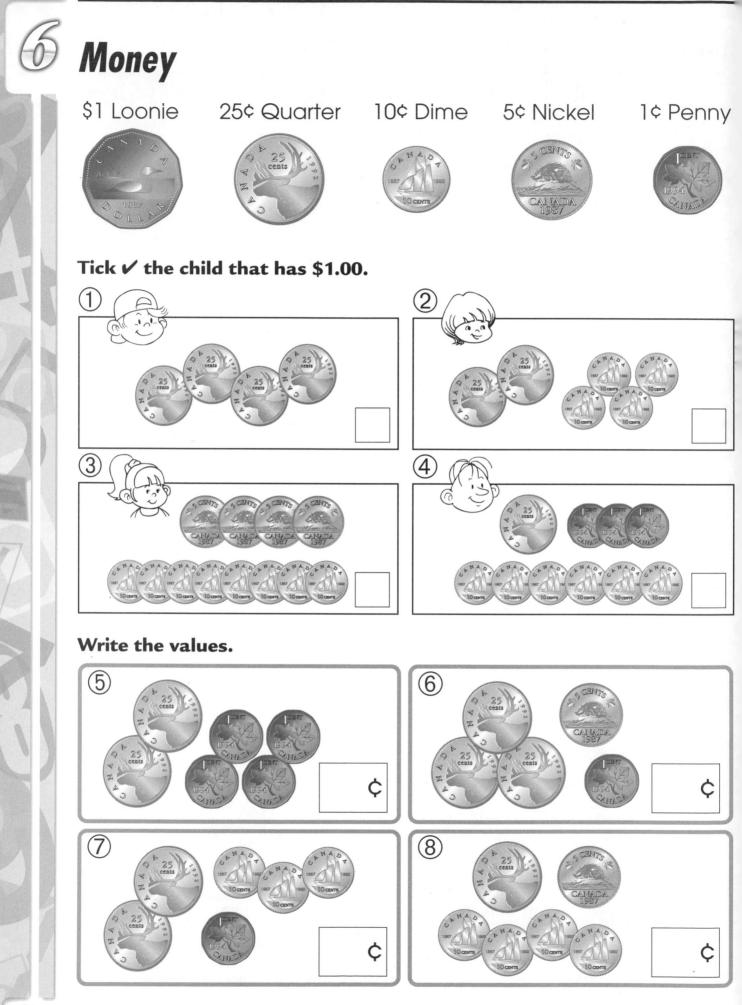

Tick ✔ the child that has $1.00.

① ②

③ ④

Write the values.

⑤ _____ ¢

⑥ _____ ¢

⑦ _____ ¢

⑧ _____ ¢

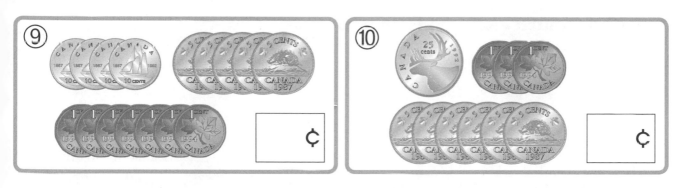

Tick ✔ the coins to match what each child says.

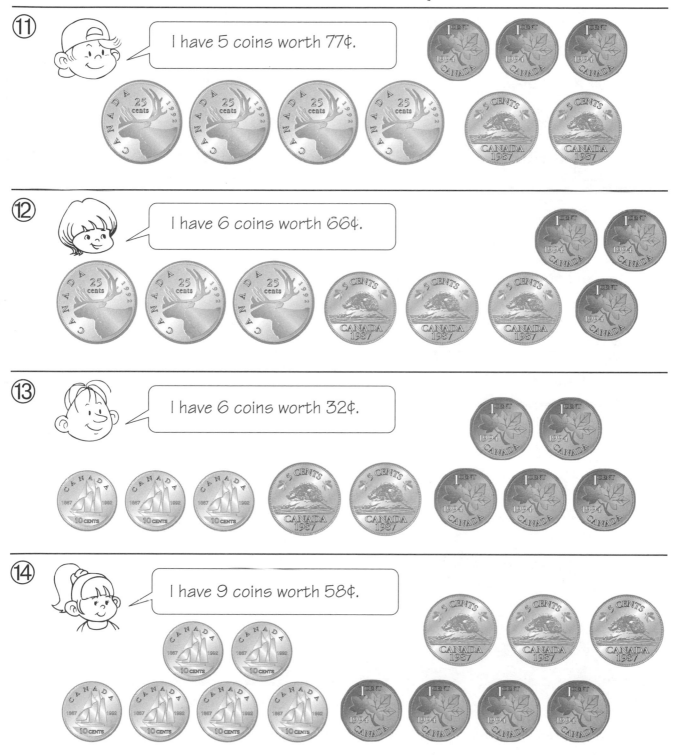

Write how much each child has left.

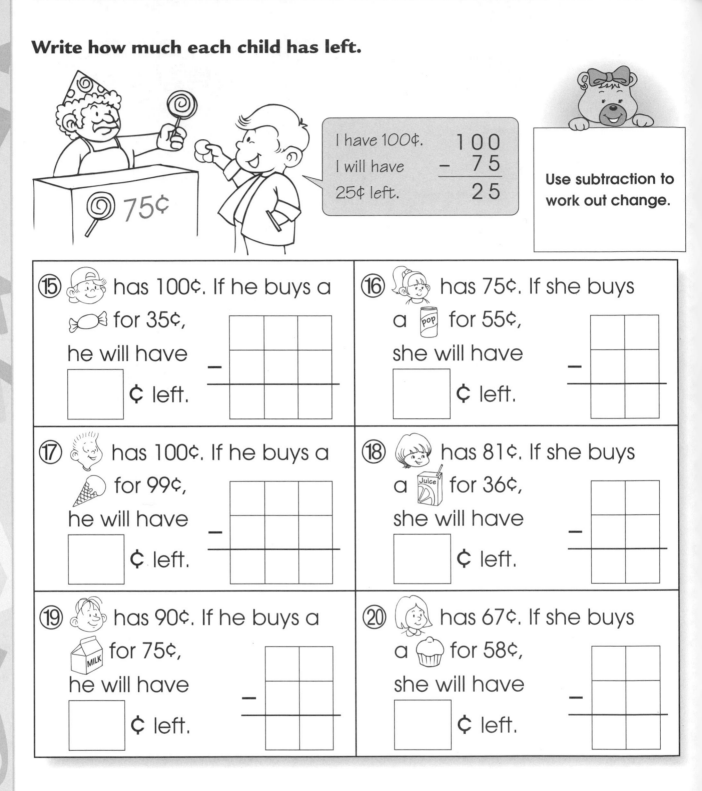

I have 100¢.
I will have
25¢ left.

```
  100
−  75
   25
```

Use subtraction to work out change.

⑮ has 100¢. If he buys a 🍬 for 35¢, he will have ⬜ ¢ left.

⑯ has 75¢. If she buys a 🥤 for 55¢, she will have ⬜ ¢ left.

⑰ has 100¢. If he buys a 🍦 for 99¢, he will have ⬜ ¢ left.

⑱ has 81¢. If she buys a 🧃 for 36¢, she will have ⬜ ¢ left.

⑲ has 90¢. If he buys a 🥛 for 75¢, he will have ⬜ ¢ left.

⑳ has 67¢. If she buys a 🧁 for 58¢, she will have ⬜ ¢ left.

Write the price of each thing. Then tick ✔ what each child has bought.

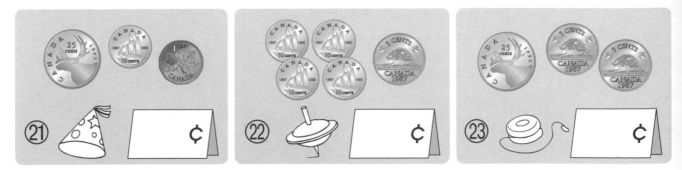

㉑ ___ ¢

㉒ ___ ¢

㉓ ___ ¢

7 Lines

How did the children ski yesterday, going straight or curved? Tick ✔ the right answers.

Straight line

Curved line

	①	②	③	④
Straight	☐	☐	☐	☐
Curved	☐	☐	☐	☐

What could you draw along to get a straight line? Circle Yes or No.

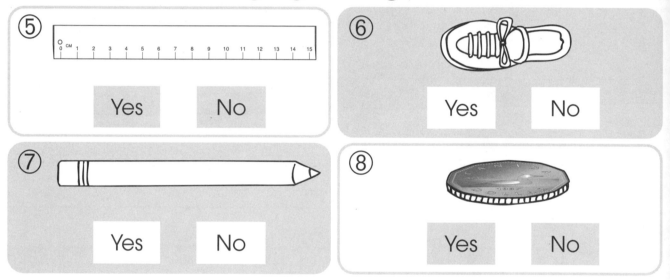

⑤ Yes   No

⑥ Yes   No

⑦ Yes   No

⑧ Yes   No

What could you use to get curves? Circle Yes or No.

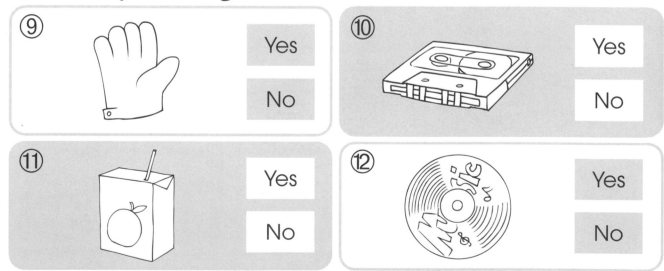

⑨ Yes   No

⑩ Yes   No

⑪ Yes   No

⑫ Yes   No

Colour the things with parallel lines.

⑬ ⑭ ⑮ ⑯

Parallel lines

Look at the lines and answer the questions.

⑰ How many straight lines? _____

⑱ _____ is a curved line.

⑲ How many pairs of parallel lines? _____

⑳ _____ and _____ are a pair of parallel lines.

_____ and _____ are a pair of parallel lines, too.

a. ——————
b. ∿∿∿
c. ——————
d. ——————
e. ——————

ACTIVITY

Help Nicky draw the lines.

Ⓐ

1. Draw a parallel line 3 rows to the left of line A.

2. Draw a parallel line 4 rows to the right of line A.

3. Are the lines you drew parallel?   Yes / No

8 2D Figures

These are Nicky's cookies. Name their shapes. Write the letters only.

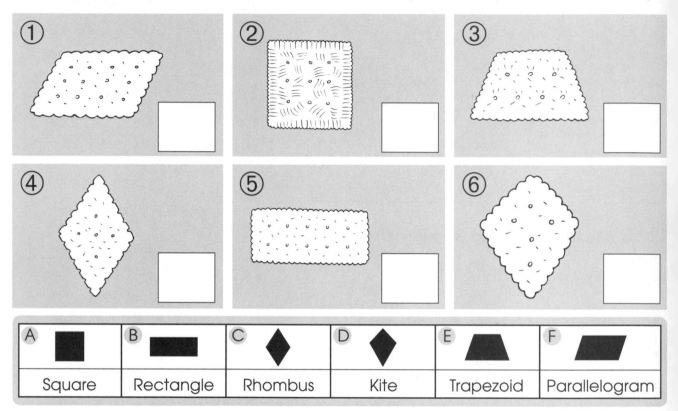

① ☐

② ☐

③ ☐

④ ☐

⑤ ☐

⑥ ☐

A ◼	B ▬	C ◆	D ◆	E ⬗	F ▰
Square	Rectangle	Rhombus	Kite	Trapezoid	Parallelogram

Nicky helps his mom make some cookies. Finish what he says.

⑦ It has _____ sides, _____ vertices and _____ pair of parallel lines. It is a _____ trapezoid _____ .

Side →
Right angle ↗
Vertex (plural = vertices)

⑧ It has _____ sides, _____ vertices, _____ right angles and _____ pairs of parallel lines. It is a _____ .

⑨ It has _____ equal sides, _____ vertices, _____ right angles and _____ pairs of parallel lines. It is a _____ .

⑩ It has _____ equal sides, _____ vertices, _____ right angles and _____ pairs of parallel lines. It is a _____ .

Draw a line or lines to show how each group of shapes can be made.

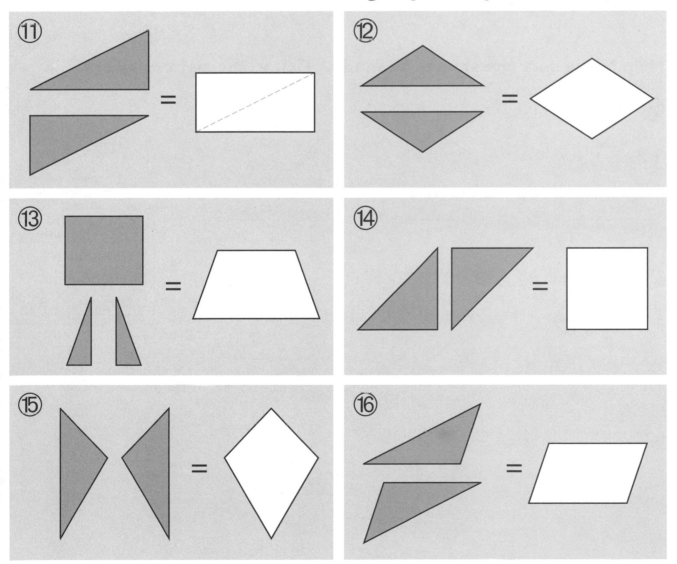

Look how Nicky folded and cut each piece of square paper. Circle the shapes he could get when he opened the paper.

You may follow what I did to find the answers.

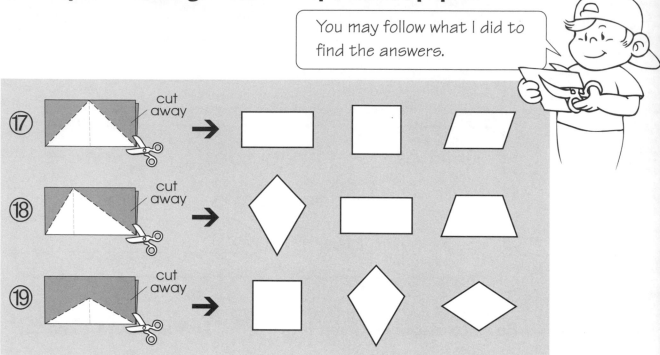

Help Nicky sort the shapes he made. Tick ✔ the right answers.

⑳ Which is __NOT__ a pentagon?

㉑ Which is __NOT__ a hexagon?

Shapes	No. of sides
Pentagon	5
Hexagon	6
Octagon	8

㉒ Which is __NOT__ an octagon?

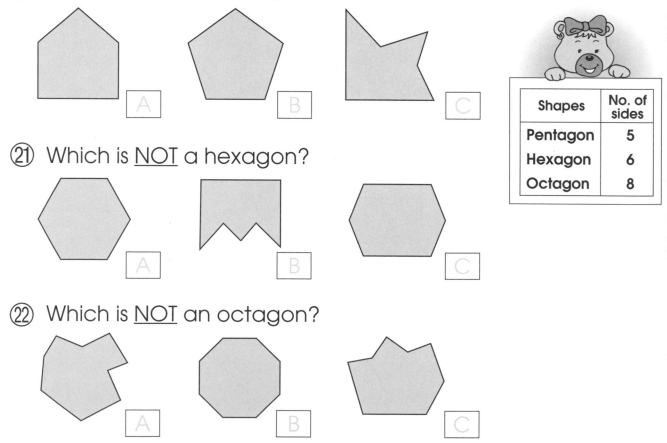

㉓ Which is a regular pentagon?

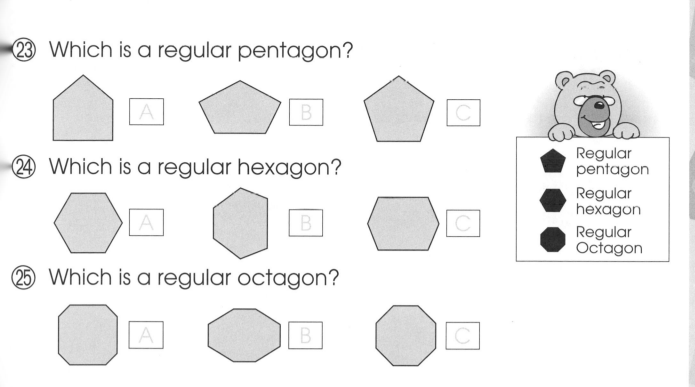

A | B | C

㉔ Which is a regular hexagon?

A | B | C

| Regular pentagon |
| Regular hexagon |
| Regular Octagon |

㉕ Which is a regular octagon?

A | B | C

Join the dots to form the shapes. Then write the number of sides and vertices in each shape.

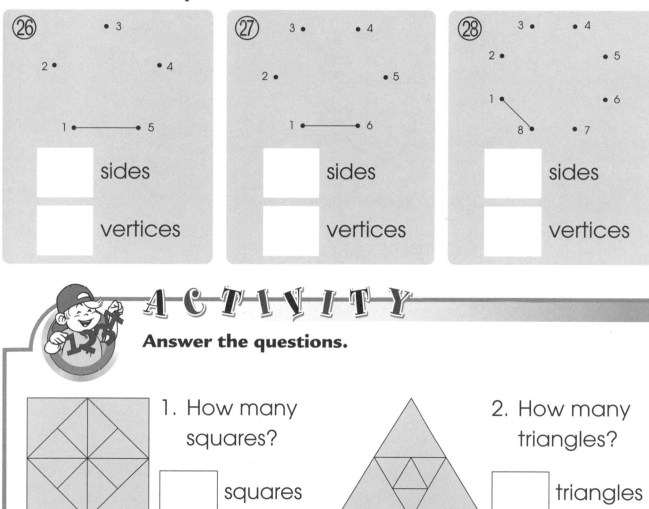

㉖
• 3
2 •   • 4
1 •———• 5

☐ sides

☐ vertices

㉗
3 •   • 4
2 •   • 5
1 •———• 6

☐ sides

☐ vertices

㉘
3 •   • 4
2 •   • 5
1 •   • 6
8 •   • 7

☐ sides

☐ vertices

ACTIVITY

Answer the questions.

1. How many squares?

☐ squares

2. How many triangles?

☐ triangles

Pictographs

Here are the favourite sports in Nicky's class. Tick ✔ the right answers.

one picture for one person

| Hockey | Baseball | Skiing | Soccer | Swimming | Skating | Basketball |

① Which is the most popular sport?   A [basketball]   B [hockey]   C [skating]

② Which is the next most popular sport?

   A [skiing]   B [hockey]   C [basketball]

③ Which sports do more people like than [skiing]?

   A [basketball] and [swimming]   B [hockey] and [skating]   C [hockey] and [basketball]

④ Which sports do fewer people like than [skating]?

   A [basketball] and [swimming]   B [swimming] and [soccer]   C [soccer] and [baseball]

⑤ How many people in Nicky's class?   A 31   B 32   C 33

Nicky and his friends are counting their toy cars. Look at the table to complete the graph and circle the right answers.

⑥ Colour the ⬜ to complete the graph.

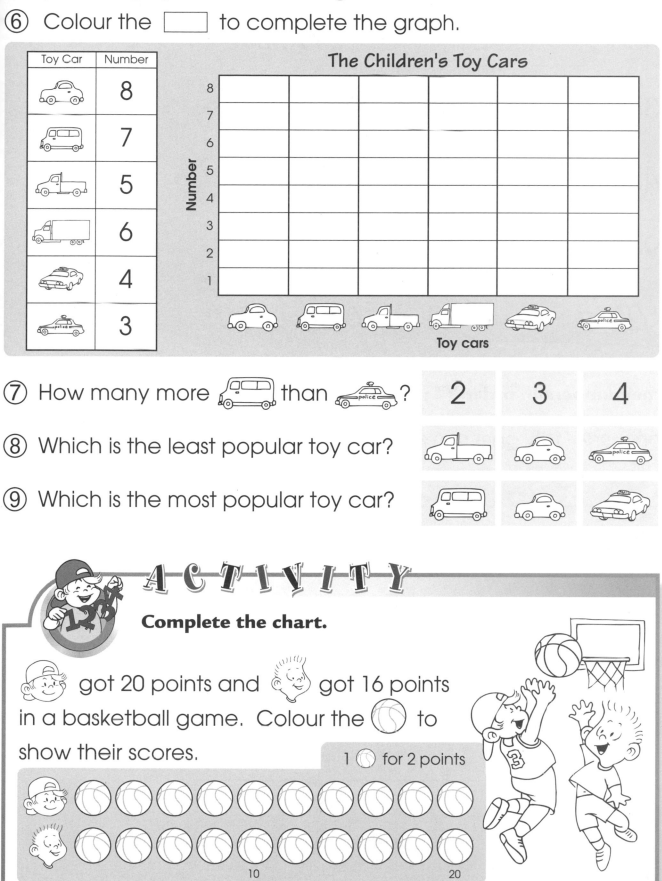

Toy Car	Number
🚗	8
🚐	7
🛻	5
🚚	6
🚓	4
🚓	3

The Children's Toy Cars

Number

Toy cars

⑦ How many more 🚐 than 🚓?   2   3   4

⑧ Which is the least popular toy car?   🛻   🚗   🚓

⑨ Which is the most popular toy car?   🚐   🚗   🚓

ACTIVITY

Complete the chart.

👦 got 20 points and 👦 got 16 points in a basketball game. Colour the ⚪ to show their scores.

1 ⚪ for 2 points

10   20

Fill in the boxes. (6 marks)

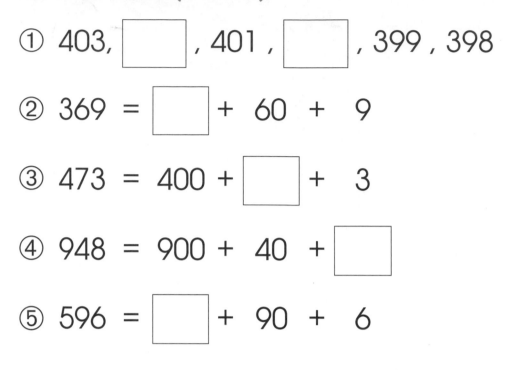

① 403, ☐ , 401 , ☐ , 399 , 398

② 369 = ☐ + 60 + 9

③ 473 = 400 + ☐ + 3

④ 948 = 900 + 40 + ☐

⑤ 596 = ☐ + 90 + 6

Put the numbers in order. (4 marks)

⑥ 200, 206, 198, 203, 230 from the largest to the smallest.

_____

⑦ 467, 523, 500, 489, 471 from the smallest to the largest.

_____

Write the numbers in words. (4 marks)

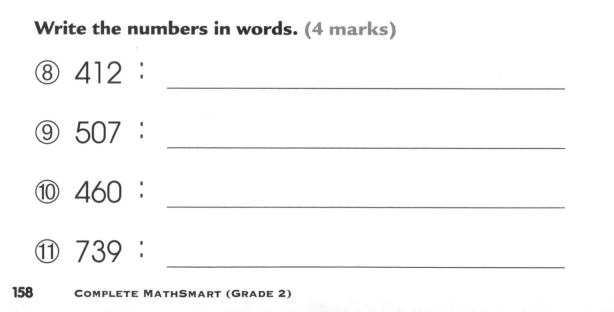

⑧ 412 ⋮ _____

⑨ 507 ⋮ _____

⑩ 460 ⋮ _____

⑪ 739 ⋮ _____

Write the answers. (24 marks)

⑫ 27 − 18 = ☐

⑬ 342 + 89 = ☐

⑭ 432 + 199 = ☐

⑮ 75 − 26 = ☐

⑯ 57 − 18 + 9 = ☐

⑰ 13 + 29 − 4 = ☐

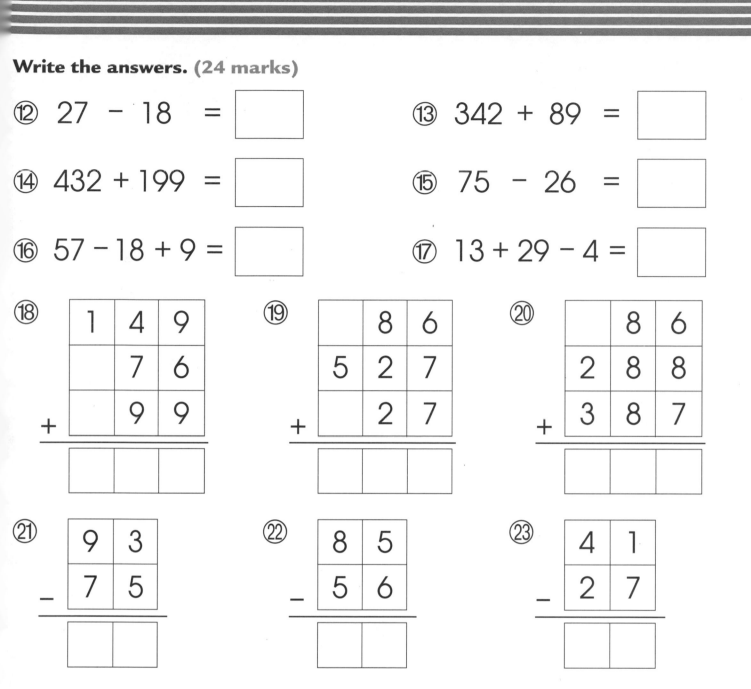

⑱
	1	4	9
		7	6
+		9	9

⑲
		8	6
	5	2	7
+		2	7

⑳
		8	6
	2	8	8
+	3	8	7

㉑
	9	3
−	7	5

㉒
	8	5
−	5	6

㉓
	4	1
−	2	7

Put the numbers in the right boxes. (10 marks)

25 71 59 24

40 36 49 28

45 26 18 19

17 48 27 63

㉔ 5's table

㉕ 8's table

㉖ 5's and 9's tables

㉗ 6's and 8's tables

㉘ 7's and 9's tables

Fill in the boxes. (13 marks)

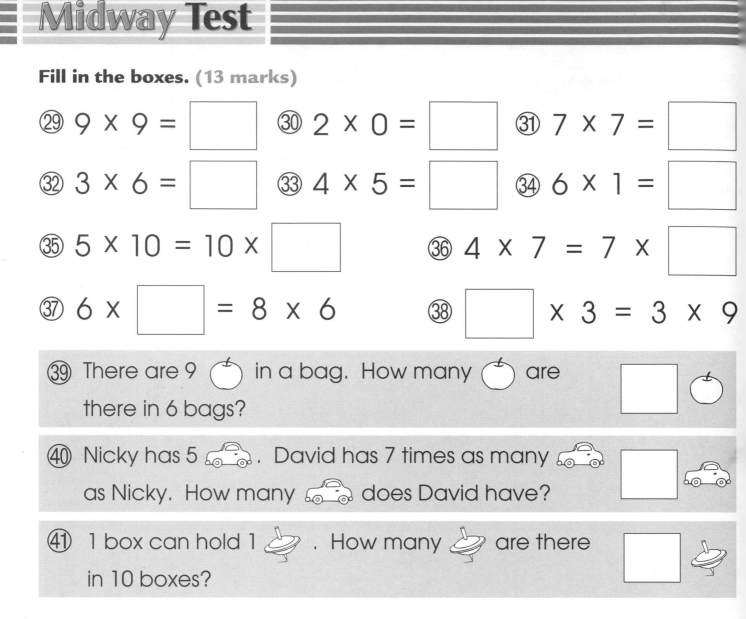

㉙ 9 × 9 = ☐   ㉚ 2 × 0 = ☐   ㉛ 7 × 7 = ☐

㉜ 3 × 6 = ☐   ㉝ 4 × 5 = ☐   ㉞ 6 × 1 = ☐

㉟ 5 × 10 = 10 × ☐   ㊱ 4 × 7 = 7 × ☐

㊲ 6 × ☐ = 8 × 6   ㊳ ☐ × 3 = 3 × 9

㊴ There are 9 🍎 in a bag. How many 🍎 are there in 6 bags?   ☐ 🍎

㊵ Nicky has 5 🚗. David has 7 times as many 🚗 as Nicky. How many 🚗 does David have?   ☐ 🚗

㊶ 1 box can hold 1 🪀 . How many 🪀 are there in 10 boxes?   ☐ 🪀

Tick ✔ the name of each shape. Then fill in the blanks. (12 marks)

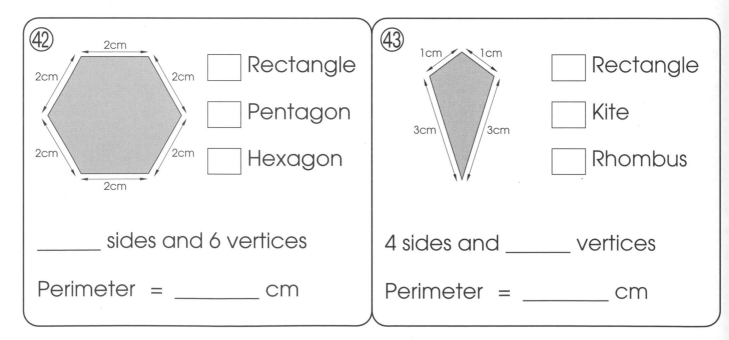

㊷

2cm, 2cm, 2cm, 2cm, 2cm, 2cm

☐ Rectangle
☐ Pentagon
☐ Hexagon

_____ sides and 6 vertices

Perimeter = _____ cm

㊸

1cm, 1cm, 3cm, 3cm

☐ Rectangle
☐ Kite
☐ Rhombus

4 sides and _____ vertices

Perimeter = _____ cm

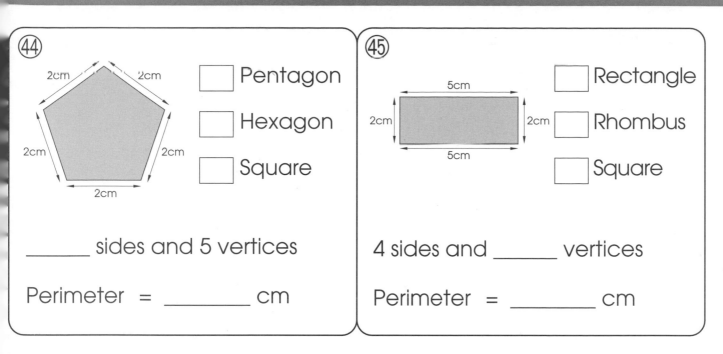

44

2cm 2cm
2cm 2cm
   2cm

☐ Pentagon

☐ Hexagon

☐ Square

_____ sides and 5 vertices

Perimeter = _____ cm

45

5cm
2cm   2cm
5cm

☐ Rectangle

☐ Rhombus

☐ Square

4 sides and _____ vertices

Perimeter = _____ cm

Write the times. (4 marks)

46 _____ minutes past _____

47 _____ minutes to _____

48

49

Look at the calendar and answer the questions. (3 marks)

50 What day is April 7th? _____

51 What date is the 3rd Saturday in April?

_____

52 What day is May 2nd? _____

| APRIL | | | | | | |
SUN	MON	TUE	WED	THUR	FRI	SAT
	1	2	3	4	5	6
7	8	9	10	11	12	13
14	15	16	17	18	19	20
21	22	23	24	25	26	27
28	29	30				

Draw the lines on the geoboard. (3 marks)

53 Draw a straight line from C to D.

54 Draw a curved line from E to F.

55 Draw a line parallel to AB, and label it Y.

Match and write the temperatures. (6 marks)

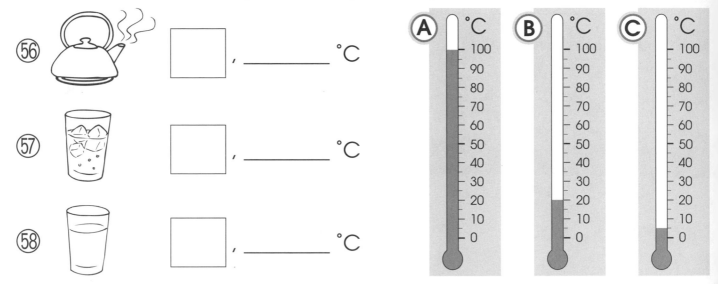

56 [ ] , _____ °C

57 [ ] , _____ °C

58 [ ] , _____ °C

Write the values. (3 marks)

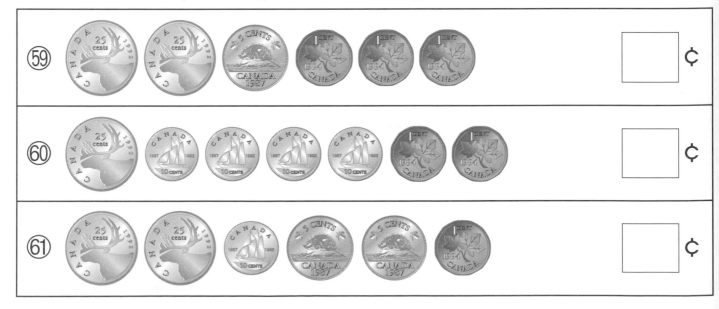

59 [ ] ¢

60 [ ] ¢

61 [ ] ¢

Tick ✔ the coins you get in change. (4 marks)

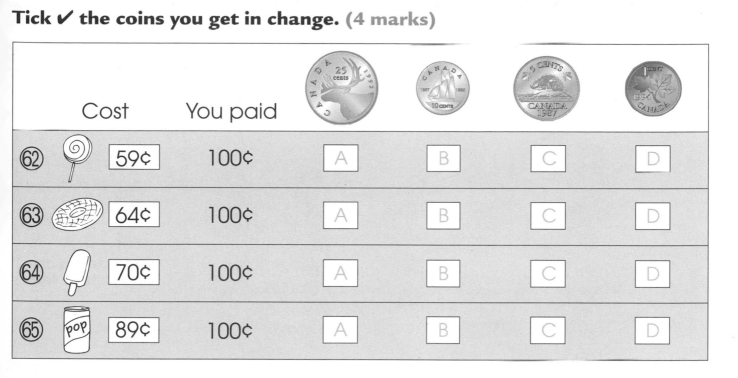

	Cost	You paid	25¢	10¢	5¢	1¢
62	59¢	100¢	A	B	C	D
63	64¢	100¢	A	B	C	D
64	70¢	100¢	A	B	C	D
65	89¢	100¢	A	B	C	D

Read the pictograph and tick ✔ the right answers. (4 marks)

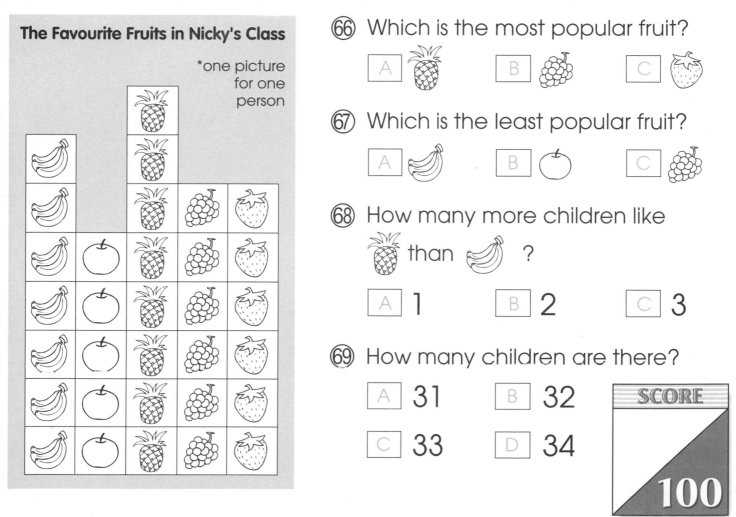

The Favourite Fruits in Nicky's Class

*one picture for one person

66) Which is the most popular fruit?
   A   B   C

67) Which is the least popular fruit?
   A   B   C

68) How many more children like 🍍 than 🍌 ?
   A 1   B 2   C 3

69) How many children are there?
   A 31   B 32
   C 33   D 34

SCORE

100

4-digit Numbers

How many apples has Nicky counted for his uncle? Write the numbers.

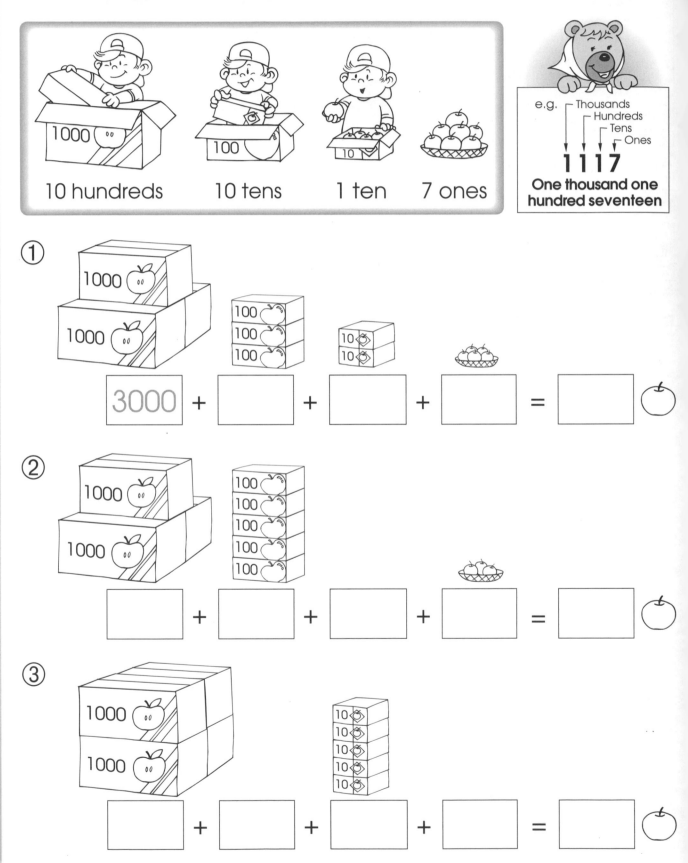

| 10 hundreds | 10 tens | 1 ten | 7 ones |

e.g. Thousands
       Hundreds
       Tens
       Ones

1 1 1 7

One thousand one hundred seventeen

① 1000 · 1000 · 100 100 100 · 10 10 · apples

3000 + ⬜ + ⬜ + ⬜ = ⬜

② 1000 · 1000 · 100 100 100 100 100 · apples

⬜ + ⬜ + ⬜ + ⬜ = ⬜

③ 1000 · 1000 · 10 10 10 10 10

⬜ + ⬜ + ⬜ + ⬜ = ⬜

Nicky counts the apples with an abacus. Write the numbers.

④
thousands hundreds tens ones

4000 + _____ + _____ + _____

= _____

⑤
thousands hundreds tens ones

_____ + _____ + _____ + _____

= _____

Write the numbers in ▢ **.**

⑥

Sept 16, 1999

Pay to: Stanley Smith

Three thousand four hundred sixteen

$ _____

/100 dollars

Trust Bank

Big Bucks

⑦ There were seven thousand and thirty-one apples sold last week.

Number of Apples Sold

ACTIVITY

Pead what the children say. Then write the numbers in the boxes.

1. It is between 2500 and 2504.

2. It is between one thousand and one thousand twenty.

3. The hundreds digit of this number is 4.

4. The thousands digit of this number is 3.

11

More about Addition and Subtraction

Nicky helps his uncle count the number of apples sold each week. Write the numbers.

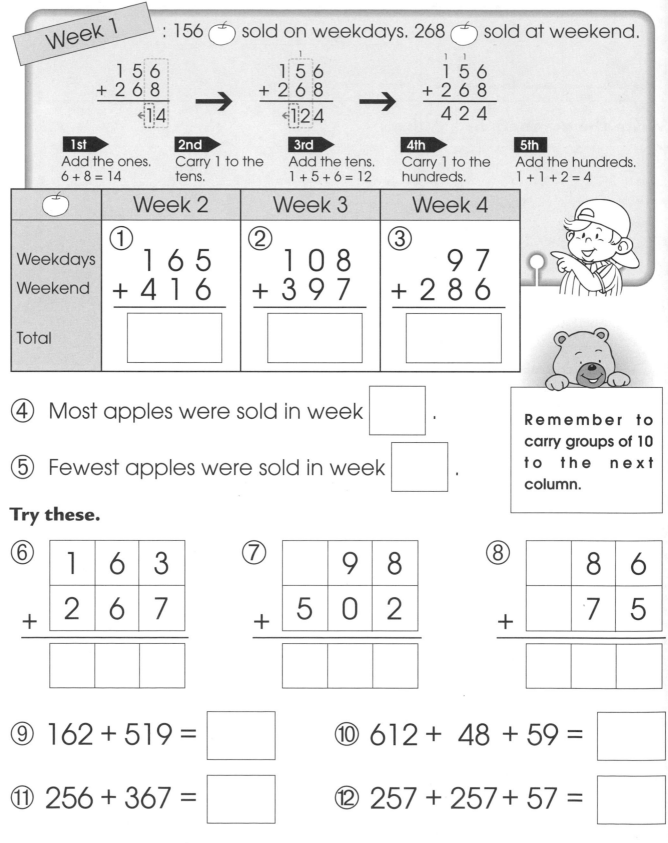

Week 1 : 156 🍎 sold on weekdays. 268 🍎 sold at weekend.

$$
\begin{array}{r}
1\ 5\ 6 \\
+\ 2\ 6\ 8 \\
\hline
1\ 4
\end{array}
\rightarrow
\begin{array}{r}
^1 \\
1\ 5\ 6 \\
+\ 2\ 6\ 8 \\
\hline
1\ 2\ 4
\end{array}
\rightarrow
\begin{array}{r}
^1\ ^1 \\
1\ 5\ 6 \\
+\ 2\ 6\ 8 \\
\hline
4\ 2\ 4
\end{array}
$$

1st Add the ones. 6 + 8 = 14

2nd Carry 1 to the tens.

3rd Add the tens. 1 + 5 + 6 = 12

4th Carry 1 to the hundreds.

5th Add the hundreds. 1 + 1 + 2 = 4

🍎	Week 2	Week 3	Week 4
Weekdays Weekend	① $\begin{array}{r}1\ 6\ 5\\+\ 4\ 1\ 6\\\hline\end{array}$	② $\begin{array}{r}1\ 0\ 8\\+\ 3\ 9\ 7\\\hline\end{array}$	③ $\begin{array}{r}9\ 7\\+\ 2\ 8\ 6\\\hline\end{array}$
Total			

④ Most apples were sold in week ☐ .

⑤ Fewest apples were sold in week ☐ .

Remember to carry groups of 10 to the next column.

Try these.

⑥
$$
\begin{array}{r}
1\ 6\ 3 \\
+\ 2\ 6\ 7 \\
\hline
\end{array}
$$

⑦
$$
\begin{array}{r}
9\ 8 \\
+\ 5\ 0\ 2 \\
\hline
\end{array}
$$

⑧
$$
\begin{array}{r}
8\ 6 \\
+\ 7\ 5 \\
\hline
\end{array}
$$

⑨ 162 + 519 = ☐

⑩ 612 + 48 + 59 = ☐

⑪ 256 + 367 = ☐

⑫ 257 + 257 + 57 = ☐

Nicky and Tim help sell the apples. Write the numbers.

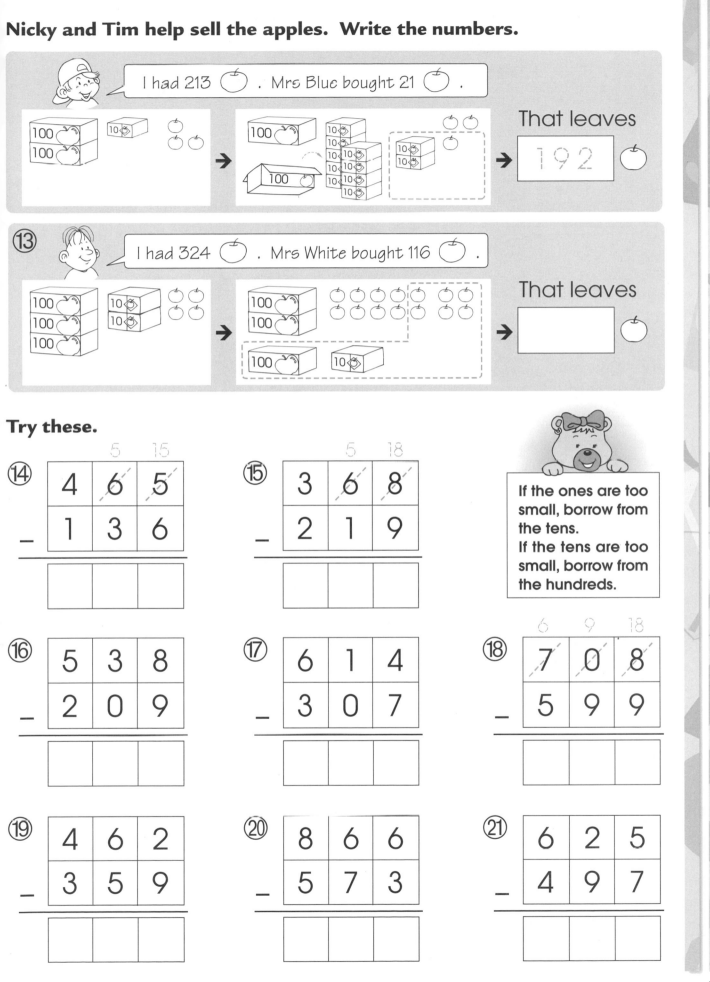

I had 213 🍎. Mrs Blue bought 21 🍎.

That leaves

192 🍎

⑬ I had 324 🍎. Mrs White bought 116 🍎.

That leaves

🍎

Try these.

If the ones are too small, borrow from the tens.
If the tens are too small, borrow from the hundreds.

⑭
```
  5  15
4  6  5
```
- 1 3 6

⑮
```
  5  18
3  6  8
```
- 2 1 9

⑯
```
5  3  8
```
- 2 0 9

⑰
```
6  1  4
```
- 3 0 7

⑱
```
 6  9  18
7  0  8
```
- 5 9 9

⑲
```
4  6  2
```
- 3 5 9

⑳
```
8  6  6
```
- 5 7 3

㉑
```
6  2  5
```
- 4 9 7

Help Nicky write the numbers.

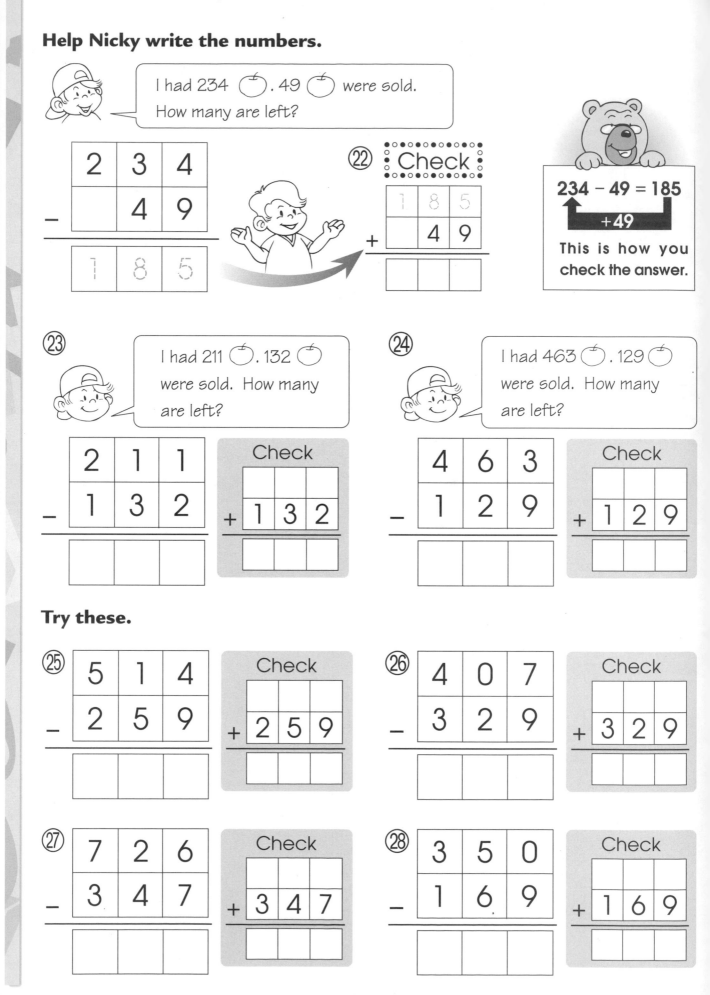

I had 234 🍎. 49 🍎 were sold. How many are left?

$$\begin{array}{r} 2\ 3\ 4 \\ -\quad 4\ 9 \\ \hline 1\ 8\ 5 \end{array}$$

㉒ **Check**

$$\begin{array}{r} 1\ 8\ 5 \\ +\quad 4\ 9 \\ \hline \end{array}$$

234 − 49 = 185
+49
This is how you check the answer.

㉓ I had 211 🍎. 132 🍎 were sold. How many are left?

$$\begin{array}{r} 2\ 1\ 1 \\ -\ 1\ 3\ 2 \\ \hline \end{array}$$

Check
$$\begin{array}{r} +\ 1\ 3\ 2 \\ \hline \end{array}$$

㉔ I had 463 🍎. 129 🍎 were sold. How many are left?

$$\begin{array}{r} 4\ 6\ 3 \\ -\ 1\ 2\ 9 \\ \hline \end{array}$$

Check
$$\begin{array}{r} +\ 1\ 2\ 9 \\ \hline \end{array}$$

Try these.

㉕
$$\begin{array}{r} 5\ 1\ 4 \\ -\ 2\ 5\ 9 \\ \hline \end{array}$$

Check
$$\begin{array}{r} +\ 2\ 5\ 9 \\ \hline \end{array}$$

㉖
$$\begin{array}{r} 4\ 0\ 7 \\ -\ 3\ 2\ 9 \\ \hline \end{array}$$

Check
$$\begin{array}{r} +\ 3\ 2\ 9 \\ \hline \end{array}$$

㉗
$$\begin{array}{r} 7\ 2\ 6 \\ -\ 3\ 4\ 7 \\ \hline \end{array}$$

Check
$$\begin{array}{r} +\ 3\ 4\ 7 \\ \hline \end{array}$$

㉘
$$\begin{array}{r} 3\ 5\ 0 \\ -\ 1\ 6\ 9 \\ \hline \end{array}$$

Check
$$\begin{array}{r} +\ 1\ 6\ 9 \\ \hline \end{array}$$

Follow the apple trails. Write the numbers.

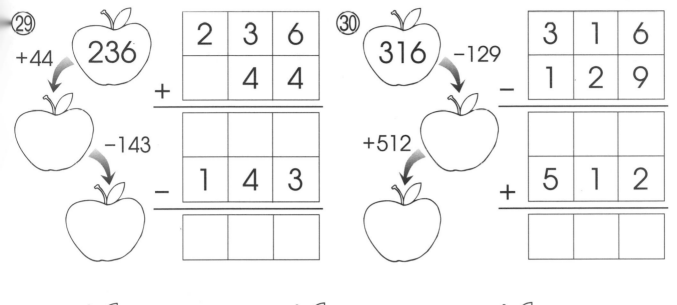

㉙

+44 236

−143

	2	3	6
+		4	4
−	1	4	3

㉚

316 −129

+512

	3	1	6
−	1	2	9
+	5	1	2

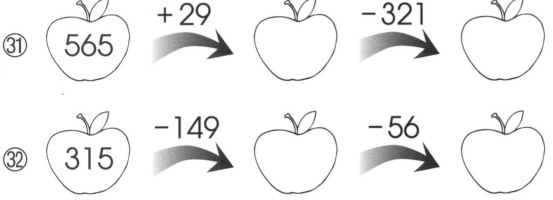

㉛ 565   + 29   − 321

㉜ 315   − 149   − 56

A C T I V I T Y

Use a calculator to find the answers. Remember to clear your calculator after each question.

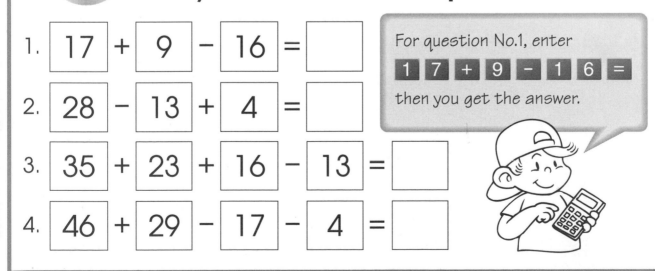

1. 17 + 9 − 16 =

2. 28 − 13 + 4 =

3. 35 + 23 + 16 − 13 =

4. 46 + 29 − 17 − 4 =

For question No.1, enter

1 7 + 9 − 1 6 =

then you get the answer.

12 Division

Nicky and his friends are sharing their snacks. Circle each share/group of snacks and write the numbers.

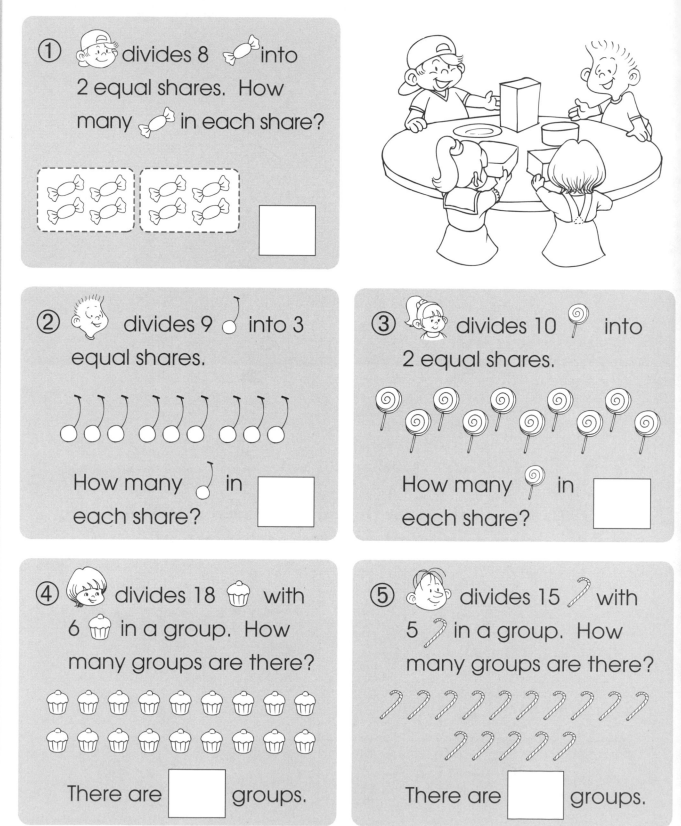

① divides 8 🍬 into 2 equal shares. How many 🍬 in each share?

② divides 9 🍒 into 3 equal shares.

How many 🍒 in each share?

③ divides 10 🍭 into 2 equal shares.

How many 🍭 in each share?

④ divides 18 🧁 with 6 🧁 in a group. How many groups are there?

There are ⬜ groups.

⑤ divides 15 🍬 with 5 🍬 in a group. How many groups are there?

There are ⬜ groups.

See how Nicky's mom puts the cookies into the bags. Write the numbers.

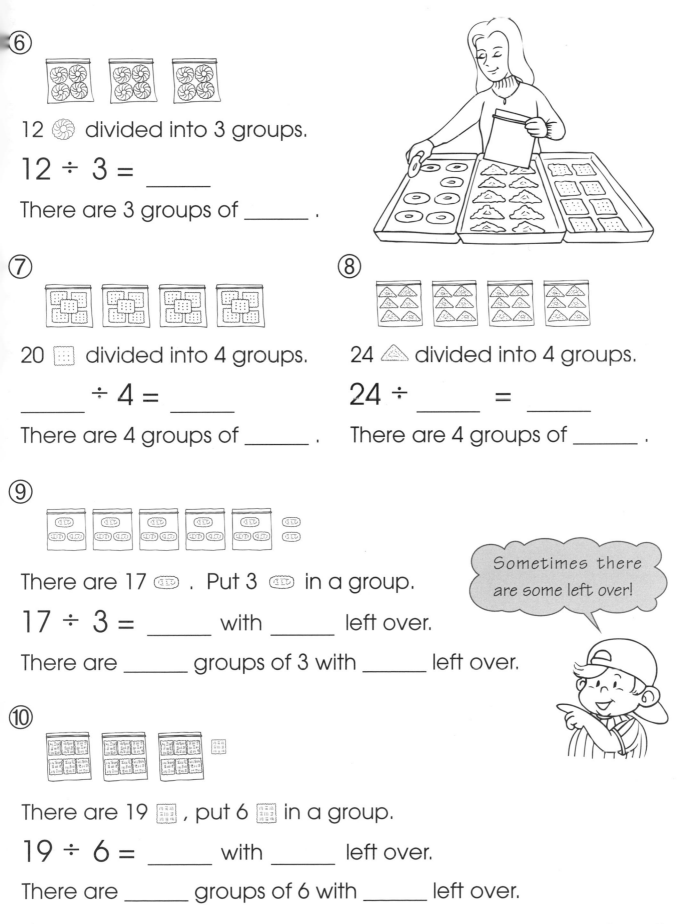

⑥

12 🍪 divided into 3 groups.

12 ÷ 3 = _____

There are 3 groups of _____ .

⑦

20 ▦ divided into 4 groups.

_____ ÷ 4 = _____

There are 4 groups of _____ .

⑧

24 △ divided into 4 groups.

24 ÷ _____ = _____

There are 4 groups of _____ .

⑨

There are 17 ⬭ . Put 3 ⬭ in a group.

17 ÷ 3 = _____ with _____ left over.

There are _____ groups of 3 with _____ left over.

> Sometimes there are some left over!

⑩

There are 19 ▥ , put 6 ▥ in a group.

19 ÷ 6 = _____ with _____ left over.

There are _____ groups of 6 with _____ left over.

Look at the cookies and answer the questions.

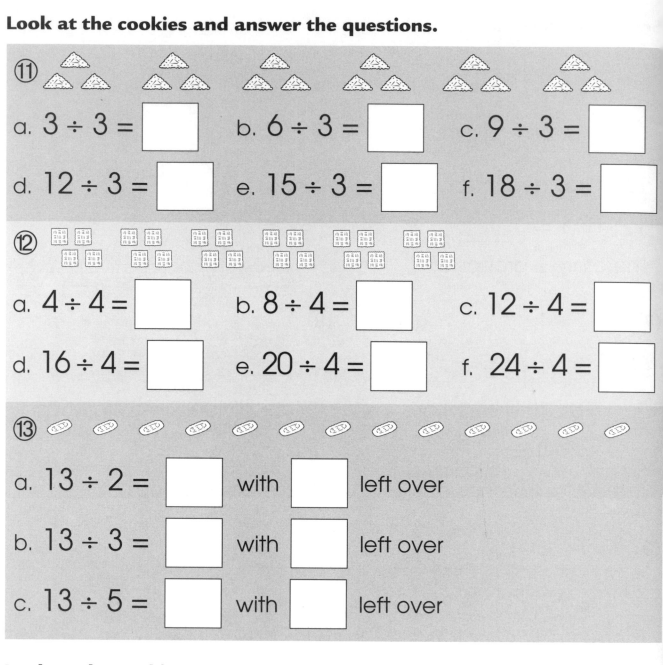

⑪

a. $3 \div 3 = \boxed{}$ b. $6 \div 3 = \boxed{}$ c. $9 \div 3 = \boxed{}$

d. $12 \div 3 = \boxed{}$ e. $15 \div 3 = \boxed{}$ f. $18 \div 3 = \boxed{}$

⑫

a. $4 \div 4 = \boxed{}$ b. $8 \div 4 = \boxed{}$ c. $12 \div 4 = \boxed{}$

d. $16 \div 4 = \boxed{}$ e. $20 \div 4 = \boxed{}$ f. $24 \div 4 = \boxed{}$

⑬

a. $13 \div 2 = \boxed{}$ with $\boxed{}$ left over

b. $13 \div 3 = \boxed{}$ with $\boxed{}$ left over

c. $13 \div 5 = \boxed{}$ with $\boxed{}$ left over

Look at the cookies and write the numbers.

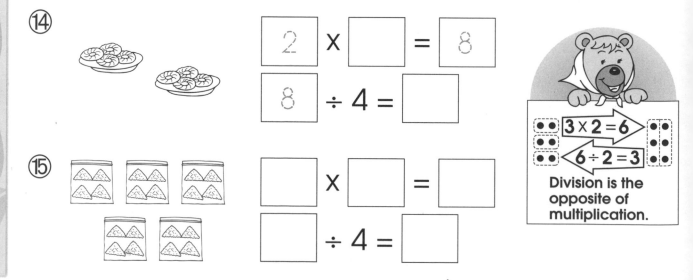

⑭

$2 \times \boxed{} = 8$

$8 \div 4 = \boxed{}$

⑮

$\boxed{} \times \boxed{} = \boxed{}$

$\boxed{} \div 4 = \boxed{}$

$3 \times 2 = 6$
$6 \div 2 = 3$

Division is the opposite of multiplication.

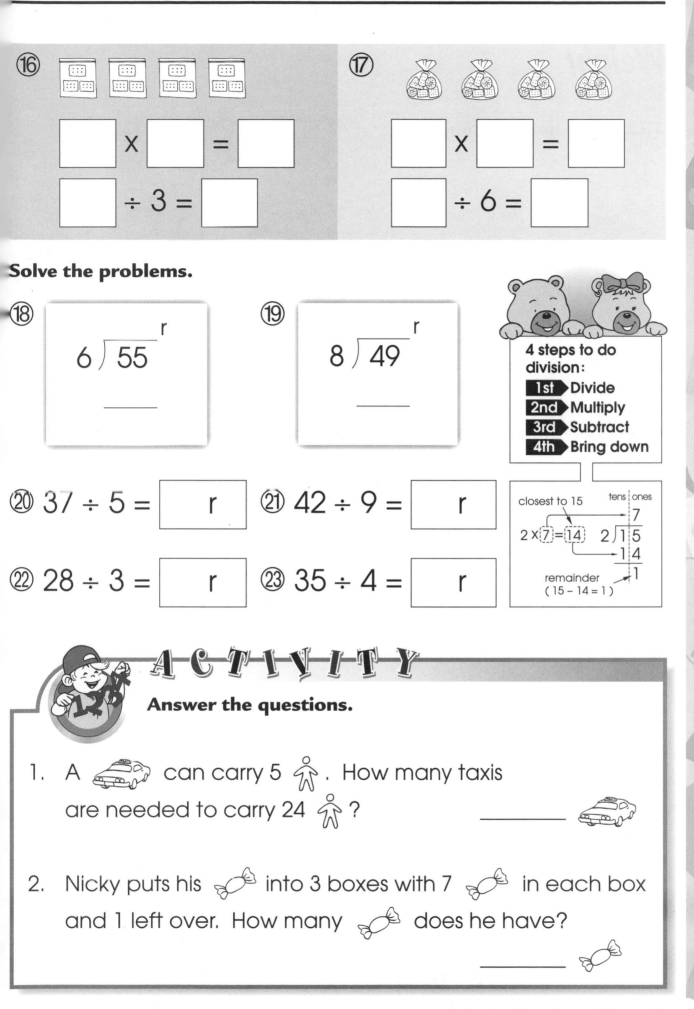

⑯ □ × □ = □

□ ÷ 3 = □

⑰ □ × □ = □

□ ÷ 6 = □

Solve the problems.

⑱ 6) 55 ____ r

⑲ 8) 49 ____ r

4 steps to do division:

1st ▶ Divide
2nd ▶ Multiply
3rd ▶ Subtract
4th ▶ Bring down

⑳ 37 ÷ 5 = □ r

㉑ 42 ÷ 9 = □ r

㉒ 28 ÷ 3 = □ r

㉓ 35 ÷ 4 = □ r

closest to 15

2 × 7 = 14   2) 1 5

                  tens ¦ ones
                       7
                       1 5
                       1 4

remainder
(15 − 14 = 1)   1

ACTIVITY

Answer the questions.

1. A 🚕 can carry 5 👤 . How many taxis are needed to carry 24 👤 ?   _____

2. Nicky puts his 🍬 into 3 boxes with 7 🍬 in each box and 1 left over. How many 🍬 does he have?

_____

Tick ✔ the heavier things.

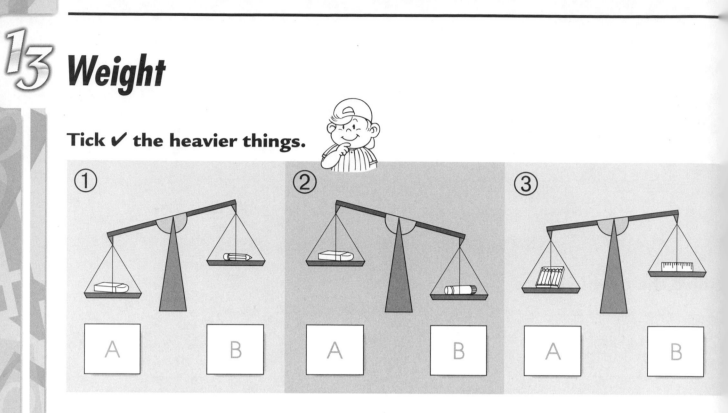

① A ☐   B ☐

② A ☐   B ☐

③ A ☐   B ☐

Help Nicky weigh his toy cars with marbles. Fill in the blanks.

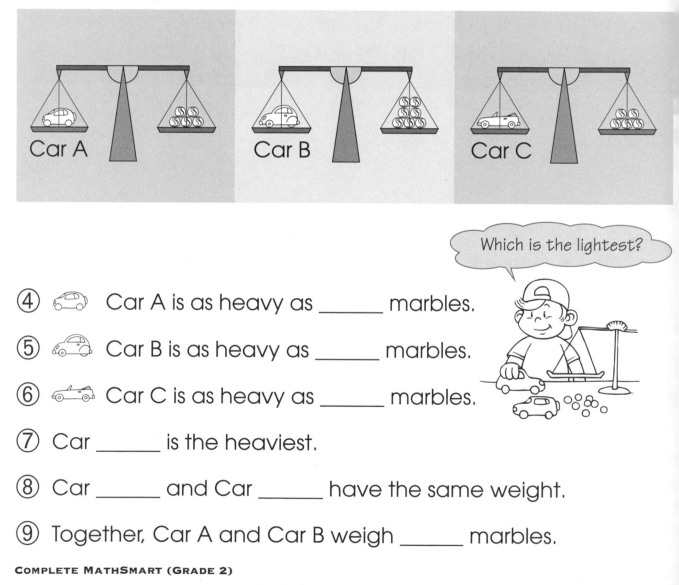

Car A   Car B   Car C

Which is the lightest?

④ Car A is as heavy as _____ marbles.

⑤ Car B is as heavy as _____ marbles.

⑥ Car C is as heavy as _____ marbles.

⑦ Car _____ is the heaviest.

⑧ Car _____ and Car _____ have the same weight.

⑨ Together, Car A and Car B weigh _____ marbles.

Write the weights of the things.

We weigh heavy things in kilograms. We weigh light things in grams.

⑩ pencil weighs ⬚ g.

⑪ car weighs ⬚ g.

⑫ chips weighs ⬚ g.

⑬ bananas weighs ⬚ g.

⑭ grapes weighs ⬚ g.

We usually use single units to show quantities.
Remember: 1 kg = 1000 g

ACTIVITY

Tick ✔ the right answers.

1. When a scale is balanced,

   A   the things on both sides weigh the same.

   B   the things on both sides are of the same size.

2. Which groups of things can balance?

   A   2 | 100g | and 1 | 300g | SUGAR

   B   1 | 300g | and 2 🍬

14 Angles

Help Nicky put the angles in order. Write the letters.

① From the largest to the smallest: _____ , _____ , _____

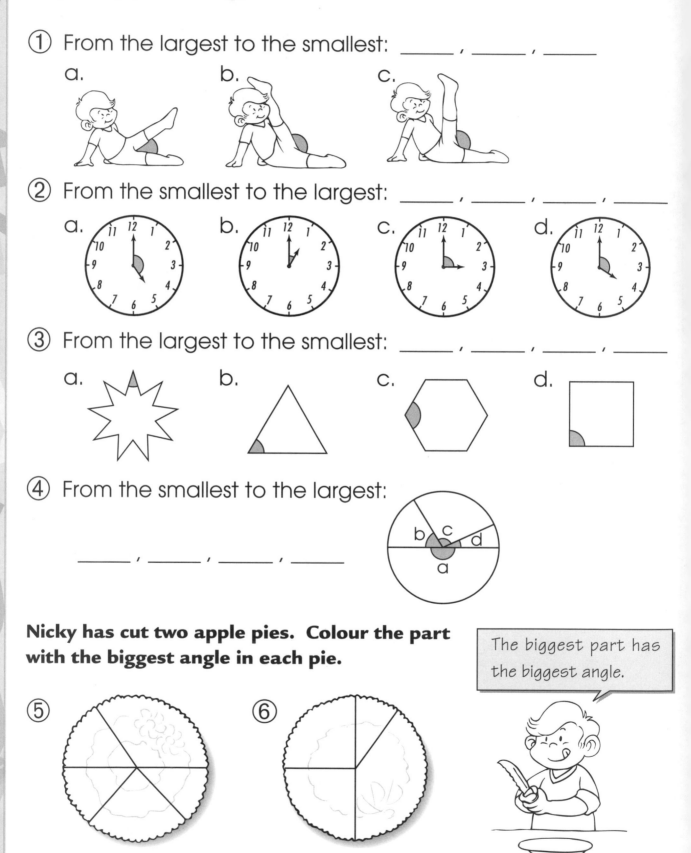

a.

b.

c.

② From the smallest to the largest: _____ , _____ , _____ , _____

a.

b.

c.

d.

③ From the largest to the smallest: _____ , _____ , _____ , _____

a.

b.

c.

d.

④ From the smallest to the largest:

_____ , _____ , _____ , _____

Nicky has cut two apple pies. Colour the part with the biggest angle in each pie.

> The biggest part has the biggest angle.

⑤

⑥

Count and write the number of right angles ⌐ in each shape.

⑦ _____

⑧ _____

⑨ _____

⑩ _____

⑪ _____

⑫ _____

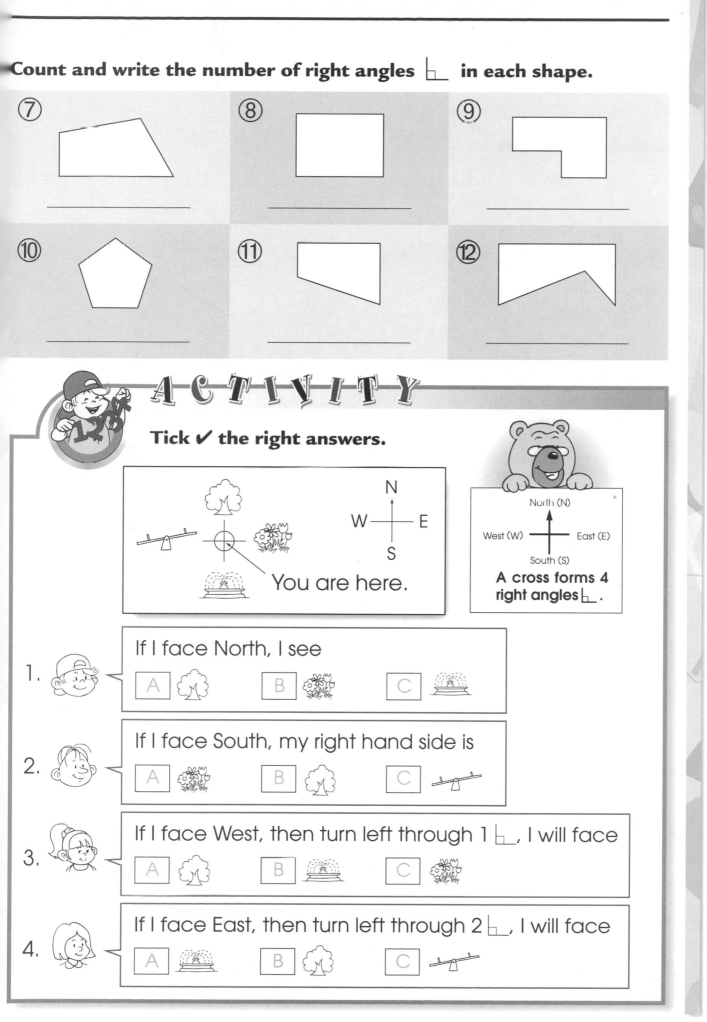

ACTIVITY

Tick ✔ the right answers.

N
W ┼ E
S

You are here.

North (N)
West (W) ──── East (E)
South (S)

A cross forms 4 right angles ⌐.

1. If I face North, I see

   A 🌳   B 🌷   C ⛲

2. If I face South, my right hand side is

   A 🌷   B 🌳   C 🛝

3. If I face West, then turn left through 1 ⌐, I will face

   A 🌳   B ⛲   C 🌷

4. If I face East, then turn left through 2 ⌐, I will face

   A ⛲   B 🌳   C 🛝

Colour the shapes.

① Colour the prisms yellow.

② Colour the pyramids green

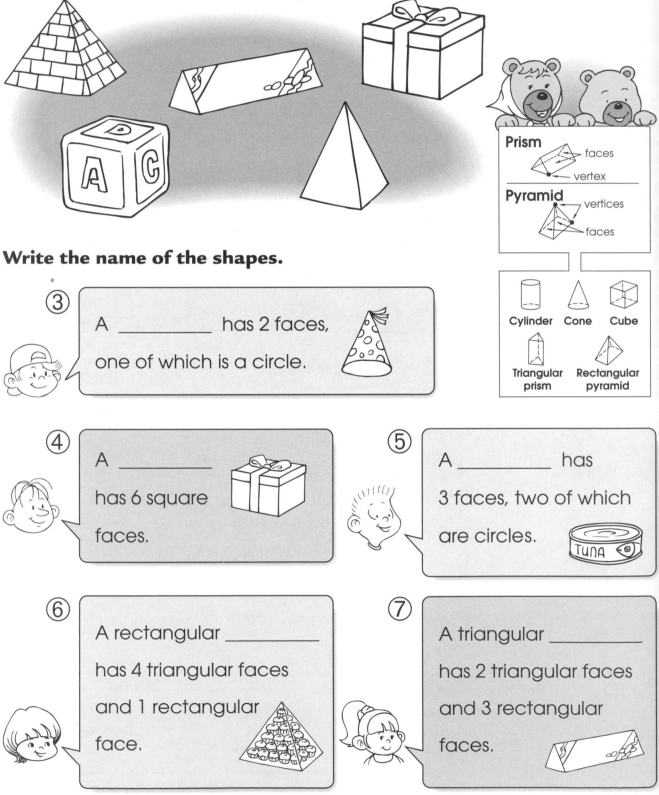

Prism — faces — vertex

Pyramid — vertices — faces

Cylinder   Cone   Cube

Triangular prism   Rectangular pyramid

Write the name of the shapes.

③ A _____ has 2 faces, one of which is a circle.

④ A _____ has 6 square faces.

⑤ A _____ has 3 faces, two of which are circles.

⑥ A rectangular _____ has 4 triangular faces and 1 rectangular face.

⑦ A triangular _____ has 2 triangular faces and 3 rectangular faces.

In each group, circle the face that does not belong to the solid.

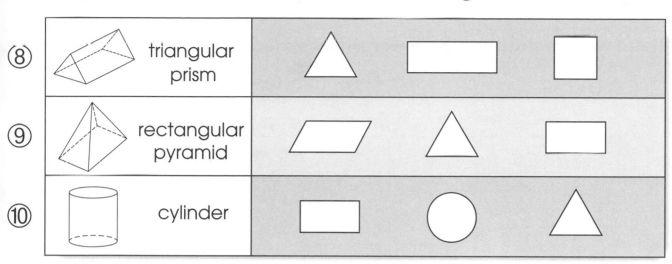

⑧ triangular prism

⑨ rectangular pyramid

⑩ cylinder

How many solids can you see? Write the numbers.

⑪ ☐ cone

⑫ ☐ cylinders

⑬ ☐ cubes

⑭ ☐ triangular prism

⑮ ☐ rectangular pyramids

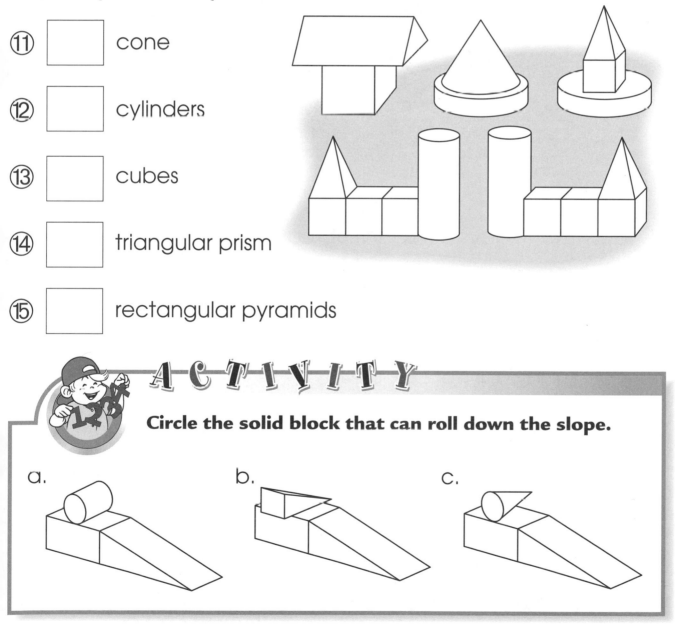

ACTIVITY

Circle the solid block that can roll down the slope.

a.

b.

c.

16 Block Graphs

Read Nicky's graph and answer the questions.

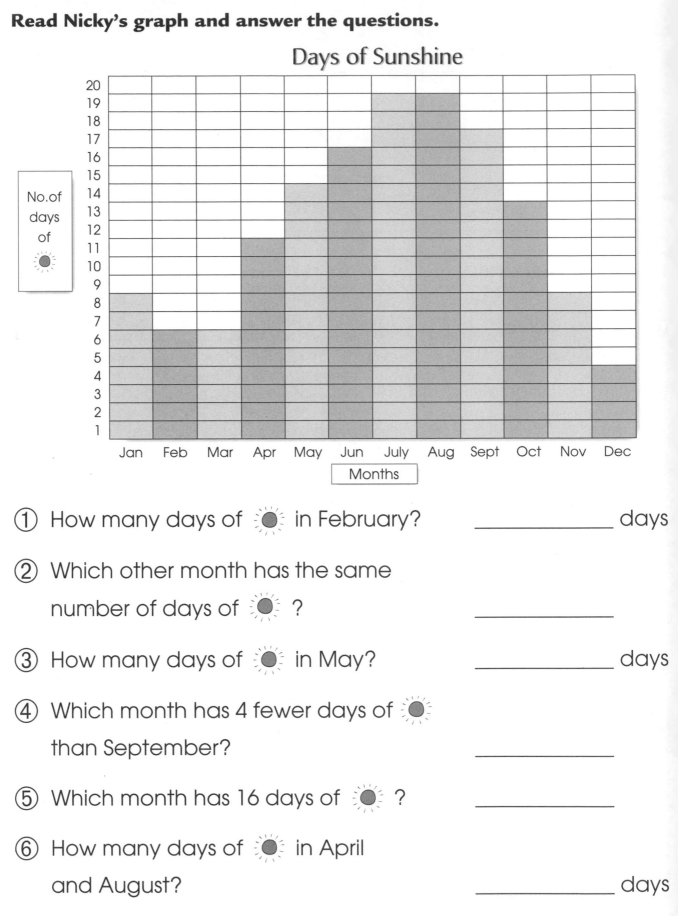

Days of Sunshine

① How many days of ☀ in February? _____ days

② Which other month has the same
number of days of ☀ ? _____

③ How many days of ☀ in May? _____ days

④ Which month has 4 fewer days of ☀
than September? _____

⑤ Which month has 16 days of ☀ ? _____

⑥ How many days of ☀ in April
and August? _____ days

Look at the table and answer the questions.

	Nicky	Tim	Jill	Katie	David	Lily
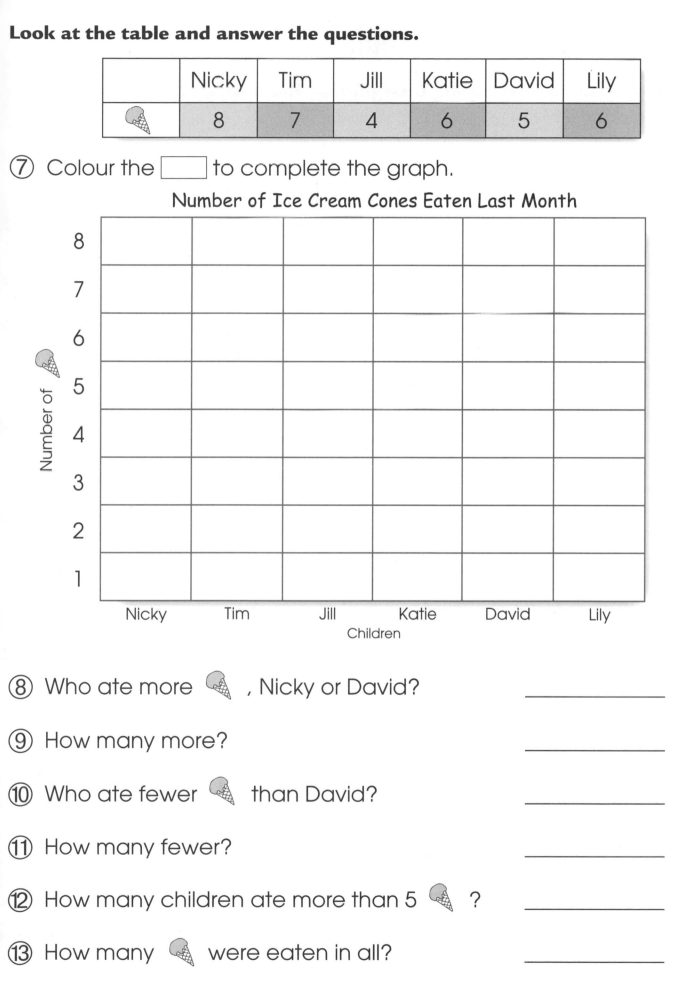	8	7	4	6	5	6

⑦ Colour the ☐ to complete the graph.

Number of Ice Cream Cones Eaten Last Month

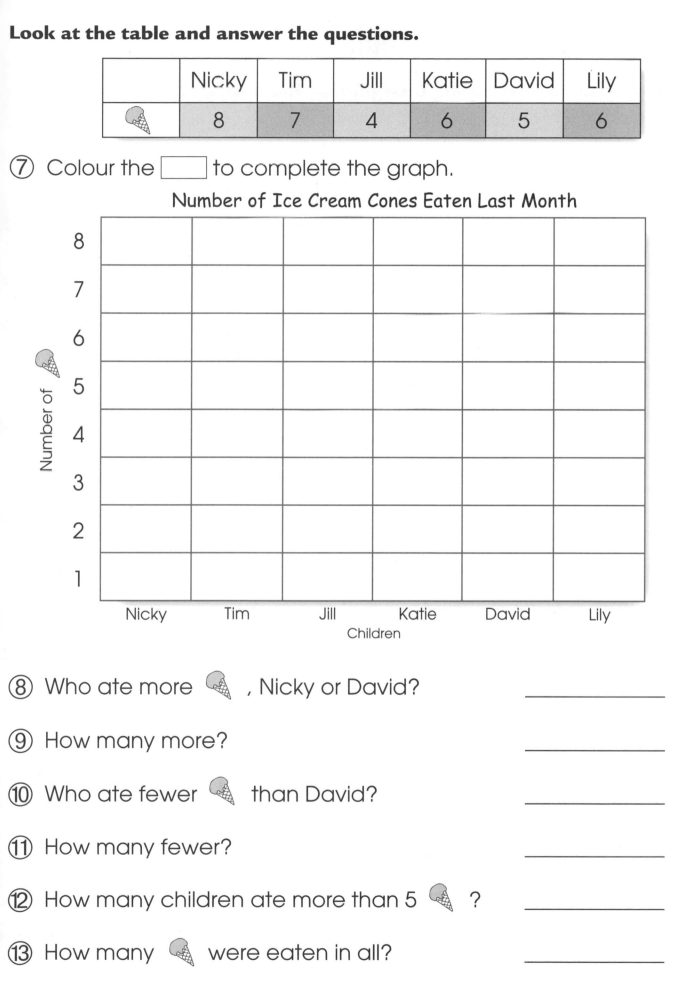

⑧ Who ate more 🍦, Nicky or David? _____

⑨ How many more? _____

⑩ Who ate fewer 🍦 than David? _____

⑪ How many fewer? _____

⑫ How many children ate more than 5 🍦? _____

⑬ How many 🍦 were eaten in all? _____

17 Fractions and Decimals

The children are sharing their pizzas. Read what they say and colour the pizzas.

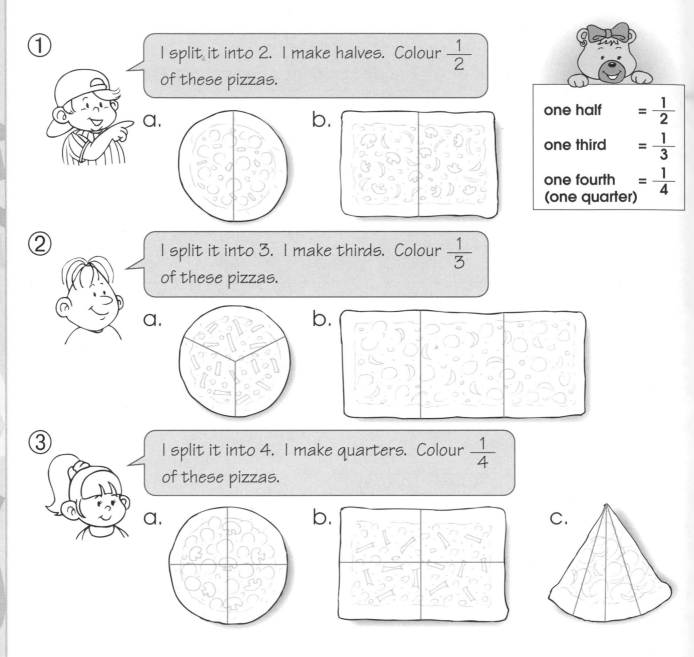

① *I split it into 2. I make halves. Colour $\frac{1}{2}$ of these pizzas.*

a. b.

one half $= \frac{1}{2}$

one third $= \frac{1}{3}$

one fourth (one quarter) $= \frac{1}{4}$

② *I split it into 3. I make thirds. Colour $\frac{1}{3}$ of these pizzas.*

a. b.

③ *I split it into 4. I make quarters. Colour $\frac{1}{4}$ of these pizzas.*

a. b. c.

Tick ✔ the right answer for the shaded part of each shape.

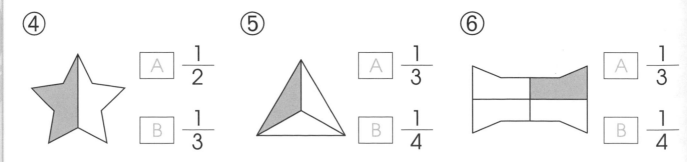

④ A $\frac{1}{2}$ B $\frac{1}{3}$

⑤ A $\frac{1}{3}$ B $\frac{1}{4}$

⑥ A $\frac{1}{3}$ B $\frac{1}{4}$

Read what Nicky says. Then write the fractions and decimals of the shaded parts of each shape.

10 tenths make 1.

$\frac{2}{10}$ are shaded; $\frac{2}{10}$ can also be written as 0.2 .

2 tenths

decimal point

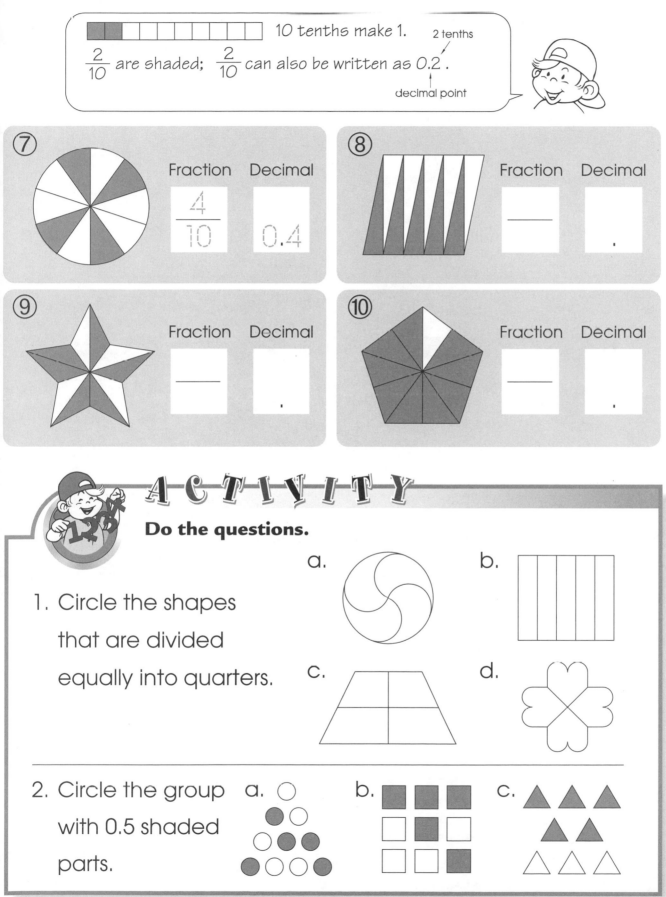

⑦ Fraction $\frac{4}{10}$ Decimal 0.4

⑧ Fraction ___ Decimal .

⑨ Fraction ___ Decimal .

⑩ Fraction ___ Decimal .

ACTIVITY

Do the questions.

1. Circle the shapes that are divided equally into quarters.

a.

b.

c.

d.

2. Circle the group with 0.5 shaded parts.

a.

b.

c.

Transformations

How are the coins transformed? Tick ✔ the right answers.

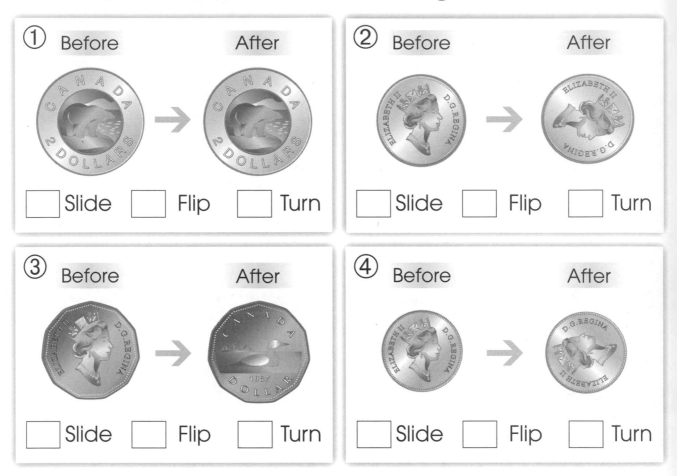

① Before   After

☐ Slide   ☐ Flip   ☐ Turn

② Before   After

☐ Slide   ☐ Flip   ☐ Turn

③ Before   After

☐ Slide   ☐ Flip   ☐ Turn

④ Before   After

☐ Slide   ☐ Flip   ☐ Turn

Read what Nicky says and draw the shapes.

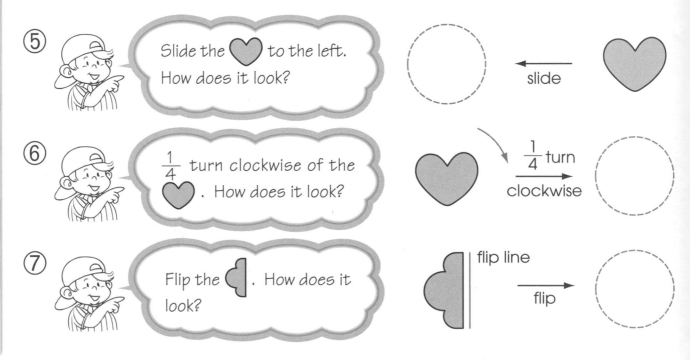

⑤ Slide the ♥ to the left. How does it look?

← slide

⑥ $\frac{1}{4}$ turn clockwise of the ♥ . How does it look?

$\frac{1}{4}$ turn clockwise

⑦ Flip the ◖. How does it look?

flip line
flip

Read what Tim says and draw the transformed figures.

⑩ Flip the arrow over the line.

⑪ $\frac{1}{4}$ turn clockwise.

⑫ Slide it to the right.

⑬ Flip it over the line.

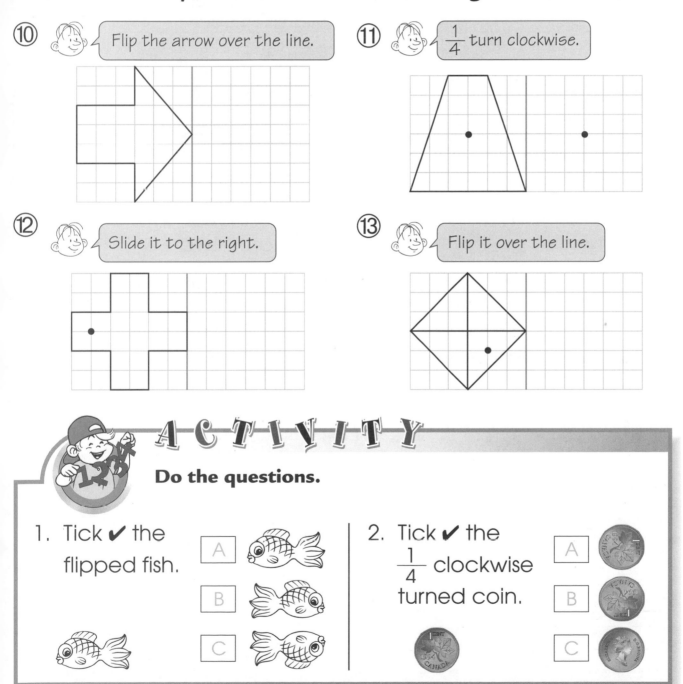

ACTIVITY

Do the questions.

1. Tick ✔ the flipped fish.
   - A
   - B
   - C

2. Tick ✔ the $\frac{1}{4}$ clockwise turned coin.
   - A
   - B
   - C

Write the numbers and letters to match the beads. (12 marks)

	Number	Letter			Number	Letter
① Th H T O				② Th H T O		
③ Th H T O				④ Th H T O		
⑤ Th H T O				⑥ Th H T O		

A	Five thousand six hundred and two
C	Six thousand five hundred twenty-two
E	Six thousand six hundred twenty

B	Five thousand five hundred and two
D	Five thousand six hundred twenty-two
F	Six thousand five hundred twenty

Find the answers. (19 marks)

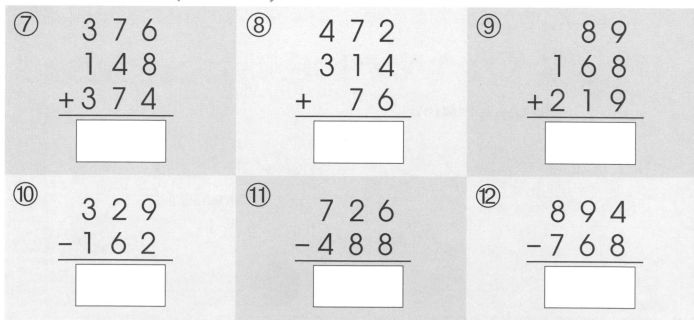

⑦
```
  3 7 6
  1 4 8
+ 3 7 4
───────
```

⑧
```
  4 7 2
  3 1 4
+   7 6
───────
```

⑨
```
    8 9
  1 6 8
+ 2 1 9
───────
```

⑩
```
  3 2 9
- 1 6 2
───────
```

⑪
```
  7 2 6
- 4 8 8
───────
```

⑫
```
  8 9 4
- 7 6 8
───────
```

⑬
```
    5 2 3
      8 8
  +   6 7
  ┌───────┐
  │       │
  └───────┘
```

⑭
```
    3 1 9
    1 0 9
  +   5 7
  ┌───────┐
  │       │
  └───────┘
```

⑮
```
      6 6
    2 8 7
  +   4 9
  ┌───────┐
  │       │
  └───────┘
```

⑯
```
    4 6 3
  - 2 7 6
  ┌───────┐
  │       │
  └───────┘
```

⑰
```
    3 1 9
  - 2 6 9
  ┌───────┐
  │       │
  └───────┘
```

⑱
```
    5 0 4
  - 1 7 8
  ┌───────┐
  │       │
  └───────┘
```

⑲
```
    3 2 6
  - 1 7 9
  ┌───────┐
  │       │
  └───────┘
  +   7 3
  ┌───────┐
  │       │
  └───────┘
```

⑳
```
    2 7 2
  +   6 9
  ┌───────┐
  │       │
  └───────┘
  - 2 0 8
  ┌───────┐
  │       │
  └───────┘
```

㉑
```
    1 6 7
  -   9 9
  ┌───────┐
  │       │
  └───────┘
  + 2 1 5
  ┌───────┐
  │       │
  └───────┘
```

㉒ $209 + 316 + 58 =$ ☐

㉓ $462 - 333 =$ ☐

㉔ $601 - 273 + 64 =$ ☐

㉕ $514 - 327 =$ ☐

Find the answers. (18 marks)

㉖ 14 ● grouped in threes. How many groups?

$14 \div 3 =$ _____ r _____

There are _____ groups of 3 ● with _____ left over.

㉗ 17 ● grouped in sixes. How many groups?

17 ÷ 6 = _____ r _____

There are _____ groups of 6 ● with _____ left over.

㉘ 18 ● grouped in fours. How many groups?

18 ÷ 4 = _____ r _____

There are _____ groups of 4 ● with _____ left over.

㉙ 4) 25 r

㉚ 8) 71 r

㉛ 7) 59 r

㉜ 9) 63 r

㉝ 6) 29 r

㉞ 5) 47 r

Look at the pictures and write the answers. (4 marks)

㉟
[ ] x 4 = 24

24 ÷ 4 = [ ]

㊱
[ ] x 3 = 30

30 ÷ 3 = [ ]

Solve the problems. (14 marks)

㊲ There are 16 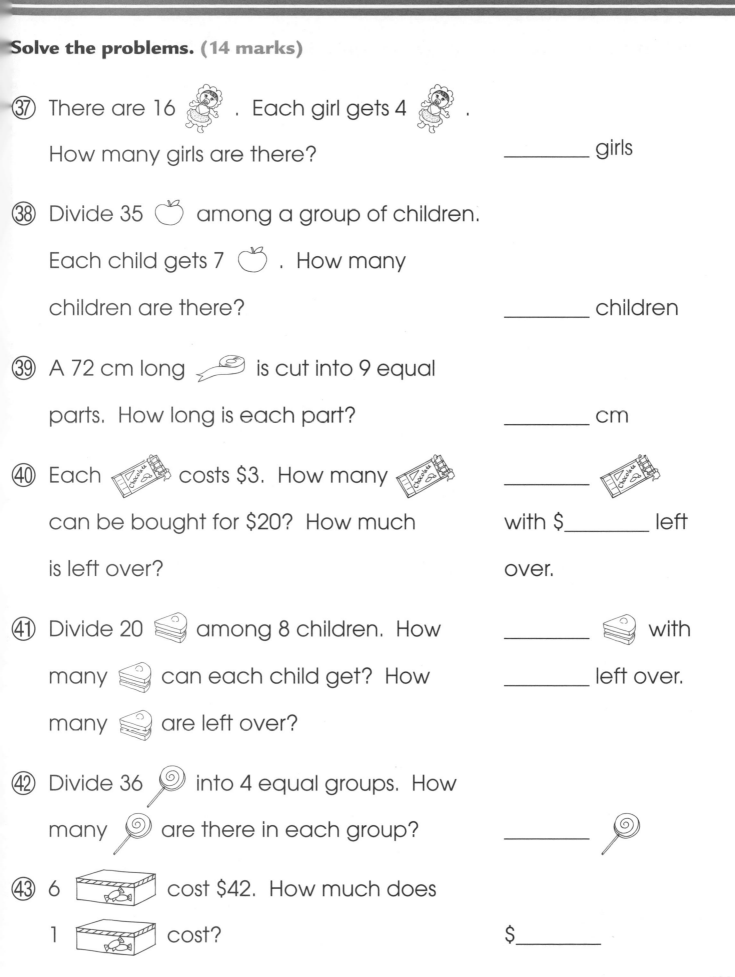 . Each girl gets 4 . How many girls are there?

_____ girls

㊳ Divide 35 🍎 among a group of children. Each child gets 7 🍎 . How many children are there?

_____ children

㊴ A 72 cm long 🎀 is cut into 9 equal parts. How long is each part?

_____ cm

㊵ Each 🍫 costs $3. How many 🍫 can be bought for $20? How much is left over?

_____ 🍫 with $_____ left over.

㊶ Divide 20 🍰 among 8 children. How many 🍰 can each child get? How many 🍰 are left over?

_____ 🍰 with _____ left over.

㊷ Divide 36 🍭 into 4 equal groups. How many 🍭 are there in each group?

_____ 🍭

㊸ 6 📦 cost $42. How much does 1 📦 cost?

$_____

Look at the pictures and answer the questions. (6 marks)

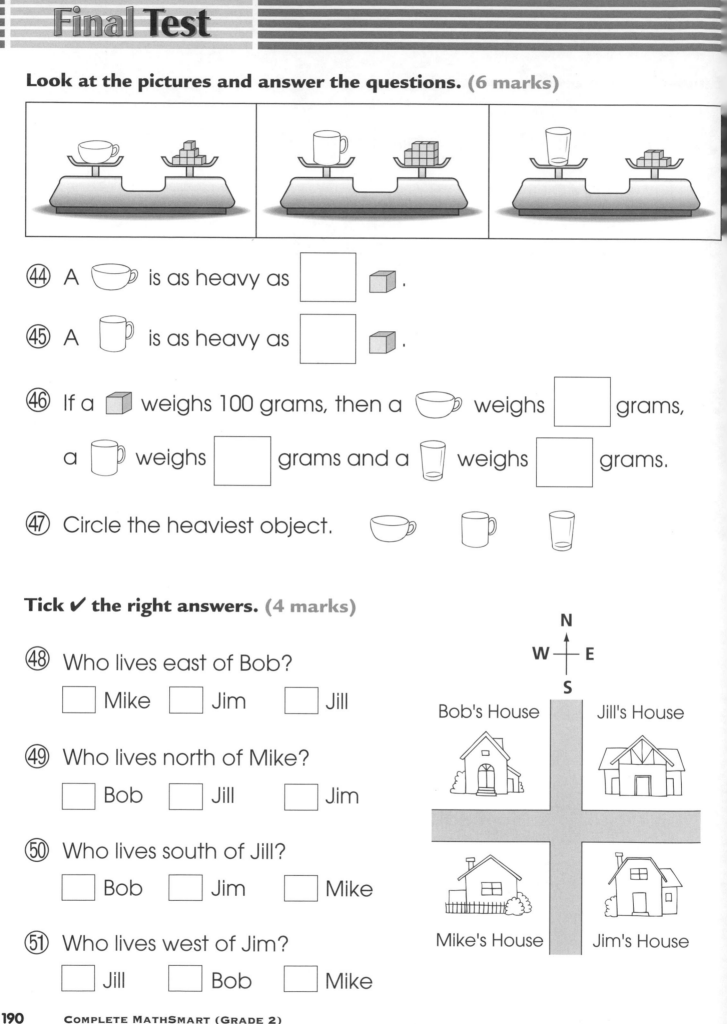

㊽ A ☕ is as heavy as [ ] 🔲.

㊺ A 🍵 is as heavy as [ ] 🔲.

㊻ If a 🔲 weighs 100 grams, then a ☕ weighs [ ] grams, a 🍵 weighs [ ] grams and a 🥛 weighs [ ] grams.

㊼ Circle the heaviest object.   ☕   🍵   🥛

Tick ✔ the right answers. (4 marks)

㊽ Who lives east of Bob?

[ ] Mike   [ ] Jim   [ ] Jill

㊾ Who lives north of Mike?

[ ] Bob   [ ] Jill   [ ] Jim

㊿ Who lives south of Jill?

[ ] Bob   [ ] Jim   [ ] Mike

51 Who lives west of Jim?

[ ] Jill   [ ] Bob   [ ] Mike

Bob's House   Jill's House

Mike's House   Jim's House

Look at the picture and write the numbers. (5 marks)

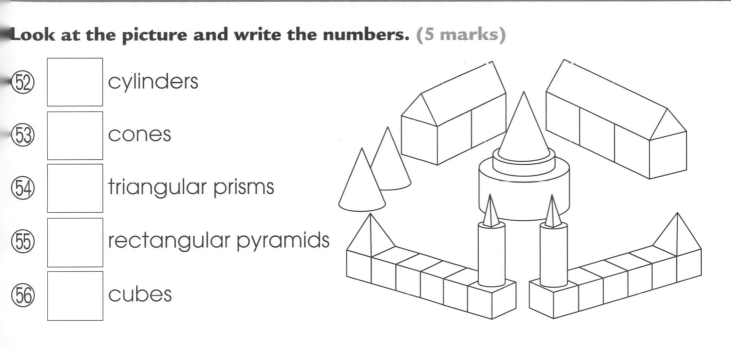

㊾ 52 ☐ cylinders

㊿ 53 ☐ cones

54 ☐ triangular prisms

55 ☐ rectangular pyramids

56 ☐ cubes

Read the graph and tick ✔ the right answers. (4 marks)

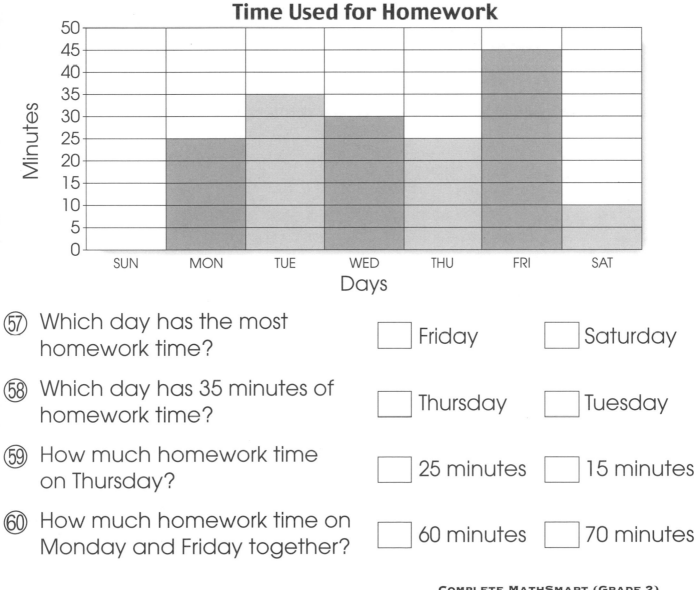

Time Used for Homework

57 Which day has the most homework time? ☐ Friday ☐ Saturday

58 Which day has 35 minutes of homework time? ☐ Thursday ☐ Tuesday

59 How much homework time on Thursday? ☐ 25 minutes ☐ 15 minutes

60 How much homework time on Monday and Friday together? ☐ 60 minutes ☐ 70 minutes

How much is shaded in each shape? Tick ✔ the right answers. (3 marks)

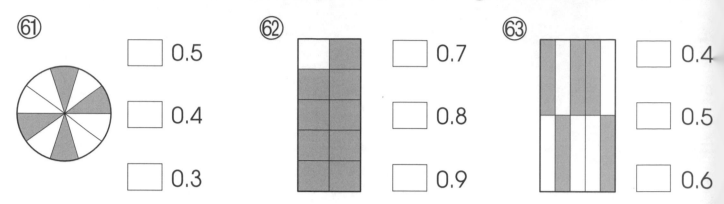

⑥¹ ☐ 0.5 ☐ 0.4 ☐ 0.3

⑥² ☐ 0.7 ☐ 0.8 ☐ 0.9

⑥³ ☐ 0.4 ☐ 0.5 ☐ 0.6

Write the fraction of the eaten apples in each group. (3 marks)

⑥⁴ ⑥⁵ ⑥⁶

How are the shapes transformed? Write the letters. (4 marks)

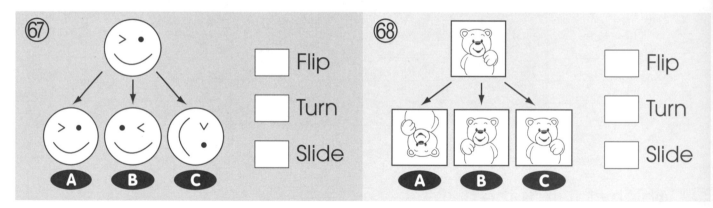

⑥⁷ ☐ Flip ☐ Turn ☐ Slide

A B C

⑥⁸ ☐ Flip ☐ Turn ☐ Slide

A B C

Draw the transformed shapes. (4 marks)

⑥⁹ Flip it over the line.

⑦⁰ $\frac{1}{4}$ turn clockwise.

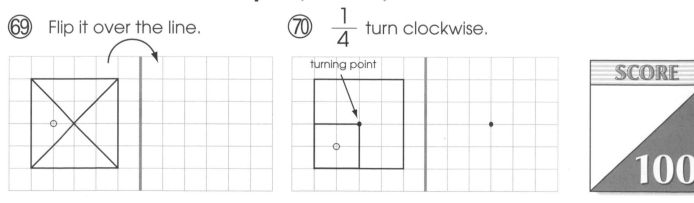

turning point

SCORE

100

Section IV

Overview

In Section III, children were encouraged to connect ideas from numbers, measurement, geometry, patterning and graphs, as they were introduced to the different strands of mathematics. They had the basic concepts of using addition, subtraction, multiplication and division in simple problem-solving activities.

In this section, integrated activities in the form of story problems involve children in the applications of arithmetic, graphing and measurement skills as described in the Grade 2 curriculum and beyond.

While calculators may be used where necessary, children should be encouraged to do calculations mentally whenever possible.

3-digit Numbers

The children estimate the number of jelly beans in a jar. Answer the questions.

	Stella	Peggy	Sam	Max	Craig
Estimated number of jelly beans	178	193	145	180	213

①   Who estimates the smallest number?   _____

②   Who estimates the largest number?   _____

③   What is the smallest estimated number? Write the number in words.

_____

④   What is the largest estimated number? Write the number in words.

_____

⑤   Put the numbers in order, from the smallest to the largest.

_____

⑥   How many of the estimated numbers are smaller than 190? _____

⑦   How many of the estimated numbers are larger than 190? _____

There are 190 jelly beans in the jar. The winner is the one who gives the estimated number closest to 190. Help the children answer the questions.

⑧   Who is the winner?   _____

⑨   Who is the second winner?   _____

Matthew kept a record of the number of ice cream cones sold each month in summer at his store. Use his table to answer the questions.

	May	June	July	August	September
Number of 🍦 sold	774	810	988	910	780

⑩ In which month did he sell the most 🍦 ?

_____

⑪ In which month did he sell the fewest 🍦 ?

_____

⑫ In which months did he sell more than 900 🍦 ?

_____

⑬ In which months did he sell fewer than 900 🍦 ?

_____

⑭ What is the difference between the number of 🍦 sold in June and in August?   _____ 🍦

⑮ How many more 🍦 did he sell in September than in May?   _____ 🍦

⑯ Put the months in order, from the one which sold the most 🍦 to the one which sold the fewest.

_____

⑰ Matthew sold 100 fewer 🍦 in April than in May. How many 🍦 were sold in April? Write the number in words.

_____

Addition and Subtraction

Peggy, Sue and Sarah use beads to make necklaces and bracelets. See how many beads they use. Then answer the questions.

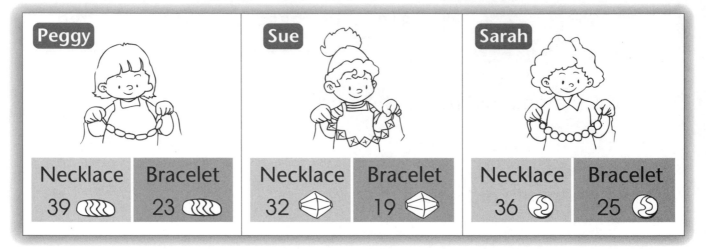

① How many  does Peggy use in all?

_____ = _____   _____

② How many ◇ does Sue use in all?

_____ = _____   _____ ◇

③ How many ⑤ does Sarah use in all?

_____ = _____   _____ ⑤

④ How many more  does Peggy use for her necklace than her bracelet?

_____ = _____   _____ more

⑤ How many more ◇ does Sue use for her necklace than her bracelet?

_____ = _____   _____ more ◇

⑥ How many beads do the girls use to make their bracelets?

_____ = _____   _____ beads

Many people took part in a race to raise money for Heart Research. See how they participated in the race. Use the table to answer the questions.

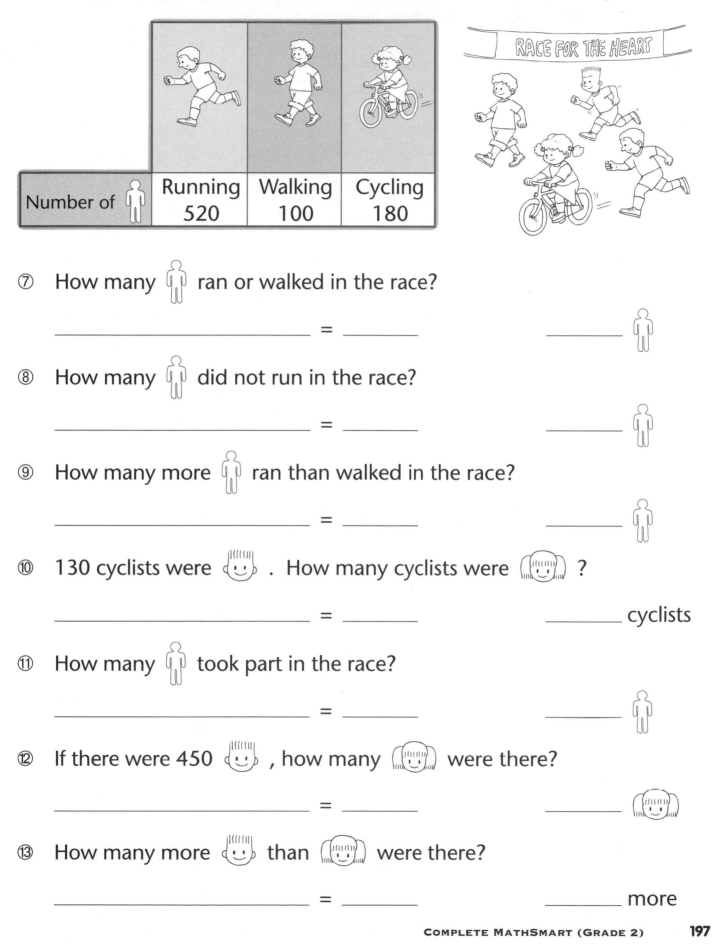

Number of 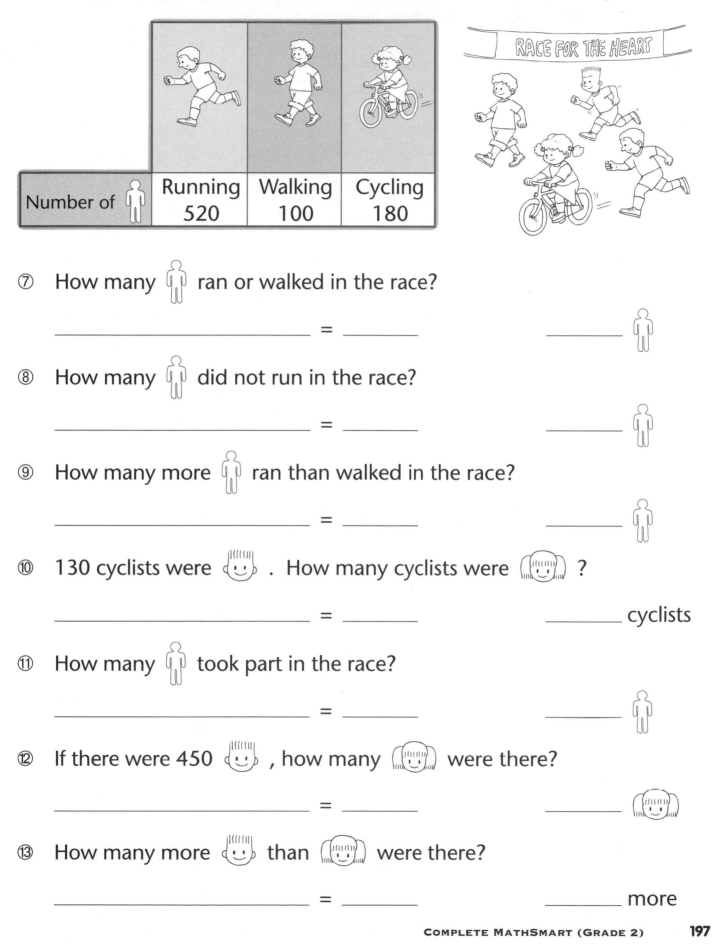	Running 520	Walking 100	Cycling 180

⑦ How many 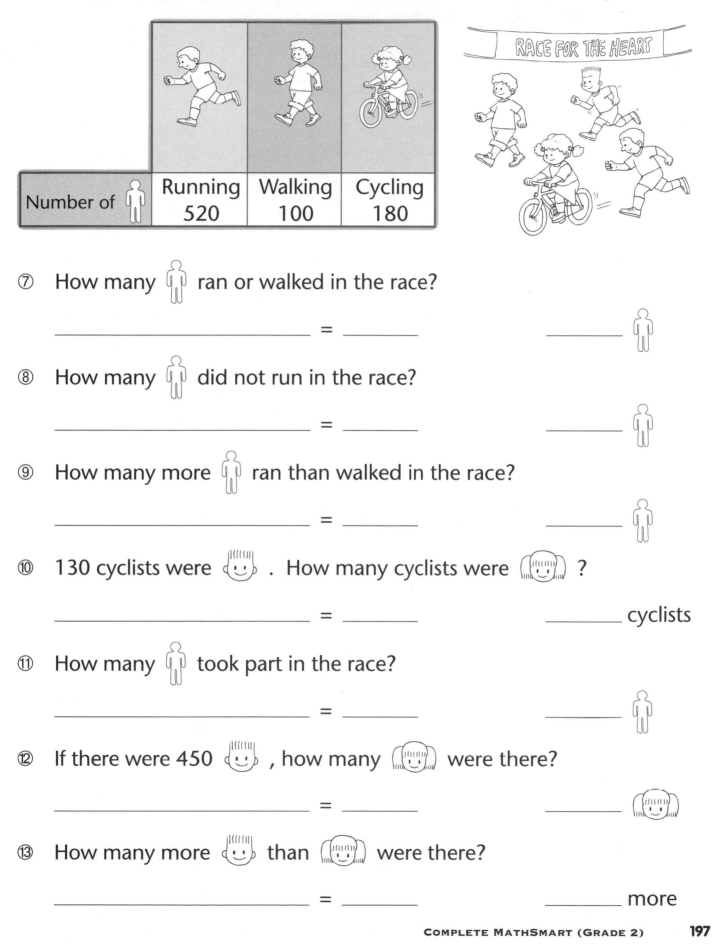 ran or walked in the race?

_____ = _____ _____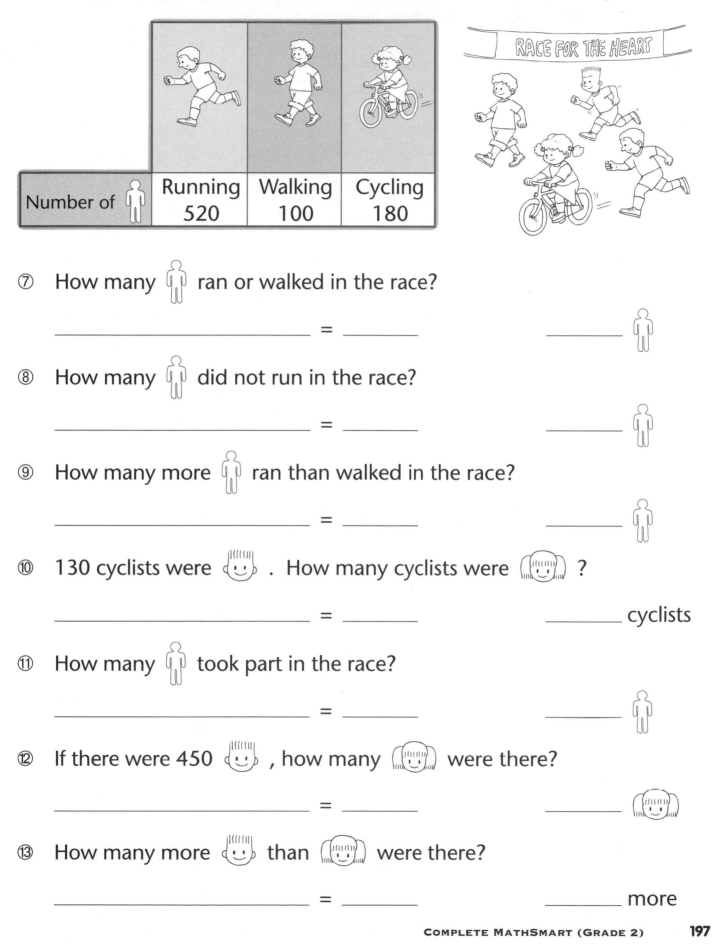

⑧ How many 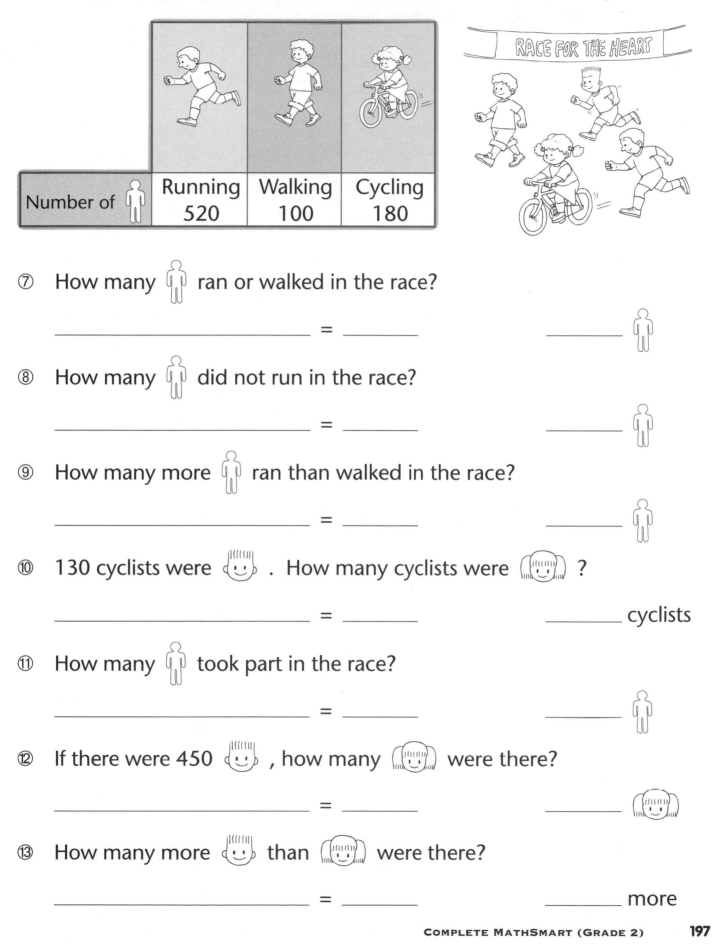 did not run in the race?

_____ = _____ _____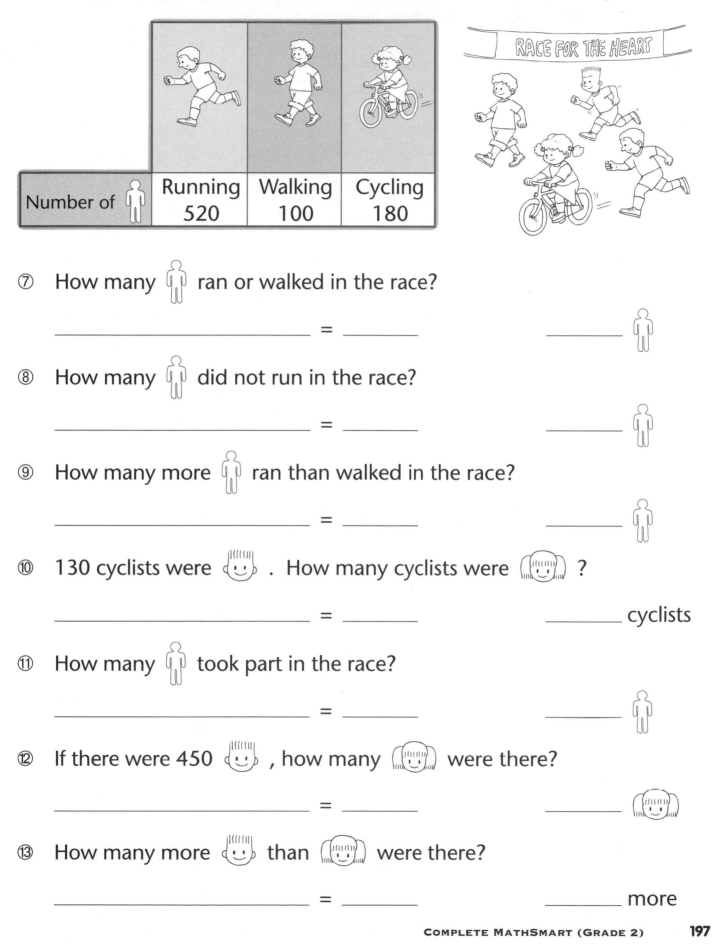

⑨ How many more ran than walked in the race?

_____ = _____ _____

⑩ 130 cyclists were . How many cyclists were ?

_____ = _____ _____ cyclists

⑪ How many took part in the race?

_____ = _____ _____

⑫ If there were 450 , how many were there?

_____ = _____ _____

⑬ How many more than were there?

_____ = _____ _____ more

See how many hamburgers, hot dogs and sandwiches Henry sold in the past two weeks. Answer the questions and check ✔ the correct answers.

1st week	138	109	123
2nd week	158	105	147

⑭ In which week were more  sold? _____ week

⑮ In which week were more  sold? _____ week

⑯ In which week were more  sold? _____ week

⑰ In the 1st week, which item did Henry sell the most?

Ⓐ    Ⓑ   Ⓒ

⑱ In the 2nd week, which item did Henry sell the most?

Ⓐ   Ⓑ   Ⓒ

⑲ In the 2nd week, which item did Henry sell the least?

Ⓐ   Ⓑ   Ⓒ

⑳ How many more  did Henry sell in the 2nd week than in the 1st week?

_____ = _____   _____ more

㉑ How many did he sell in all?

_____ = _____

㉒ How many more 🌭 did Henry sell in the 1st week than in the 2nd week?

_____ = _____   _____ more 🌭

㉓ How many 🌭 did he sell in all?

_____ = _____   _____ 🌭

㉔ How many more 🥪 did Henry sell in the 2nd week than in the 1st week?

_____ = _____   _____ more 🥪

㉕ How many 🥪 did he sell in all?

_____ = _____   _____ 🥪

㉖ What is the total number of the three items sold in the 1st week?

_____ = _____   _____

㉗ What is the total number of the three items sold in the 2nd week?

_____ = _____   _____

㉘ In the 1st week, 75 of the 🍔 sold were with cheese. How many 🍔 sold were without cheese?

_____ = _____   _____ 🍔

㉙ In the 2nd week, 89 of the 🥪 sold were with ham. How many 🥪 sold were without ham?

_____ = _____   _____ 🥪

See how Graham lays the tiles. Then fill in the blanks.

① Entrance

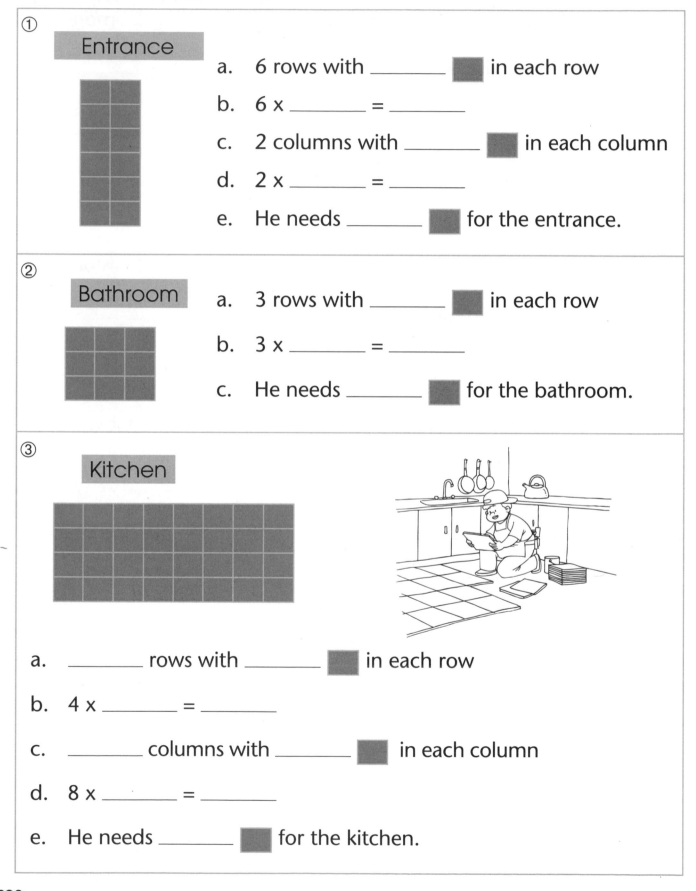

a.   6 rows with _____  in each row

b.   6 x _____ = _____

c.   2 columns with _____  in each column

d.   2 x _____ = _____

e.   He needs _____  for the entrance.

② Bathroom

a.   3 rows with _____  in each row

b.   3 x _____ = _____

c.   He needs _____  for the bathroom.

③ Kitchen

a.   _____ rows with _____  in each row

b.   4 x _____ = _____

c.   _____ columns with _____  in each column

d.   8 x _____ = _____

e.   He needs _____  for the kitchen.

Help Ted the farmer solve the problems.

④

a. One dog has _____ legs.

b. How many legs do 3 dogs have?

3 x _____ = _____   _____ legs

⑤

a. One cat has _____ ears.

b. How many ears do 5 cats have?

_____ x _____ = _____   _____ ears

⑥

a. One hen lays _____ eggs.

b. How many eggs do 2 hens lay?

_____ x _____ = _____   _____ eggs

⑦

a. One spider has _____ legs.

b. How many legs do 4 spiders have?

_____ x _____ = _____   _____ legs

⑧

a. One basket holds _____ carrots.

b. How many carrots do 3 baskets hold?

_____ x _____ = _____   _____ carrots

⑨

a. One bag holds _____ corn cobs.

b. How many corn cobs do 6 bags hold?

_____ x _____ = _____   _____ corn cobs

It is Laura's birthday. Help her check ✔ the correct answers and solve the problems.

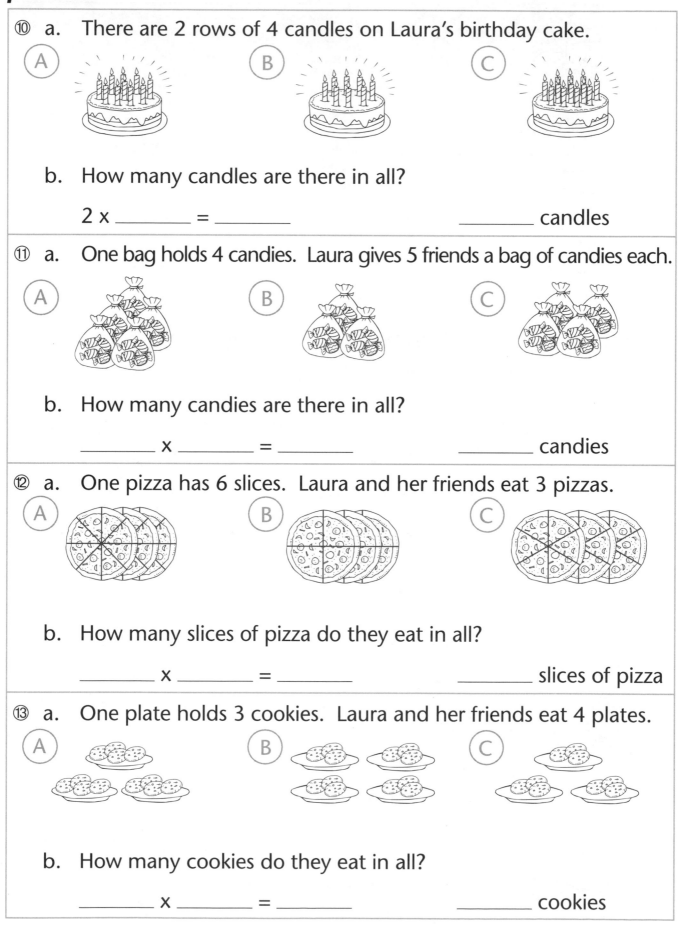

⑩ a. There are 2 rows of 4 candles on Laura's birthday cake.

A   B   C

b. How many candles are there in all?

2 x _____ = _____   _____ candles

⑪ a. One bag holds 4 candies. Laura gives 5 friends a bag of candies each.

A   B   C

b. How many candies are there in all?

_____ x _____ = _____   _____ candies

⑫ a. One pizza has 6 slices. Laura and her friends eat 3 pizzas.

A   B   C

b. How many slices of pizza do they eat in all?

_____ x _____ = _____   _____ slices of pizza

⑬ a. One plate holds 3 cookies. Laura and her friends eat 4 plates.

A   B   C

b. How many cookies do they eat in all?

_____ x _____ = _____   _____ cookies

⑭ Laura invites 8 friends. Each friend eats 6 chocolates. How many chocolates do they eat in all?

_____ x _____ = _____   _____ chocolates

⑮ There are 6 straws in a box. How many straws are there in 7 boxes?

_____ x _____ = _____   _____ straws

⑯ There are 2 balloons in a bag. How many balloons are there in 9 bags?

_____ x _____ = _____   _____ balloons

⑰ There are 6 plates in a pile. How many plates are there in 4 piles?

_____ x _____ = _____   _____ plates

⑱ There are 5 forks in a cup. How many forks are there in 5 cups?

_____ x _____ = _____   _____ cups

⑲ One child eats 4 marshmallows. How many marshmallows do 5 children eat in all?

_____ x _____ = _____   _____ marshmallows

⑳ One plate holds 3 brownies. How many brownies are there on 2 plates?

_____ x _____ = _____   _____ brownies

Read what the children say. Then check ✔ the coins and write the amounts.

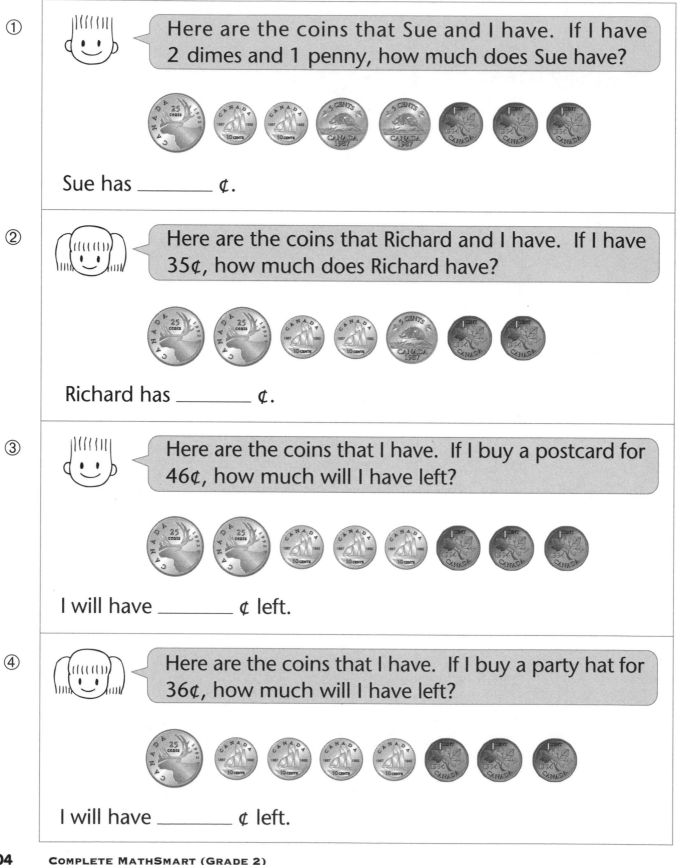

① Here are the coins that Sue and I have. If I have 2 dimes and 1 penny, how much does Sue have?

Sue has _____ ¢.

② Here are the coins that Richard and I have. If I have 35¢, how much does Richard have?

Richard has _____ ¢.

③ Here are the coins that I have. If I buy a postcard for 46¢, how much will I have left?

I will have _____ ¢ left.

④ Here are the coins that I have. If I buy a party hat for 36¢, how much will I have left?

I will have _____ ¢ left.

Pat wants to buy some beads to make bracelets. See what kinds of beads she buys and answer the questions.

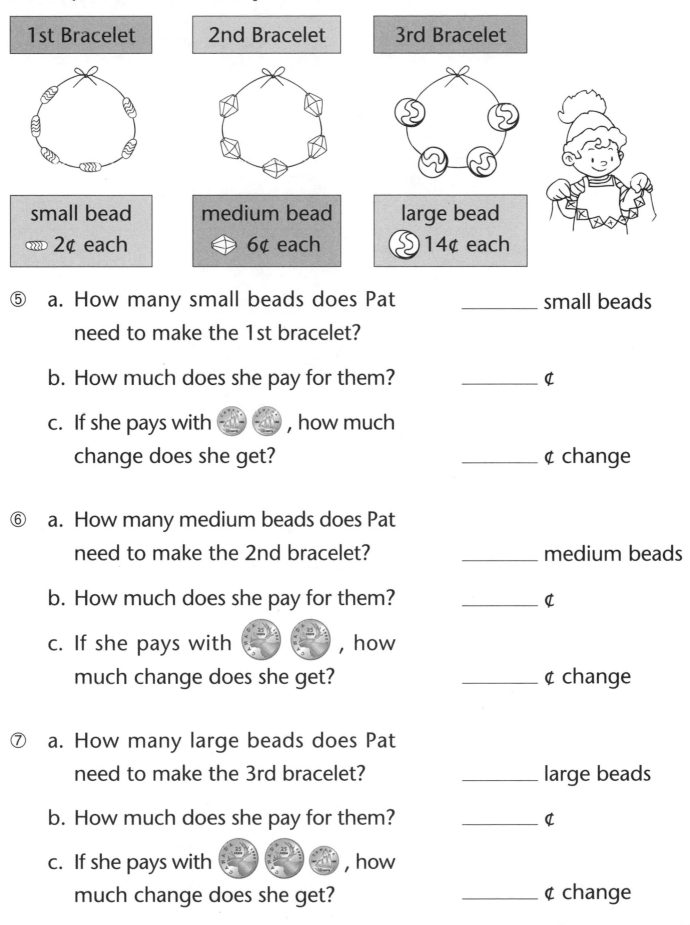

1st Bracelet   2nd Bracelet   3rd Bracelet

small bead
🪱 2¢ each

medium bead
◈ 6¢ each

large bead
🌀 14¢ each

⑤ a. How many small beads does Pat need to make the 1st bracelet?   _____ small beads

   b. How much does she pay for them?   _____ ¢

   c. If she pays with 🪙 🪙 , how much change does she get?   _____ ¢ change

⑥ a. How many medium beads does Pat need to make the 2nd bracelet?   _____ medium beads

   b. How much does she pay for them?   _____ ¢

   c. If she pays with 🪙 🪙 , how much change does she get?   _____ ¢ change

⑦ a. How many large beads does Pat need to make the 3rd bracelet?   _____ large beads

   b. How much does she pay for them?   _____ ¢

   c. If she pays with 🪙 🪙 🪙 , how much change does she get?   _____ ¢ change

Write how much each snack costs and see what the children buy. Help them solve the problems.

⑧								¢
⑨								¢
⑩								¢
⑪								¢

⑫ How much does Emma pays for a 🍪 and a 🧁 ?

_____ + _____ = _____

She pays _____ ¢.

+ _____

⑬ Paula pays 🪙🪙 for a 🥨. How much change does she get?

_____ – _____ = _____

She get _____ ¢ change.

– _____

⑭ How much more does a 🧀 cost than a 🧁 ?

_____ = _____

A 🧀 costs _____ ¢ more than a 🧁 .

⑮ How much do 2 🥨 cost?

_____ = _____

2 🥨 cost _____ ¢.

⑯ Jennifer buys a 🍪 and a 🥨. How much does she pay in all?

_____ = _____

She pays _____ ¢ in all.

⑰ Derek has 85¢. If he buys a 🧁 , how much has he left?

_____ = _____

He has _____ ¢ left.

⑱ Molly buys 2 🧁 and 1 🍪 . How much does she pay in all?

_____ = _____

She pays _____ ¢ in all.

⑲ Kevin gets 🪙 🪙 🪙 change from 🪙 🪙 .
What snack did he buy?

_____ = _____

He bought a _____ .

Pictographs

Look at the graph. Then answer the questions.

Favourite Footwear in Mrs Starkman's Class

Boots

Running shoes

Sandals

Dress shoes

Slippers

①   Which type of footwear is the least popular? _____

②   Which type of footwear is the most popular? _____

③   Which type of footwear is the next most popular? _____

④   Which type of footwear do fewer children like
than slippers? _____

⑤   Which type of footwear is as popular as slippers? _____

⑥   How many more children like sandals than
dress shoes? _____

⑦   How many children like running shoes or boots? _____

⑧   How many children are in Mrs Starkman's class? _____

Here are the records of the baseball teams. Look at the graph and answer the questions.

Number of Games Won

The Hawks · The Cubs · The Herons · The Rangers · The Lotus · The Jays

Team

⑨ Which team has won 7 games? _____

⑩ Which team has won 5 games? _____

⑪ How many teams have won more than 6 games? _____ teams

⑫ Which team has won 2 more games than The Cubs? _____

⑬ Which team has the best record? _____

⑭ Which team has the worst record? _____

⑮ The Rangers have played 12 games. How many games did they lose? _____ games

Ted has recorded the results of the hockey games. Use the table to complete the pictograph and answer the questions.

Team	Toronto	Rochester	Philadelphia	Buffalo	New York
Number of games won	5	8	4	6	7

⑯ Colour the boxes to complete the graph.

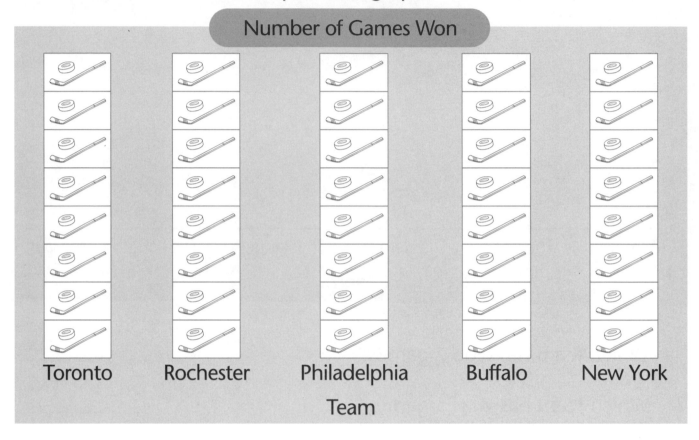

Number of Games Won

Toronto   Rochester   Philadelphia   Buffalo   New York

Team

⑰ Which team has the best record? _____

⑱ Which team has the worst record? _____

⑲ Which team has won 6 games? _____

⑳ How many teams have won 6 games or more? _____ teams

㉑ Buffalo has played 11 games. How many games did they lose? _____ games

㉒ Toronto has lost 7 games. How many games did they play in all? _____ games

Uncle Jim has recorded his customers' favourite sandwiches. Use his record to complete the pictograph and answer the questions.

Sandwich	Ham	Corned Beef	Roast Beef	Egg Salad	Chicken	Tuna Salad
Number of customers						

㉓ Colour the boxes to complete the graph.

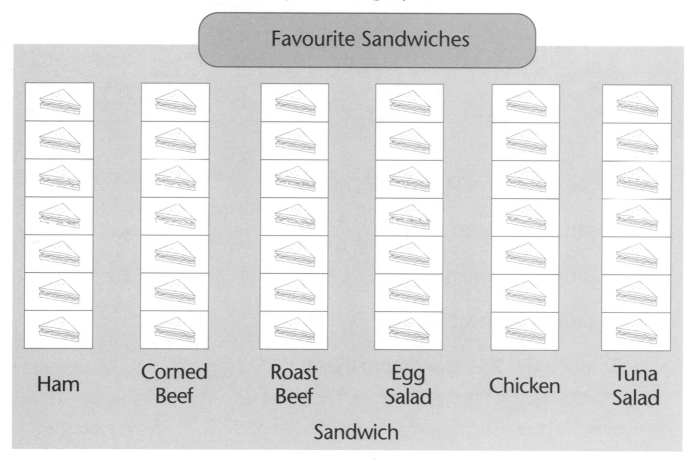

Favourite Sandwiches

Ham　　Corned Beef　　Roast Beef　　Egg Salad　　Chicken　　Tuna Salad

Sandwich

㉔ Which is the most popular sandwich?　　_____

㉕ Which is the least popular sandwich?　　_____

㉖ How many customers like beef sandwiches?　　_____

㉗ How many customers like salad sandwiches?　　_____

㉘ How many more customers like ham sandwiches than chicken sandwiches?　　_____

UNIT 6 — More about Addition and Subtraction

See how much Ron and his friends earned in the past 2 months. Answer the questions.

	April	May
Ron	$145	$108
Dan	$213	$96
Ada	$177	$82
Roberta	$59	$134

① Who earned the most in April? _____

② Who earned the least in April? _____

③ Who earned the most in May? _____

④ Who earned the least in May? _____

⑤ How much did Ron earn altogether?

_____ = _____ $ _____

⑥ How much did Dan earn altogether?

_____ = _____ $ _____

⑦ How much more did Ada earn in April than in May?

_____ = _____ $ _____ more

⑧ How much more did Roberta earn in May than in April?

_____ = _____ $ _____ more

Scientists counted the number of Canada Geese and Mallard Ducks at different places along Lake Ontario. Use the table to answer the questions.

Place	Number of 🦢	Number of 🦆
Hamilton	150	32
Oakville	165	64
Mississauga	178	45
Toronto	197	58

⑨ Where are the most 🦢 found? _____

⑩ Where are the most 🦆 found? _____

⑪ How many 🦢 and 🦆 were found in Hamilton?

_____ = _____   _____ 🦢 🦆

⑫ How many 🦢 and 🦆 were found in Oakville?

_____ = _____   _____ 🦢 🦆

⑬ How many 🦢 and 🦆 were found in Mississauga?

_____ = _____   _____ 🦢 🦆

⑭ How many 🦢 and 🦆 were found in Toronto?

_____ = _____   _____ 🦢 🦆

⑮ How many more 🦢 and 🦆 were found in Toronto than in Hamilton?

_____ = _____   _____ more 🦢 🦆

See how many students are in each school. Answer the questions.

Name of School	Number of Students
Cedar	154
Pine	326
Spruce	105
Maple	302

⑯ 72 students in Cedar School are . How many are in Cedar school?

_____ = _____   _____

⑰ 124 students in Maple School are . How many are in Maple school?

_____ = _____   _____

⑱ 97 students in Pine School wear . How many students in Pine School do not wear ?

_____ = _____   _____ students

⑲ 35 students in Spruce School have blond hair. How many students in Spruce School do not have blond hair?

_____ = _____   _____ students

⑳ If Cedar School and Pine School have a joint Sports Day and all students participate, how many students will there be in all?

_____ = _____   _____ students

This year Simon's Sports Store sold a lot of bicycles, tricycles, skateboards and scooters. Help Simon solve the problems.

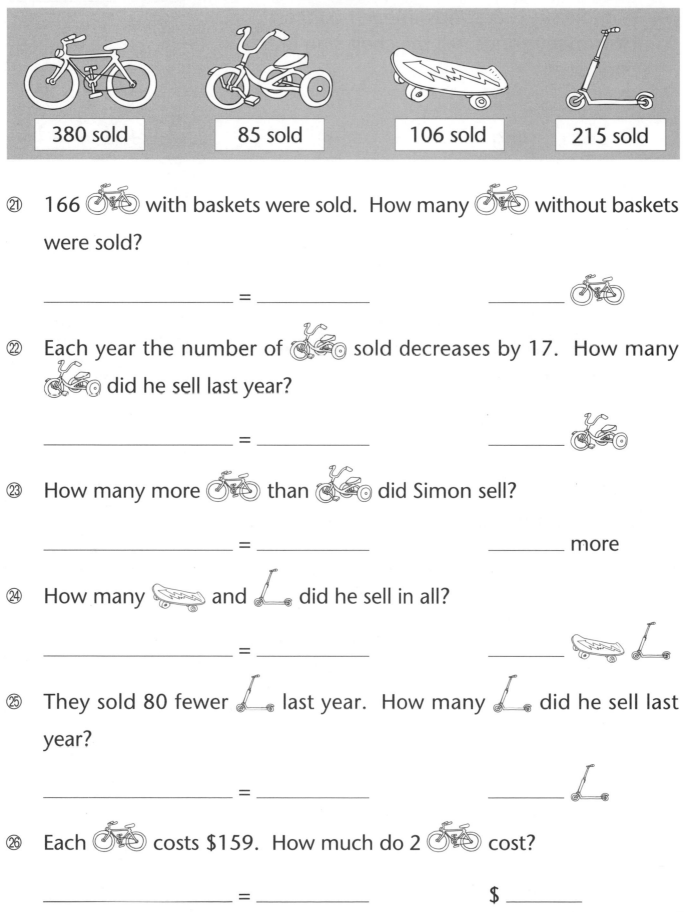

380 sold   85 sold   106 sold   215 sold

㉑ 166 🚲 with baskets were sold. How many 🚲 without baskets were sold?

_____ = _____   _____ 🚲

㉒ Each year the number of 🛺 sold decreases by 17. How many 🛺 did he sell last year?

_____ = _____   _____ 🛺

㉓ How many more 🚲 than 🛺 did Simon sell?

_____ = _____   _____ more

㉔ How many 🛹 and 🛴 did he sell in all?

_____ = _____   _____ 🛹 🛴

㉕ They sold 80 fewer 🛴 last year. How many 🛴 did he sell last year?

_____ = _____   _____ 🛴

㉖ Each 🚲 costs $159. How much do 2 🚲 cost?

_____ = _____ $ _____

Ivan goes to a music show. Help him solve the problems.

① A choir sings 9 songs in each concert. How many songs will the choir sing in 3 concerts?

3 x _____ = _____

_____ song

② A violin has 4 strings. How many strings are there on 5 violins?

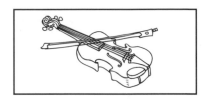

_____ x _____ = _____

_____ strings

③ A guitar has 6 strings. How many strings are there on 4 guitars?

_____ x _____ = _____

_____ strings

④ A piano has 2 pedals. How many pedals are there on 7 pianos?

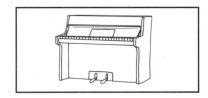

_____ x _____ = _____

_____ pedals

⑤ A Chinese flute has 6 finger-holes. How many finger-holes are there on 5 Chinese flutes?

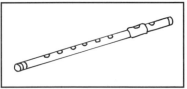

_____ x _____ = _____

_____ finger-holes

⑥ A drum has 2 drum-sticks. How many drum-sticks are there on 8 drums?

_____ x _____ = _____

_____ drum-sticks

See how much money each girl has. Fill in the blanks and answer the questions.

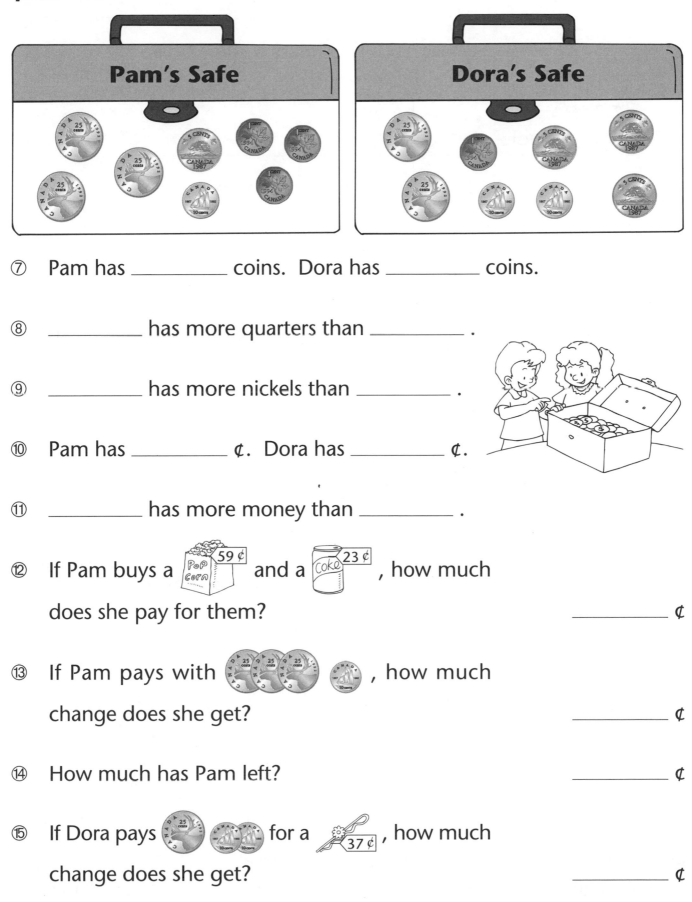

⑦ Pam has _____ coins. Dora has _____ coins.

⑧ _____ has more quarters than _____ .

⑨ _____ has more nickels than _____ .

⑩ Pam has _____ ¢. Dora has _____ ¢.

⑪ _____ has more money than _____ .

⑫ If Pam buys a [POP corn 59¢] and a [Coke 23¢], how much does she pay for them? _____ ¢

⑬ If Pam pays with [25 cents] [25 cents] [25 cents] [10 cents], how much change does she get? _____ ¢

⑭ How much has Pam left? _____ ¢

⑮ If Dora pays [25 cents] [10 cents] [10 cents] for a [37¢], how much change does she get? _____ ¢

The table shows the number of boys and girls at each school. Complete the table and answer the questions.

⑯ Trafalgar School	(boy)	Two hundred ninety-five	
	(girl)		312
⑰ Meadows School	(boy)	Two hundred seventy-three	
	(girl)		298
⑱ Glenview School	(boy)		301
	(girl)	Two hundred ninety	

⑲ Put the schools in order, from the one with the most boys to the one with the fewest.

_____ , _____ , _____

⑳ Put the schools in order, from the one with the most girls to the one with the fewest.

_____ , _____ , _____

㉑ Which school has more boys than girls? _____

㉒ How many students attend Trafalgar School? _____ students

㉓ How many students attend Meadows School? _____ students

㉔ How many students attend Glenview School? _____ students

㉕ How many more girls than boys are there at Trafalgar School? _____ more

Simon and his friends joined the Summer Reading Programme. See how many books they read. Answer the questions.

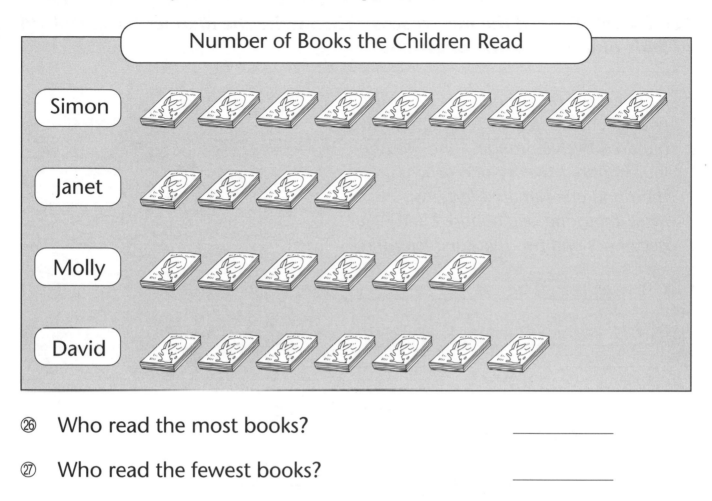

Number of Books the Children Read

Simon

Janet

Molly

David

㉖ Who read the most books? _____

㉗ Who read the fewest books? _____

㉘ How many more books did Janet need to read to catch up with Molly? _____ more books

㉙ How many more books did David read than Janet? _____ more books

㉚ Simon read 4 books about dinosaurs. How many of his books were not about dinosaurs? _____ books

㉛ Did the girls read more books than the boys? _____

㉜ For every 3 books each child read, he or she would get a prize. How many prizes would Simon get? _____ prizes

㉝ How many prizes would David get? _____ prizes

Read what Richard the farmer says. Then write the number for each kind of fruit and answer the questions.

I have two thousand three hundred twenty-one apples, three thousand two hundred twelve oranges, one thousand four hundred twenty-one peaches, two thousand one hundred forty-two pears, three thousand one hundred thirty-four nectarines and two thousand forty-three kiwi.

① _____ 🍎

② _____ 🍊

③ _____ 🍑

④ _____ 🍐

⑤ _____ 🍑

⑥ _____ 🥝

⑦ Which kind of fruit does Richard have the most? _____

⑧ Which kind of fruit does Richard have the least? _____

⑨ How many kinds of fruit does Richard have that are more than three thousand? _____

⑩ If Richard sells one thousand 🍎 to the market, how many 🍎 will be left? Write the number in words.

_____

⑪ If Richard gets five hundred 🍑 from Tim, how many 🍑 will he have in all? Write the number in words.

_____

Dave went to the Royal Ontario Museum and learned all about dinosaurs. Look at the table and answer the questions.

Dinosaur	Length (cm)
Tyrannosarus	1200
Diplodocus	2600
Brachiosaurus	2200
Plesiosaurus	1800
Brontosaurus	2100
Triceratops	600
Giganotosaurus	1300

⑫   Which dinosaur was the longest?   _____

⑬   Which dinosaur was the second longest?   _____

⑭   How much longer was Brachiosaurus than Tyrannosaurus?   _____ cm

⑮   What is the difference in length between Diplodocus and Triceratops?   _____ cm

⑯   Which dinosaur was longer than Tyrannosaurus but shorter than Plesiosaurus?   _____

⑰   How long was Brontosaurus? Write its length in words.

_____

⑱   How long was Giganotosaurus? Write its length in words.

_____

Mrs Ling and Mrs Ford buy some lottery tickets to support the Canadian Cancer Society. Help them put the tickets in order and answer the questions.

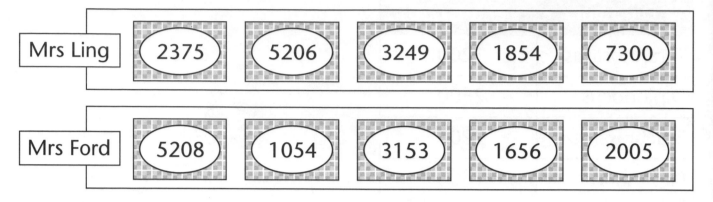

⑲ Help Mrs Ling put the tickets in order, from the largest to the smallest.

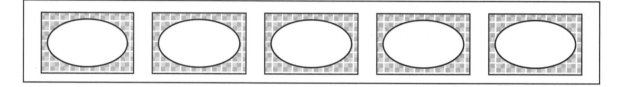

⑳ Help Mrs Ford put the tickets in order, from the largest to the smallest.

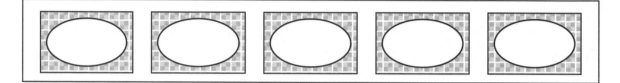

㉑ Write the smallest number of Mrs Ling's tickets in words.

_____

㉒ Write the largest number of Mrs Ford's tickets in words.

_____

㉓ How many tickets with 2 in the hundreds place does Mrs Ling have? What are they?

_____ tickets; _____

㉔ How many tickets with 5 in the tens place does Mrs Ford have? What are they?

_____ tickets; _____

Sam's factory supplies markers to different stores. The markers come in boxes of different sizes. Complete the table and answer the questions.

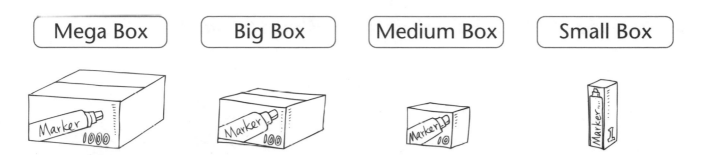

| Mega Box | Big Box | Medium Box | Small Box |

	Mega Box	Big Box	Medium Box	Small Box	Total Number of Markers
㉕ Max's Mart	2	3	1	4	
㉖ Toby's Shop	3	1	0	5	
㉗ Ranis Retail				0	1470
㉘ Tedd Depot			6		2069

㉙ Which store orders the most number of 〈Marker〉 ? _____

㉚ Which store orders the least number of 〈Marker〉 ? _____

㉛ Max's Mart sold 800 〈Marker〉 last month. How many big boxes of 〈Marker〉 did it sell in all? _____ big boxes

㉜ Toby's Shop sold 70 〈Marker〉 last week. How many medium boxes of 〈Marker〉 did it sell in all? _____ medium boxes

㉝ Ranis Retail sells 5 mega boxes of 〈Marker〉 a year. How many 〈Marker〉 does it sell in all? _____ 〈Marker〉

Division

See how the children share their food. Write the numbers.

① Chad and Sue share 8 🍎. How many 🍎 does each child get?

🍎🍎🍎🍎🍎🍎🍎🍎

$8 \div 2 =$ _____

Each child gets _____ 🍎.

② 5 children share 15 🍬. How many 🍬 does each child get?

🍬🍬🍬🍬🍬🍬🍬🍬🍬🍬🍬🍬🍬🍬🍬

$15 \div 5 =$ _____   Each child gets _____ 🍬.

③ 4 children share 12 🍪. How many 🍪 does each child get?

🍪🍪🍪🍪🍪🍪🍪🍪🍪🍪🍪🍪

$12 \div 4 =$ _____   Each child gets _____ 🍪.

④ 3 children share 18 🍭. How many 🍭 does each child get?

🍭🍭🍭🍭🍭🍭🍭🍭🍭🍭🍭🍭🍭🍭🍭🍭🍭🍭

$18 \div 3 =$ _____   Each child gets _____ 🍭.

⑤ 6 children share 12 🍓. How many 🍓 does each child get?

🍓🍓🍓🍓🍓🍓🍓🍓🍓🍓🍓🍓

$12 \div 6 =$ _____   Each child gets _____ 🍓.

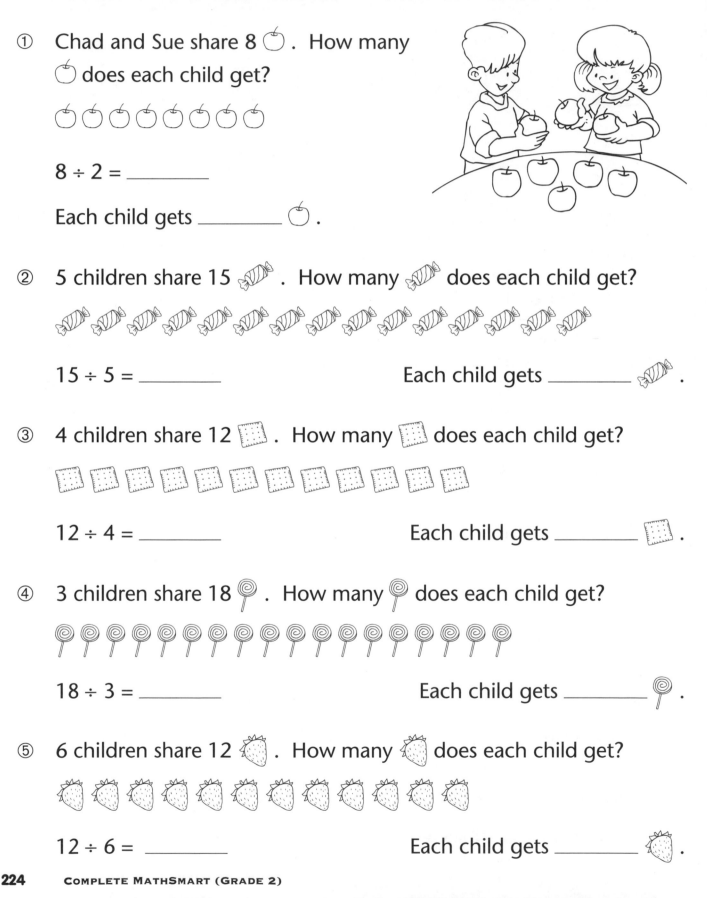

Mrs Starkman wants to sew some buttons on the clothes. Help her draw the buttons and write the numbers.

⑥   Divide 25 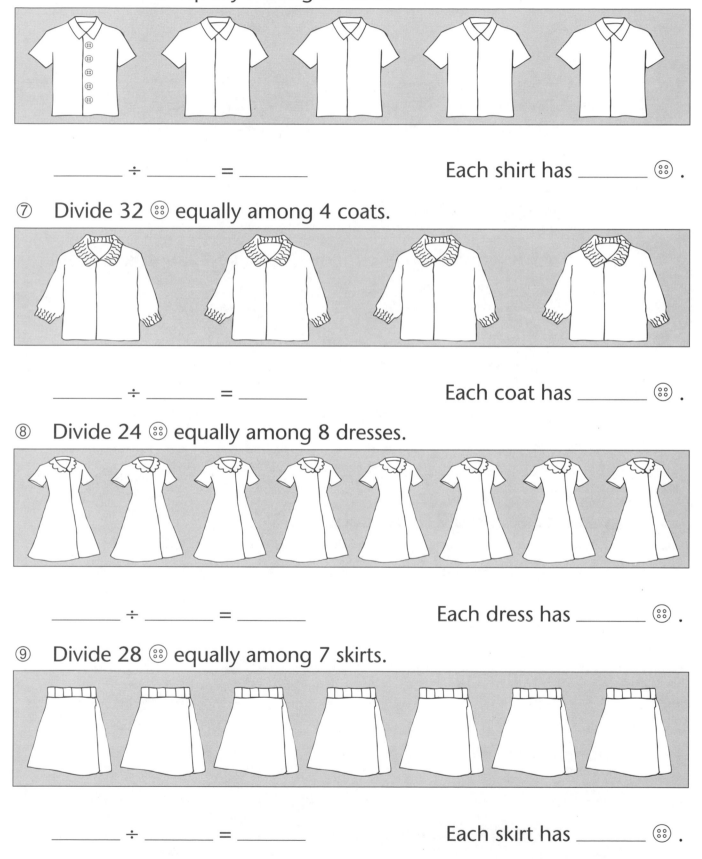 equally among 5 shirts.

_____ ÷ _____ = _____   Each shirt has _____ ⊞ .

⑦   Divide 32 ⊞ equally among 4 coats.

_____ ÷ _____ = _____   Each coat has _____ ⊞ .

⑧   Divide 24 ⊞ equally among 8 dresses.

_____ ÷ _____ = _____   Each dress has _____ ⊞ .

⑨   Divide 28 ⊞ equally among 7 skirts.

_____ ÷ _____ = _____   Each skirt has _____ ⊞ .

Help Dale the farmer solve the problems.

⑩ A cow has 4 legs. How many cows have 20 legs?

_____ ÷ _____ = _____

_____ cows have 20 legs.

⑪ Each hen lays 3 eggs. How many hens lay 27 eggs?

_____ ÷ _____ = _____

_____ hens lay 27 eggs.

⑫ Each cat has 8 whiskers. How many cats have 72 whiskers?

_____ ÷ _____ = _____

_____ cats have 72 whiskers.

⑬ A basket holds 7 corn cobs. How many baskets hold 21 corn cobs?

_____ ÷ _____ = _____

_____ baskets hold 21 corn cobs.

⑭ A bag holds 4 potatoes. How many bags hold 20 potatoes?

_____ ÷ _____ = _____

_____ bags hold 20 potatoes.

⑮ A box holds 5 bunches of celery. How many boxes hold 10 bunches of celery?

_____ ÷ _____ = _____

_____ boxes hold 10 bunches of celery.

5 girls go apple-picking. Help them solve the problems.

⑯ The girls pick 40 apples in all and put 4 apples in each basket. How many baskets do they need?

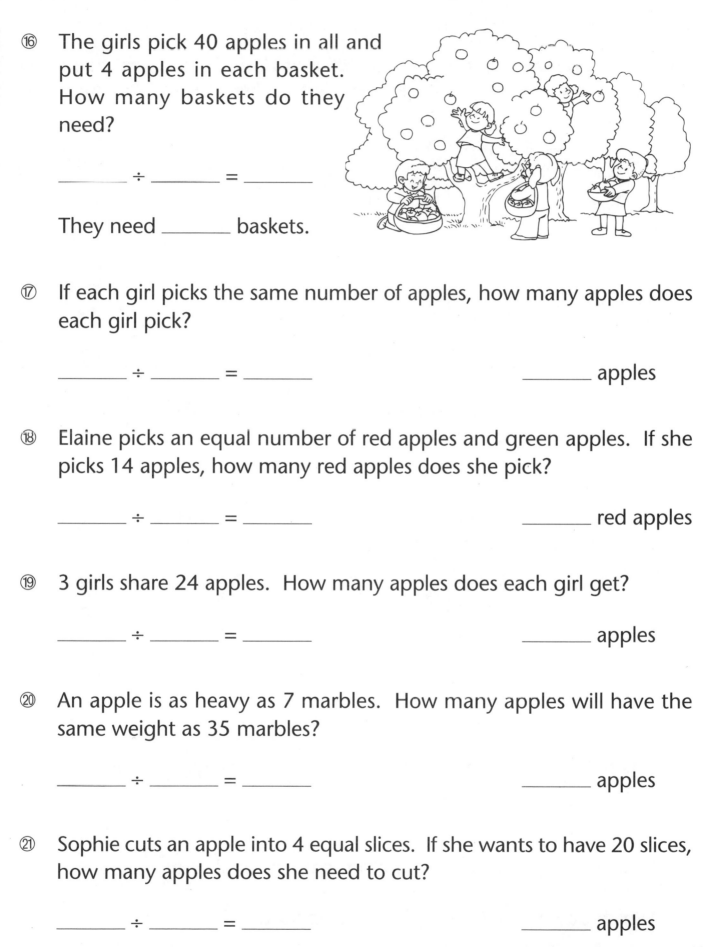

_____ ÷ _____ = _____

They need _____ baskets.

⑰ If each girl picks the same number of apples, how many apples does each girl pick?

_____ ÷ _____ = _____   _____ apples

⑱ Elaine picks an equal number of red apples and green apples. If she picks 14 apples, how many red apples does she pick?

_____ ÷ _____ = _____   _____ red apples

⑲ 3 girls share 24 apples. How many apples does each girl get?

_____ ÷ _____ = _____   _____ apples

⑳ An apple is as heavy as 7 marbles. How many apples will have the same weight as 35 marbles?

_____ ÷ _____ = _____   _____ apples

㉑ Sophie cuts an apple into 4 equal slices. If she wants to have 20 slices, how many apples does she need to cut?

_____ ÷ _____ = _____   _____ apples

Measurement

Jason measured the temperature at different times for the past two days. Help him write the times and temperatures. Then answer the questions.

①

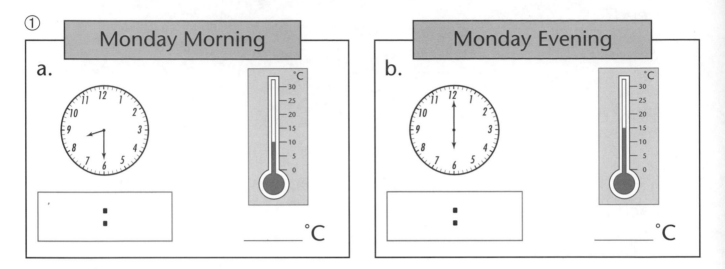

Monday Morning

a. _____:_____

_____ °C

Monday Evening

b. _____:_____

_____ °C

c. The morning temperature was _____ higher / lower than the evening temperature.

②

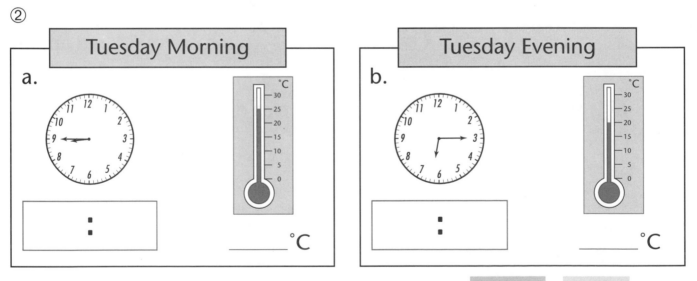

Tuesday Morning

a. _____:_____

_____ °C

Tuesday Evening

b. _____:_____

_____ °C

c. The morning temperature was _____ higher / lower than the evening temperature.

③ Which day had a higher morning temperature? _____

④ Which day had a lower evening temperature? _____

Mr Richards organized a track event at Riverview School. Look at the 6 best times for the 400-m race and answer the questions.

The 6 Best Times	
Adam	2 min 50 s
Bob	3 min 10 s
Carol	3 min 3 s
Daren	2 min 58 s
Eva	2 min 55 s
Frank	3 min 15 s

⑤　How long was the race? 　　　　　　　　　_____ metres

⑥　Who won the race? 　　　　　　　　　_____

⑦　Who came 2nd? 　　　　　　　　　_____

⑧　Who came 5th? 　　　　　　　　　_____

⑨　What was the time difference between the

　　best runner and the second best runner? 　_____ seconds

Read what Mr Richards says. Then answer the questions.

> *Today is Wednesday, May 15. Yesterday, the children practised running from 9:30 a.m. to 11:00 a.m. On the coming Saturday, we will have a swimming gala. It will start at 9:15 a.m. and last 4 hours.*

⑩　How long did the children practise running? 　_____ minutes

⑪　What date will they have a swimming gala? 　_____

⑫　When will the swimming gala end? 　_____

10 More about Multiplication and Division

Mrs Kerr is dividing her plants into window boxes. Write the numbers.

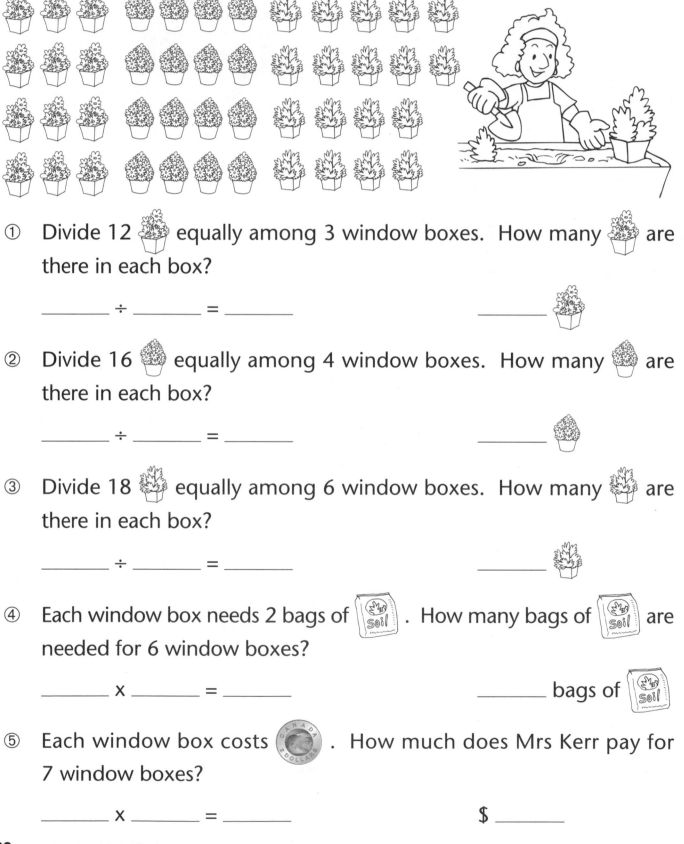

① Divide 12 🪴 equally among 3 window boxes. How many 🪴 are there in each box?

_____ ÷ _____ = _____   _____

② Divide 16 🪴 equally among 4 window boxes. How many 🪴 are there in each box?

_____ ÷ _____ = _____   _____

③ Divide 18 🪴 equally among 6 window boxes. How many 🪴 are there in each box?

_____ ÷ _____ = _____   _____

④ Each window box needs 2 bags of Soil. How many bags of Soil are needed for 6 window boxes?

_____ x _____ = _____   _____ bags of Soil

⑤ Each window box costs 🪙. How much does Mrs Kerr pay for 7 window boxes?

_____ x _____ = _____ $ _____

Look at Peter's baseball cards. Help him solve the problems.

⑥ How many baseball cards does Peter have? _____ cards

⑦ If Peter divides the cards equally into 4 piles, how many cards are there in each pile?

_____ ÷ _____ = _____   _____ cards

⑧ If Peter gives 2 piles to Pam, how many cards does Pam get?

_____ x _____ = _____   _____ cards

⑨ If Pam divides the cards equally into 6 piles, how many cards are there in each pile?

_____ ÷ _____ = _____   _____ cards

⑩ If Peter gives 6 cards to Joe and puts the rest equally into 5 boxes, how many cards are there in each box?

_____ ÷ _____ = _____   _____ cards

⑪ How many cards are there in 3 boxes?

_____ x _____ = _____   _____ cards

See what Ann bought. Help her solve the problems.

⑫ How many did Ann buy in all?

_____ x _____ = _____   _____

⑬ If Ann divides all the into 4 equal groups, how many will there be in each group?

_____ ÷ _____ = _____   _____

⑭ How many did Ann buy in all?

_____ x _____ = _____   _____

⑮ If Ann divides all the into 8 equal groups, how many will there be in each group?

_____ ÷ _____ = _____   _____

⑯ How many did Ann buy in all?

_____ x _____ = _____   _____

⑰ If Ann divides all the into 3 equal groups, how many will there be in each group?

_____ ÷ _____ = _____   _____

Darren and his friends plant some saplings every summer. See how many saplings Darren plants and solve the problems.

⑱ Darren plants 7 saplings every hour. How many trees can he plant in 6 hours?

_____ x _____ = _____   _____ saplings

⑲ How long does it take him to plant 28 saplings?

_____ ÷ _____ = _____   _____ hours

⑳ He works 8 hours a day. How many saplings can he plant in one day?

_____ x _____ = _____   _____ saplings

㉑ A row has 10 saplings. How many saplings are there in 3 rows?

_____ x _____ = _____   _____ saplings

㉒ Katie has 16 stakes. She uses 2 for each sapling. How many saplings does she plant?

_____ ÷ _____ = _____   _____ saplings

㉓ Kim can plant 32 saplings in 4 hours. How many saplings can she plant in 1 hour?

_____ ÷ _____ = _____   _____ saplings

Look at the graph and fill in the blanks.

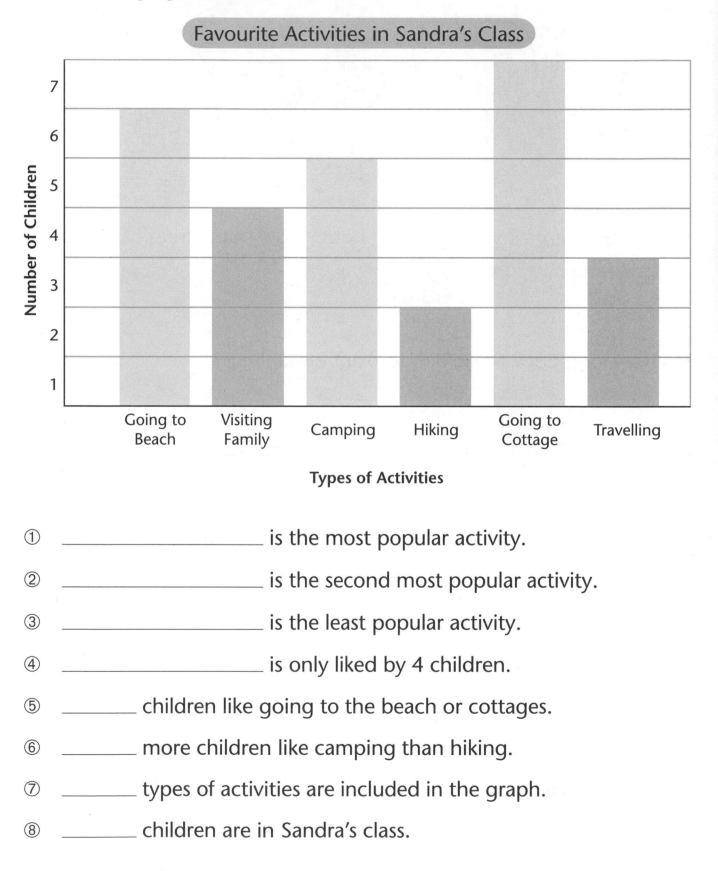

Favourite Activities in Sandra's Class

Types of Activities

① _____ is the most popular activity.

② _____ is the second most popular activity.

③ _____ is the least popular activity.

④ _____ is only liked by 4 children.

⑤ _____ children like going to the beach or cottages.

⑥ _____ more children like camping than hiking.

⑦ _____ types of activities are included in the graph.

⑧ _____ children are in Sandra's class.

Look at the graph and answer the questions.

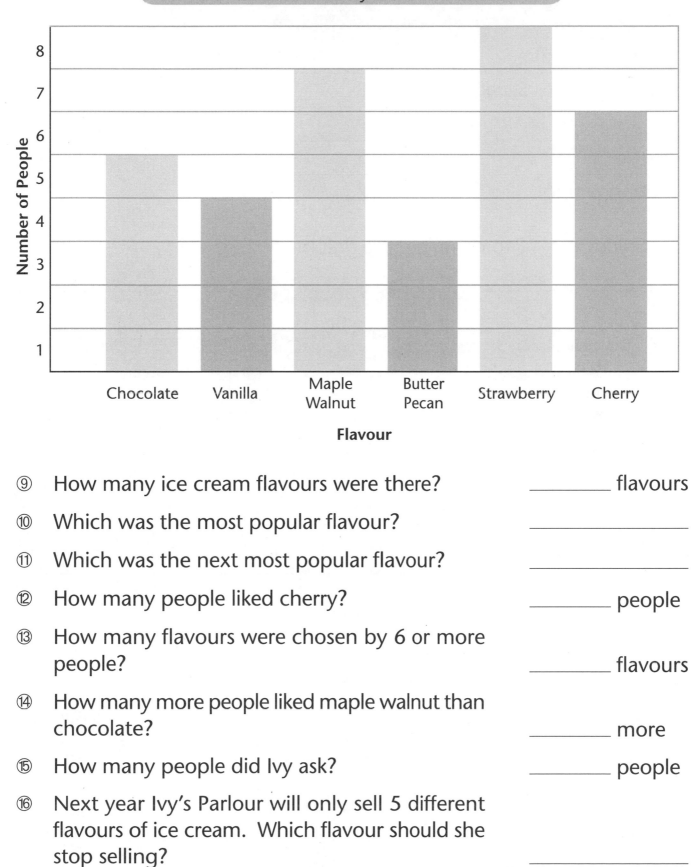

Favourite Flavours in Ivy's Ice Cream Parlour

⑨ How many ice cream flavours were there? _____ flavours

⑩ Which was the most popular flavour? _____

⑪ Which was the next most popular flavour? _____

⑫ How many people liked cherry? _____ people

⑬ How many flavours were chosen by 6 or more people? _____ flavours

⑭ How many more people liked maple walnut than chocolate? _____ more

⑮ How many people did Ivy ask? _____ people

⑯ Next year Ivy's Parlour will only sell 5 different flavours of ice cream. Which flavour should she stop selling? _____

Mr White asks the children about their favourite winter sports. Use his record to complete the graph and answer the questions.

Sport	Number of children
Downhill Skiing	11
Cross Country Skiing	8
Skating	9
Hockey	5
Tobogganing	7

⑰ Colour the ☐ to complete the graph.

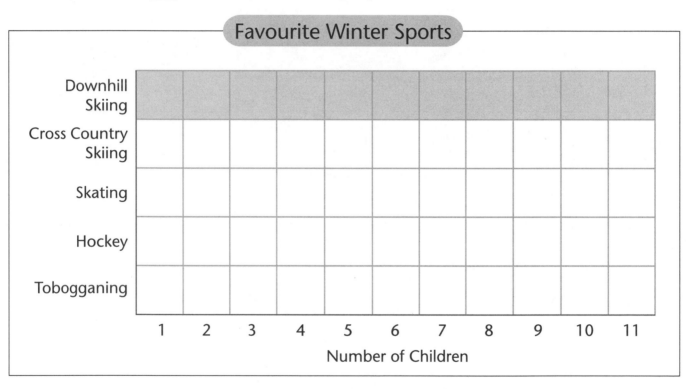

⑱ Which is the most favourite winter sport? _____

⑲ How many children like skiing? _____ children

⑳ How many children like skating or hockey? _____ children

㉑ How many more children like skating than tobogganing? _____ more

㉒ How many children did Mr White ask? _____ children

Jamie asks his classmates about the number of children in their families. Use his record to complete the graph and answer the questions.

Number of children in each family	1	2	3	4	5 or more
Number of families	4	6	3	1	2

㉓ Colour the ☐ to complete the graph.

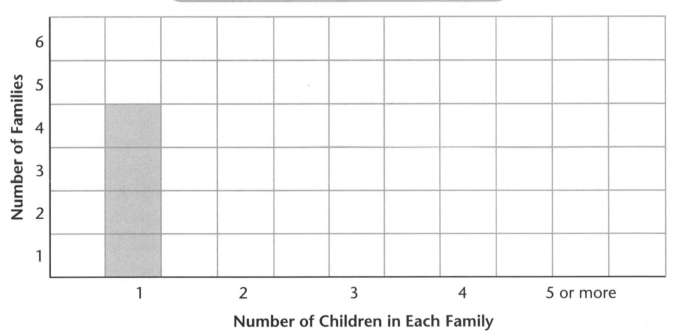

Number of Children in Each Family

㉔ What is the most usual number of children in a family? _____

㉕ How many families have 3 children? _____ families

㉖ How many families have 5 or more children? _____ families

㉗ How many children in the class have no brothers or sisters? _____ children

㉘ How many children did Jamie ask? _____ children

㉙ If Jamie has 3 brothers and no sisters, how many children are there in his family? _____ children

The 8 cards below are put face down on the table. See what they say and answer the questions.

Every time one of us picks a card and puts it back. Then we will shuffle the 8 cards and put them face down for the next player.

① Is a player more likely to pick a 2 or a 3? _____

② Is a player more likely to pick a 4 or a 6? _____

③ Is a player more likely to pick a ♥ or a ♦ ? _____

④ Is a player more likely to pick a ♠ or a ♣ ? _____

⑤ Which numbers is a player equally likely to pick? _____

⑥ Which number is a player most likely to pick? _____

⑦ Which number is a player unlikely to pick? _____

⑧ Is there any chance for a player to pick a 7 from the 8 cards above? _____

⑨ If the number on the card that a player guesses is the same as the one he or she picks, he or she wins the game. What number should Pam guess so as to have more chance to win? _____

⑩ If the pattern of the card that a player guesses is the same as the one he or she picks, he or she wins the game. What pattern should Pam guess so as to have more chance to win? _____

Stanley puts all his lollipops into a bag and picks one out. Help him answer the questions.

⑪ How many lollipops does Stanley have? _____ lollipops

⑫ How many lollipops are lemon flavour? _____ lollipops

⑬ How many lollipops are chocolate flavour? _____ lollipops

⑭ How many lollipops are vanilla flavour? _____ lollipops

⑮ How many lollipops are orange flavour? _____ lollipops

⑯ Is there more chance to pick a vanilla lollipop or an orange lollipop? _____ lollipop

⑰ Is there more chance to pick a lemon lollipop or a chocolate lollipop? _____ lollipop

⑱ What would be the most likely flavour to be picked from the bag? _____ flavour

⑲ Is it possible to pick a strawberry lollipop from the bag? _____

⑳ If Stanley puts 2 more vanilla lollipops into the bag, what would be the most likely flavour to be picked from that bag? _____ flavour

Gloria gets some information from the Internet. Help her put the information on the number line and answer the questions.

River	Length (km)
Amazon	7020
Mississippi	6770
Nile	7500
St. Lawrence	3500
Mackenzie	1240

① Write the names and lengths of the rivers in the boxes.

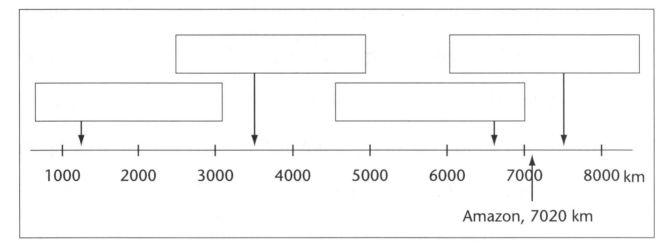

Amazon, 7020 km

② Which river is the longest? _____

③ Which river is the shortest? _____

④ Is the St. Lawrence longer than the Mississippi? _____

⑤ How many rivers are longer than 5000 km? _____ rivers

⑥ Which river is shorter than the St. Lawrence? _____

⑦ Which river is shorter than the Nile, but longer than the Mississippi? _____

⑧ The Yangtze is 5580 km long. Is the Yangtze longer than the Mackenzie? _____

Carol makes a cup of coffee and measures its temperature at different times. Write the temperatures.

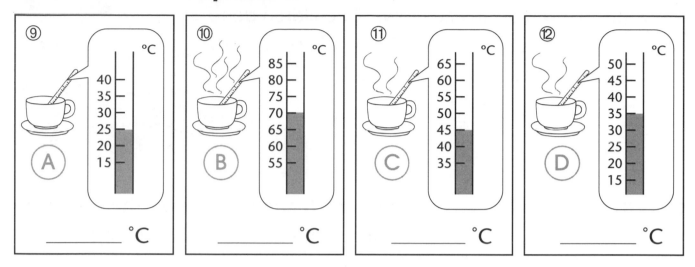

⑨ _____ °C

⑩ _____ °C

⑪ _____ °C

⑫ _____ °C

⑬ Put the pictures in order. Write the letters.

_____ , _____ , _____ , _____

Carol pours some drinks into the cups and lets Charles pick one cup. Help Charles answer the questions.

⑭ Is Charles more likely to pick pop or juice? _____

⑮ What kind of drink is Charles likely to pick? _____

⑯ What kind of drink is Charles unlikely to pick? _____

⑰ Is there any chance for Charles to pick a cup of coffee? _____

⑱ If Carol takes away 1 cup of pop, what kind of drink is Charles likely to pick? _____

⑲ If Carol takes away 1 cup of iced tea, what kind of drink is Charles unlikely to pick? _____

Mrs Ford's class go skiing. Help them solve the problems.

㉒ A bus has 4 seats in each row. 24 children go to a ski resort by bus and fill the whole bus. How many rows are there on the bus?

_____ ÷ _____ = _____

_____ rows

㉑ When they arrive at the ski resort, 8 children get off the bus every minute. How long does it take for the whole class to get off?

_____ ÷ _____ = _____   _____ minutes

㉒ 21 children ski downhill in groups of 3. How many groups are there ?

_____ ÷ _____ = _____   _____ groups

㉓ 15 children eat lunch at tables for 5 people. How many tables do they need?

_____ ÷ _____ = _____   _____ tables

㉔ Each child eats 2 chicken wings. How many chicken wings do 8 children eat?

_____ x _____ = _____   _____ chicken wings

㉕ Each child drinks 3 boxes of juice. How many boxes of juice do 9 children drink?

_____ x _____ = _____   _____ boxes of juice

㉖ Each toboggan carries 4 children. 20 children play tobogganing at the same time. How many toboggans do they need?

_____ ÷ _____ = _____   _____ toboggans

Mr Bobker's class visit the Museum. Help Mr Bobker solve the problems.

㉗ There are 6 vans going to the Museum. 5 students go in each van. How many students are there in all?

_____ x _____ = _____   _____ students

㉘ The students are divided into 3 equal groups. How many students are there in each group?

_____ x _____ = _____   _____ students

㉙ Each student gets 2 pencils from the Museum. How many pencils does a group of students get?

_____ x _____ = _____   _____ pencils

㉚ There are 8 sections on each floor. How many sections are there on 3 floors?

_____ x _____ = _____   _____ sections

㉛ Each souvenir costs 9¢. Mr Bobker buys 7 souvenirs. How much does he need to pay?

_____ x _____ = _____   _____ ¢

㉜ One of the shows at the Museum starts at 1:05 p.m. and ends at 1:40 p.m. How long does the show last?   _____ minutes

㉝ The show about electricity starts at 12:35 p.m. and last 45 minutes. When does it end?   _____

㉞ The students leave the Museum at 2:45 p.m. and return to school at 3:30 p.m. How long is the ride?   _____ minutes

Jack counted the number of cars in different colours in the parking lot. Read what he says and complete the graph. Then complete the table and fill in the blanks.

Green is the least popular colour and beige is the most popular colour. Black is the second most popular colour. Red and white are equally popular.

Number of Cars in Different Colours

㉟

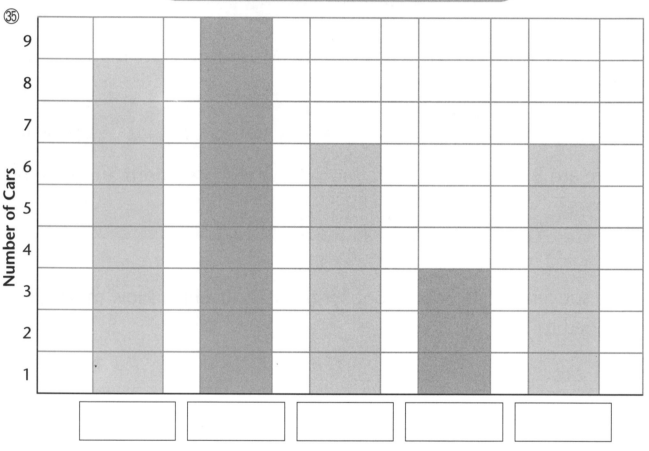

Colour

㊱

Colour	Black	Beige	Red	Green	White
Number of Cars					

㊲ There were _____ more black cars than red cars in the parking lot.

㊳ There were _____ beige or green cars in the parking lot.

㊴ Jack counted _____ cars in all.

1. 3-digit Numbers

↔ Children should understand the concept of place value and the use of zero as a place holder; otherwise, they may have difficulty in writing or reading a number with 0.

Examples

607 $\xrightarrow{\text{read}}$ sixty-seven ✗

six hundred and seven ✔

One hundred twenty-eight $\xrightarrow{\text{write}}$ 100208 ✗

128 ✔

2. Addition and Subtraction

↔ To do addition,

1st align the numbers on the right-hand side.

2nd add the numbers from right to left (starting with the ones place).

3rd carry groups of 10 from one column to the next column on the left.

Example

Align the numbers.	Add the ones and carry 1 ten to the tens column.	Add the tens.
6 7 + 2 4	1 6 7 + 2 4 1	1 6 7 + 2 4 9 1

67 + 24 = 91

↔ To do subtraction,

1st align the numbers on the right-hand side.

2nd subtract the numbers from right to left (starting with the ones place).

3rd if the number is too small to subtract, borrow 10 from the column on the left.

Example

Align the numbers.	Borrow 1 ten from the tens column; subtract the ones.	Subtract the tens.
8 2 – 1 9	7 $\cancel{8}$ 2 12 – 1 9 3	8 2 – 1 9 6 3

82 – 19 = 63

3. Multiplication

↔ Parents should pay attention to the signs their children use, as quite a few children mix up the signs of multiplication and addition. For example, they will write 3 x 3 = 9 as 3 + 3 = 9.

↔ Children need to understand that multiplication is a quick way to do addition. Initially, children learn to count in twos, fives and tens, and then proceed to count in threes, fours, etc. Parents can let their children use a number line or concrete materials to count by 2's, 5's ... so as to consolidate their concept of multiplication.

Examples   2 + 2 + 2 + 2 = 8   4 x 2 = 8

↔ Multiplying any number by 1, the number stays the same.

Examples   1 x 5 = 5   1 x 3 = 3

↔ Multiplying any number by 0, the answer is always 0.

Examples   4 x 0 = 0   0 x 7 = 0

4. Division

↔ Children should understand that division is the opposite of multiplication.

Example   5 x 2 = 10, 10 ÷ 2 = 5 and 10 ÷ 5 = 2

↔ Children can use the following steps to do division:

1st Divide	2nd Multiply	3rd Subtract	4th Bring down

Example

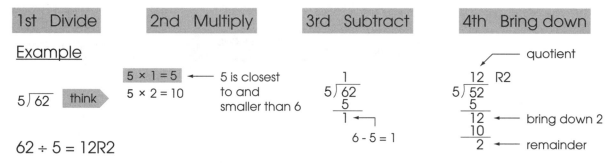

$62 ÷ 5 = 12R2$

5. Fractions and Decimals

↔ Children learn the basic concept of writing a fraction or a decimal. At the beginning, fractions should be limited to halves, thirds, fourths and tenths, and decimal numbers should be limited to one-decimal place only. Parents should encourage their children to use concrete materials and drawings to show the relationship between fractions and decimals.

Example

$\frac{3}{10}$ or 0.3 is shaded.

6. Measurement

↔ Children learn to use centimetres and metres in measuring length and distance, as well as the relationship between centimetres and metres (1 metre = 100 centimetres). Furthermore, they learn how to measure and record the perimeter and area of 2-dimensional shapes. At this stage, it is not necessary to introduce the units of perimeter and area to them.

7. Time and Temperature

↪ Children should understand the relationship between days and weeks, months and years, minutes and hours, and hours and days. Quite a few children, however, have difficulty finding intervals of time. Parents should provide more guidance and daily practice for them.

Examples

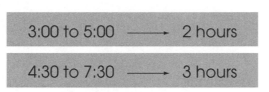

3:00 to 5:00 ⟶ 2 hours

4:30 to 7:30 ⟶ 3 hours

↪ Children learn that the thermometer is used to measure temperature. They can use the thermometer to determine whether the temperature is rising or falling and recognize that degree Celsius (°C) is the unit for recording temperature. At this stage, parents should not discuss with children the use of negative numbers to indicate temperatures below 0 °C.

8. Money

↪ Children learn to name and state the value of all coins and show their understanding of the value of each coin. They also need to know how to put coins in equivalent sets up to $1 in value. Parents should remind children that they can use subtraction to work out change.

9. Shapes

↪ At this stage, children learn some 3-dimensional figures such as prism and pyramid. Parents should encourage them to use a variety of materials such as straws and sticks to construct the skeleton of a prism or a pyramid so as to consolidate their concept of 3-dimensional figures. The 2-dimensional figures that the children may have learnt are pentagon, hexagon and octagon. They should be able to describe the attributes of regular polygons using terms such as side/sides and vertex/vertices.

Example

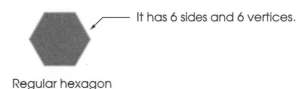

It has 6 sides and 6 vertices.

Regular hexagon

10. Transformations

→ Children learn how to demonstrate transformations, such as flips, slides and turns by using concrete materials such as cards and dice.

→ Children learn how to find a line of symmetry of a 2-dimensional figure by using paper folding or reflection in a mirror. They should understand that a symmetrical figure can have more than 1 line of symmetry.

Examples

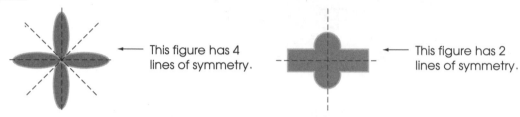

This figure has 4 lines of symmetry.

This figure has 2 lines of symmetry.

11. Pictographs and Block Graphs

→ Children need to know how to construct and label simple pictographs and block graphs by using one-to-one correspondence. Parents should encourage them to interpret the graphs and describe the information given by the graphs.

Examples

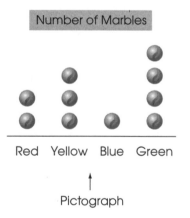

Pictograph

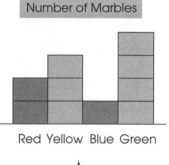

Block Graph

1 Addition and Subtraction to 20

1a. 19	b. 19	c. 19
2a. 15	b. 15	c. 15
3a. 14	b. 8	c. 14
4a. 13	b. 13	c. 9
5a. 20	b. 20	
6a. 16	b. 7	
7a. 17	b. 17	
8a. 19	b. 11	

9. 12   10. 8
11. 5   12. 9
13. 12 + 8 = 20 ; 20   14. 12 – 8 = 4 ; 4
15. 5 + 9 = 14 ; 14   16. 9 – 4 = 5 ; 5
17. 8 + 9 = 17 ; 17

2 2-digit Numbers

1. 40 ; 41 ; 43 ; 44   2. 28 ; 26 ; 25 ; 23
3. 58 ; 56 ; 55 ; 52   4. 54 ; 42 ; 37 ; 23
5. 64 ; 50 ; 25 ; 11   6. 90 ; 81 ; 47 ; 30
7.

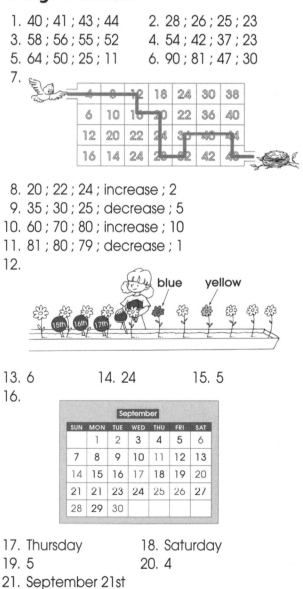

8. 20 ; 22 ; 24 ; increase ; 2
9. 35 ; 30 ; 25 ; decrease ; 5
10. 60 ; 70 ; 80 ; increase ; 10
11. 81 ; 80 ; 79 ; decrease ; 1
12.

13. 6   14. 24   15. 5
16.

September						
SUN	MON	TUE	WED	THU	FRI	SAT
		1	2	3	4	5	6
7	8	9	10	11	12	13
14	15	16	17	18	19	20
21	21	23	24	25	26	27
28	29	30				

17. Thursday   18. Saturday
19. 5   20. 4
21. September 21st
22. September 24th

23. Wednesday
24. October 2nd

25. 16	26. 9
27. 40	28. 50
29. 52	30. 38
31. 69	32. 38
33. 82	34. 35
35. 80	36. 20

3 Addition to 100

1. 35 ; 35
2. 15 ; 32 ; 47   3. 21 ; 30 ; 51

$$\begin{array}{r} 1\,5 \\ +\ 3\,2 \\ \hline 4\,7 \end{array}\qquad \begin{array}{r} 2\,1 \\ +\ 3\,0 \\ \hline 5\,1 \end{array}$$

4. 13 ; 16 ; 29   5. 22 ; 24 ; 46

$$\begin{array}{r} 1\,3 \\ +\ 1\,6 \\ \hline 2\,9 \end{array}\qquad \begin{array}{r} 2\,2 \\ +\ 2\,4 \\ \hline 4\,6 \end{array}$$

6. 52
7.

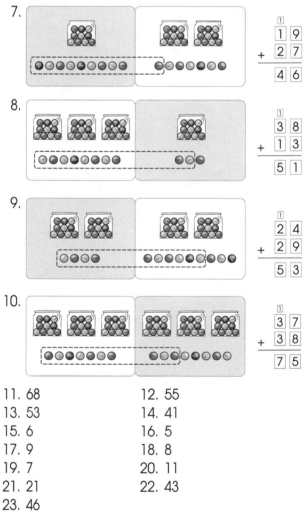

8.

9.

10.

11. 68	12. 55
13. 53	14. 41
15. 6	16. 5
17. 9	18. 8
19. 7	20. 11
21. 21	22. 43
23. 46	

24. $12 + 25 = 37$; 37

$$\begin{array}{r} \boxed{1}\ \boxed{2} \\ +\ \boxed{2}\ \boxed{5} \\ \hline \boxed{3}\ \boxed{7} \end{array}$$

25. $34 + 21 = 55$; 55

$$\begin{array}{r} \boxed{3}\ \boxed{4} \\ +\ \boxed{2}\ \boxed{1} \\ \hline \boxed{5}\ \boxed{5} \end{array}$$

26. $35 + 12 = 47$; 47

$$\begin{array}{r} \boxed{3}\ \boxed{5} \\ +\ \boxed{1}\ \boxed{2} \\ \hline \boxed{4}\ \boxed{7} \end{array}$$

27. $16 + 36 = 52$; 52

$$\begin{array}{r} ^{\boxed{1}} \\ \boxed{1}\ \boxed{6} \\ +\ \boxed{3}\ \boxed{6} \\ \hline \boxed{5}\ \boxed{2} \end{array}$$

28. $35 + 28 = 63$; 63

$$\begin{array}{r} ^{\boxed{1}} \\ \boxed{3}\ \boxed{5} \\ +\ \boxed{2}\ \boxed{8} \\ \hline \boxed{6}\ \boxed{3} \end{array}$$

4 Subtraction to 100

1. 42	2. 53	3. 36	4. 52
5. 25	6. 39	7. 46	8. 28
9. 10	10. 2	11. 7	12. 5
13. 23	14. 22	15. 21	16. 31

17. 25   18. 40

19. 32   20. 22

21. 41   22. 30

23. 21

24. 23   25. 25

26. 14   27. 34

28. 24   29. 10

30. 21   31. 5

32. $32 - 2 = 30$; 30

$$\begin{array}{r} \boxed{3}\ \boxed{2} \\ -\ \boxed{2} \\ \hline \boxed{3}\ \boxed{0} \end{array}$$

33. $45 - 4 = 41$; 41

$$\begin{array}{r} \boxed{4}\ \boxed{5} \\ -\ \boxed{4} \\ \hline \boxed{4}\ \boxed{1} \end{array}$$

34. $56 - 5 = 51$; 51

$$\begin{array}{r} \boxed{5}\ \boxed{6} \\ -\ \boxed{5} \\ \hline \boxed{5}\ \boxed{1} \end{array}$$

35. $38 - 6 = 32$; 32

$$\begin{array}{r} \boxed{3}\ \boxed{8} \\ -\ \boxed{6} \\ \hline \boxed{3}\ \boxed{2} \end{array}$$

36. $68 - 8 = 60$; 60

$$\begin{array}{r} \boxed{6}\ \boxed{8} \\ -\ \boxed{8} \\ \hline \boxed{6}\ \boxed{0} \end{array}$$

5 Shapes

1. Hexagon   2. Triangle
3. Rectangle   4.   Pentagon
5.   6.   7.
8.   9.   10.

11. 12. 13.
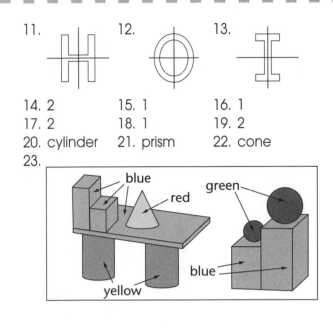

14. 2   15. 1   16. 1
17. 2   18. 1   19. 2
20. cylinder   21. prism   22. cone
23.

Midway Review

1.
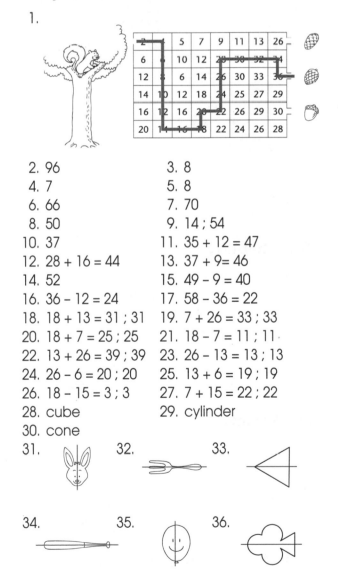

2. 96   3. 8
4. 7   5. 8
6. 66   7. 70
8. 50   9. 14 ; 54
10. 37   11. 35 + 12 = 47
12. 28 + 16 = 44   13. 37 + 9= 46
14. 52   15. 49 – 9 = 40
16. 36 – 12 = 24   17. 58 – 36 = 22
18. 18 + 13 = 31 ; 31   19. 7 + 26 = 33 ; 33
20. 18 + 7 = 25 ; 25   21. 18 – 7 = 11 ; 11
22. 13 + 26 = 39 ; 39   23. 26 – 13 = 13 ; 13
24. 26 – 6 = 20 ; 20   25. 13 + 6 = 19 ; 19
26. 18 – 15 = 3 ; 3   27. 7 + 15 = 22 ; 22
28. cube   29. cylinder
30. cone
31.   32.   33.

34.   35.   36.

6 More about Additon and Subtraction

1. 38   2. 48
3. 57   4. 62
5. 57   6. 41
7. 38   8. 52
9. 58   10. 49
11. 4   12. 8
13. 1   14. 3
15. 4   16. 6
17. 1   18. 10
19. 12   20. 15
21. 71   22. 60
23. 81   24. 72
25. 65   26. 78
27. 58   28. 79
29. 68   30. 59
31. 2   32. 3
33. 5   34. 9
35. 3   36. 7
37. 8   38. 6
39. 12   40. 10
41. 12   42. 13
43. 11 ; 18 ; 18 ; 17
44. 21 – 16 = 5 ; 21 – 5 = 16
45. 30 – 24 = 6 ; 30 – 6 = 24
46. 25 + 10 = 35 or 10 + 25 = 35 ;
    35 – 25 = 10
47. 35 ; 3
48. 29 + 5 = 34 or 5 + 29 = 34 ;
    34 – 29 = 5
49. 81 + 5 = 86 or 5 + 81 = 86 ;
    86 – 81 = 5
50. 83 – 77 = 6 ; 83 – 6 = 77
51. 77 – 69 = 8 ; 77 – 8 = 69
52. 31 + 9 = 40 or 9 + 31 = 40 ;
    40 – 31 = 9
53. 57
54. 34
55. 57 + 34 = 91 ; 91
56. 57 – 34 = 23 ; 23
57. 60 – 57 = 3 ; 3
58. 60 – 34 = 26 ; 26
59. 57 – 15 = 42 ; 42
60. 34 + 15 = 49 ; 49

7 Measurement

1. ten o'clock   2. half-past four

3. twelve o'clock   4. half-past eight
5. Alan   6. Tim
7. Rita ; Sam ; Tim   8. Tim
9. 4   10. 2
11. 5   12. 3
13. shorter   14. longer
15. B   16. C

8 Money

1a. 8   b. 8
2a. 6   b. 30
3a. 4   b. 40
4. B   5. C   6. A
7 – 9. (Suggested answers)

7a. 1 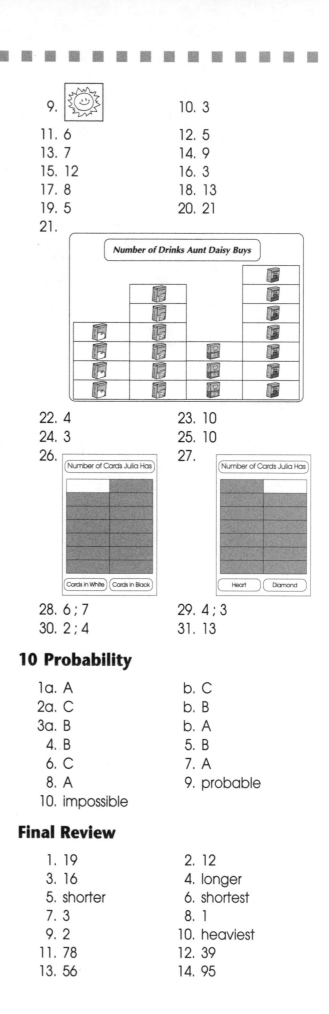 ; 1

b. 1 ; 5

8a. 2 ; 3

b. 1 ; 2 ; 3

9a. 2 ; 1 ; 3

b. 1 ; 3 ; 3

10. 24   11. 42
12. 34   13. 19
14.   15.
16. 10   17. 9
18. 6   19. 66
20. 3   21. 8
22. 59   23. 7
24. 63   25. 1
26. 4   27. 31
28. 36   29. No

9 Pictographs

1. 7   2. 3
3. 5   4. 10
5. 8   6. 12
7. No   8. 15

9.   10. 3
11. 6   12. 5
13. 7   14. 9
15. 12   16. 3
17. 8   18. 13
19. 5   20. 21
21.

Number of Drinks Aunt Daisy Buys

22. 4   23. 10
24. 3   25. 10
26.   27.

Number of Cards Julia Has

Cards in White Cards in Black

Number of Cards Julia Has

Heart Diamond

28. 6 ; 7   29. 4 ; 3
30. 2 ; 4   31. 13

10 Probability

1a. A   b. C
2a. C   b. B
3a. B   b. A
4. B   5. B
6. C   7. A
8. A   9. probable
10. impossible

Final Review

1. 19   2. 12
3. 16   4. longer
5. shorter   6. shortest
7. 3   8. 1
9. 2   10. heaviest
11. 78   12. 39
13. 56   14. 95

15. 22   16. 11

17.   18.

19. 45 + 37 = 82 ; 82
20. 48 + 29 = 77 ; 77
21. 37 – 8 = 29 ; 29
22. 45 – 15 = 30 ; 30
23. 48 + 7 = 55 ; 55
24. 29 + 29 = 58 ; 58
25. January   26. February
27. 19   28. January
29. November   30. February
31. 30   32. Montreal
33. 2   34. 76

35. 3

36. C   37. A   38. A

1 Addition and Subtraction Facts to 20

2. 14	3. 8	4. 17	5. 18
6. 12			
7. 14	8. 5	9. 4	10. 14
11. 18	12. 11	13. 13	14. 13
15. 15	16. 13		
17. 7	18. 5	19. 12	20. 3
21. 6	22. 1	23. 2	24. 0
25. 4	26. 2		
27. +	28. –	29. +	30. –
31. –	32. +	33. –	34. –
35. –	36. +	37. +	38. –

39.

12 – 6	18 – 10	6 + 2

40.

6 + 7	16 – 3	17 – 5

41.

12 + 5	20 – 4	9 + 8

42.

6 + 5	15 – 3	17 – 5

43.

19 – 8	3 + 7	16 – 6

44a. 13	b. 14	c. 15	d. 16
45a. 9	b. 10	c. 11	d. 12

46. 12 + 6 ; 18 ; 18   47. 16 – 12 ; 4 ; 4
48. 20 – 12 ; 8 ; 8   49. 10 + 5 ; 15 ; 15

Just for Fun

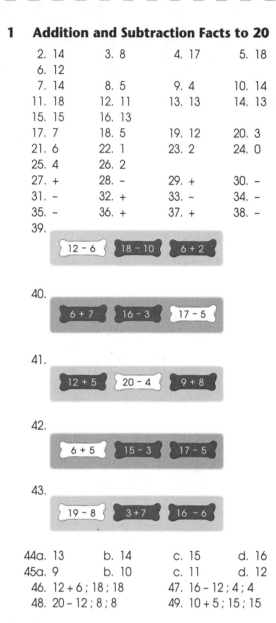

2 More about Addition Facts

1b. 5	c. 5		
2a. 8	b. 8	c. 8	
3a. 10	b. 10	c. 10	
4a. 5	b. 5	c. 5	
5a. 8	b. 8	c. 8	
6. 3	7. 7	8. 4	9. 8
10. 7	11. 6	12. 6	13. 13
14. 6	15. 17		

16. 10 + 8 = 8 + 10 → 18
17. 12 + 5 = 5 + 12 → 17
18. 4 + 15 = 15 + 4 → 19
19. 5 + 9 = 9 + 5 → 14
20. 14 + 6 = 6 + 14 → 20
21. 3 + 13 = 13 + 3 → 16

22a. 1 , 6	b. 2 , 5	c. 3 , 4	
23a. 1 , 5	b. 2 , 4	c. 3 , 3	
24a. 1 , 7	b. 2 , 6	c. 3 , 5	d. 4 , 4
25a. 1 , 8	b. 2 , 7	c. 3 , 6	d. 4 , 5
26a. 10	b. 9	c. 8	d. 7
e. 6			
27a. 8	b. 7	c. 6	d. 5
e. 4			
28a. 8	b. 8		
29a. 2 ; 6	b. 2	c. 6	

Just for Fun

2 (3 8) 7 (6 5) 4
(4 7) 5 (9 2) 3 6
6 9 (0 1) 4 (10)

3 Relating Subtraction to Addition

1. 12 ; 4 ; 8   2. 18 ; 12
3. 15 ; 6   4. 17 ; 8
5. 11 ; 6
6. 6 ; 14 ; 8 ; 14 ; 6 ; 6
7. 5 , 6 ; 11 ; 6 , 5 ; 11 ; 11 , 6 ; 5 ; 11 , 5 ; 6
8. 4 , 9 ; 13 ; 9 , 4 ; 13 ; 13 , 4 ; 9 ; 13 , 9 ; 4
9. 12 , 7 ; 19 ; 7 , 12 ; 19 ; 19 , 7 ; 12 ; 19 , 12 ; 7
10. 7 , 9 ; 16 ; 9 , 7 ; 16 ; 16 , 7 ; 9 ; 16 , 9 ; 7
11. 11 , 6 ; 17 ; 6 , 11 ; 17 ; 17 , 11 ; 6 ; 17 , 6 ; 11

12. 5 ; 5	13. 7 ; 7	14. 9	15. 10
16. 7	17. 16	18. 11	19. 8
20. 7 ; 7	21. 3 ; 3		
22. 9 ; 9	23. 8 ; 8	24. 6 ; 6	25. 4 ; 4
26. 8 ; 8	27. 7 ; 7	28. 5 ; 5	29. 9 ; 9
30. 6 ; 6	31. 6 ; 6		

Just for Fun

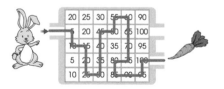

■ red
● green
▲ blue
▬ yellow

4 Adding and Subtracting Using Counting

1. 23	2. 24	3. 21	4. 16
5. 24	6. 27	7. 22	8. 21

9. 19	10. 28	11. 18	12. 26
13. 29	14. 22	15. 26	16. 18
17. 30	18. 14		
19. 57	20. 67	21. 58	22. 75
23. 72	24. 89	25. 86	26. 79
27. 66	28. 56		
29. 61	30. 84	31. 79	32. 74
33. 88	34. 82	35. 55	36. 80

37a. 4 ; 24   b. 14 ; 24   38a. 6 ; 36   b. 16 ; 36
39a. 8 ; 48   b. 18 ; 48   40a. 5 ; 55   b. 15 ; 55
41a. 0 ; 40   b. 10 ; 40   42a. 0 ; 50   b. 10 ; 50
43. 10

44.
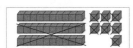
37 ; 10

45.

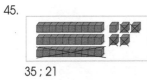
35 ; 21

46.
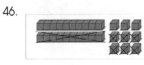
29 ; 13

47.

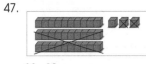
33 ; 11

48.

28 ; 13

49.

42 ; 11

50.
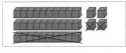
34 ; 22

Just for Fun

1.

2.

5   Adding without Regrouping I

1. 39
2.
```
   4 2
 +   4
   4 6
```
3.
```
     4
 + 5 3
   5 7
```
4.
```
   6 3
 +   5
   6 8
```
5.
```
     6
 + 4 3
   4 9
```

6. 29	7. 49	8. 38	9. 68
10. 57	11. 77	12. 89	13. 19
14. 38	15. 59	16. 67	17. 78
18. 48	19. 86	20. 29	21. 95
22. 16	23. 38	24. 68	25. 48
26. 27	27. 56	28. 27	29. 18
30. 38	31. 28	32. 66	33. 59
34. 48	35. 75	36. 87	37. 27

38. 96
39. policeman
40. 32 + 4 ; 36 ; 36   41. 20 + 6 ; 26 ; 26
42. 45 + 3 ; 48 ; 48   43. 23 + 6 ; 29 ; 29

Just for Fun

28 ; 27 ; 39 ; 19

6   Adding without Regrouping II

1. 57
2.
```
   2 2
 + 1 6
   3 8
```
3.
```
   3 4
 + 1 4
   4 8
```
4.
```
   2 0
 + 3 0
   5 0
```

5. 38	6. 77	7. 67	8. 78
9. 67	10. 58	11. 91	12. 92
13. 47	14. 73	15. 78	16. 76
17. 93	18. 88	19. 46	20. 36
21. 44	22. 47	23. 86	24. 68
25. 86	26. 88	27. 59	28. 96
29. 47	30. 38	31. 59	32. 69
33. 57	34. 78	35. 88	36. 68

37. 99
38. 38 ; 47 ; 57 ; 59 ; 68 ; 69 ; 78 ; 88 ; 99
39. 44 + 32 ; 76 ; 76   40. 53 + 46 ; 99 ; 99
41. 22 + 36 ; 58 ; 58   42. 15 + 30 ; 45 ; 45

Just for Fun

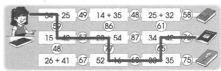

7   Adding with Regrouping I

1. 32
2.
```
   4 6
 +   8
   5 4
```
3.
```
   3 4
 +   9
   4 3
```
4.
```
     6
 + 4 5
   5 1
```

5. 24	6. 32	7. 40	8. 53
9. 65	10. 72	11. 28	12. 71
13. 83	14. 52	15. 36	16. 60
17. 44	18. 61	19. 56	20. 33
21. 61	22. 44	23. 51	24. 35

25. 70   26. 81   27. 94   28. 40
29. 43   30. 53   31. 35   32. 60
33. 72   34. 28   35. 83   36. 42
37. 34   38. 90   39. 61   40. 55
41. 70   42. 81
43. 18 + 6 ; 24 ; 24   44. 37 + 5 ; 42 ; 42
45. 28 + 8 ; 36 ; 36   46. 45 + 9 ; 54 ; 54

Just for Fun

8 Adding with Regrouping II

1. 43

2.
```
   37
 + 26
 ----
   63
```

3.
```
   35
 + 17
 ----
   52
```

4.
```
   29
 + 32
 ----
   61
```

5. 56   6. 64   7. 70   8. 82
9. 80   10. 83   11. 91   12. 63
13. 85   14. 84   15. 71   16. 96
17. 92   18. 95   19. 60   20. 70
21. 83   22. 85   23. 81   24. 84
25. 93   26. 64   27. 82   28. 91

29.
| 44 | 18 + 26 | 27 + 15 | 27 + 17 |

30.
| 65 | 32 + 33 | 36 + 29 | 22 + 33 |

31.
| 52 | 26 + 16 | 15 + 37 | 17 + 35 |

32.
| 63 | 25 + 38 | 34 + 27 | 27 + 36 |

33.
| 81 | 54 + 27 | 63 + 28 | 45 + 36 |

34.
| 74 | 36 + 38 | 29 + 45 | 27 + 37 |

35.
| 91 | 46 + 45 | 33 + 59 | 62 + 29 |

36.
| 46 | 23 + 13 | 19 + 27 | 36 + 10 |

37. 15 + 9 ; 24 ; 24   38. 36 + 49 ; 85 ; 85
39. 54 + 38 ; 92 ; 92   40. 27 + 45 ; 72 ; 72

Just for Fun

6 ; 15 ; 28 ; 45 ; 66 ; 91

Midway Review

1. 7 ; 13   2. 5 ; 11   3. 9 ; 17   4. 9 ; 13
5. 7 ; 12   6. 8 ; 8   7. 8 ; 12   8. 11 ; 11
9a. 1 , 9   b. 2 , 8   c. 3 , 7   d. 4 , 6
e. 5 , 5
10a. 10   b. 9   c. 8   d. 7
e. 6
11. 7 ; 15 ; 8 ; 15 ; 7 ; 7
12. 3 , 10 ; 13 ; 10 , 3 ; 13 ; 13 , 3 ; 10 ; 13 , 10 ; 3
13. 6 ; 6   14. 6 ; 6   15. 13   16. 16
17. 7 ; 7   18. 8 ; 8   19. 21   20. 18
21. 9 ; 9   22. 7 ; 7
23. 24   24. 41   25. 40   26. 58
27. 11   28. 63   29. 93   30. 6
31. 50   32. 74   33. 90   34. 89
35. 28   36. 22   37. 30   38. 30
39. 79   40. 75   41. 62   42. 81
43. 49   44. 85   45. 56   46. 7
47. 60 ; 60
48. 58   49. 41   50. 39

48.
```
   35
 + 23
 ----
   58
```

49.
```
   25
 + 16
 ----
   41
```

50.
```
   23
 + 16
 ----
   39
```

9 Subtracting without Regrouping I

1. 44

2.
```
   39
 -  3
 ----
   36
```

3.
```
   26
 -  3
 ----
   23
```

4.
```
   54
 -  2
 ----
   52
```

5.
```
   25
 -  5
 ----
   20
```

6. 31   7. 21   8. 43   9. 92
10. 52   11. 70   12. 82   13. 43
14. 66   15. 21   16. 55   17. 31
18. 72   19. 12   20. 93   21. 40
22. 50   23. 24   24. 32   25. 62
26. 71   27. 84   28. 91   29. 40
30. 44   31. 34   32. 53   33. 62
34. 50   35. 35   36. 81   37. 90
38. 21   39. 41   40. 81   41. 31
42. 63   43. 63   44. 52
45. 28 – 6 ; 22 ; 22
46. 59 – 5 ; 54 ; 54
47. 46 – 4 ; 42 ; 42
48. 37 – 3 ; 34 ; 34

Just for Fun

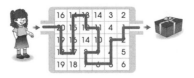

10 Subtracting without Regrouping II

1. 23

2.
```
  67
- 43
  24
```

3.
```
  55
- 15
  40
```

4.
```
  36
- 24
  12
```

5. 24   6. 23   7. 24   8. 41
9. 32   10. 30   11. 31   12. 4
13. 21   14. 22   15. 12   16. 54
17. 15   18. 10   19. 4   20. 32
21. 23   22. 22   23. 46   24. 40
25. 11   26. 14   27. 16   28. 13
29a. 34   b. 23   c. 34 ; colour a and c
30a. 22   b. 23   c. 23 ; colour b and c
31a. 16   b. 26   c. 16 ; colour a and c
32a. 45   b. 45   c. 44 ; colour a and b
33. 16 ; 16   34. 24   35. 12   36. 32

```
  96        28        67
- 72      - 16      - 35
  24        12        32
```

Just for Fun

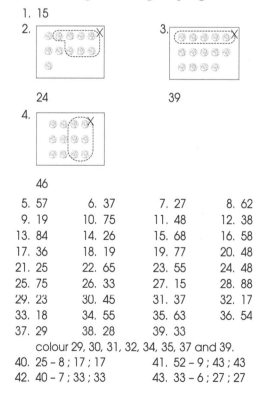

11 Subtracting with Regrouping I

1. 15

2.   24

3.   39

4.   46

5. 57   6. 37   7. 27   8. 62
9. 19   10. 75   11. 48   12. 38
13. 84   14. 26   15. 68   16. 58
17. 36   18. 19   19. 77   20. 48
21. 25   22. 65   23. 55   24. 48
25. 75   26. 33   27. 15   28. 88
29. 23   30. 45   31. 37   32. 17
33. 18   34. 55   35. 63   36. 54
37. 29   38. 28   39. 33
  colour 29, 30, 31, 32, 34, 35, 37 and 39.
40. 25 – 8 ; 17 ; 17   41. 52 – 9 ; 43 ; 43
42. 40 – 7 ; 33 ; 33   43. 33 – 6 ; 27 ; 27

Just for Fun

   54 ; 42 ; 29 ; 15 ; 0

12 Subtracting with Regrouping II

1. 26

2.   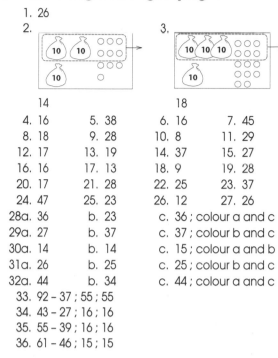   14

3.   18

4. 16   5. 38   6. 16   7. 45
8. 18   9. 28   10. 8   11. 29
12. 17   13. 19   14. 37   15. 27
16. 16   17. 13   18. 9   19. 28
20. 17   21. 28   22. 25   23. 37
24. 47   25. 23   26. 12   27. 26
28a. 36   b. 23   c. 36 ; colour a and c
29a. 27   b. 37   c. 37 ; colour b and c
30a. 14   b. 14   c. 15 ; colour a and b
31a. 26   b. 25   c. 25 ; colour b and c
32a. 44   b. 34   c. 44 ; colour a and c
33. 92 – 37 ; 55 ; 55
34. 43 – 27 ; 16 ; 16
35. 55 – 39 ; 16 ; 16
36. 61 – 46 ; 15 ; 15

Just for Fun

   SINGER

13 Estimating Sums and Differences

1. 30   2. 40   3. 50   4. 40
5. 60   6. 80   7. 80   8. 90
9. 40   10. 20
11. 30   12. 20   13. 50   14. 60
15. 10   16. 80   17. 10   18. 50
19. 10   20. 70   21. 100   22. 0
23a. 66   b. 70
24a. 44   25a. 53
  b.   b.
```
  20            10
+ 30          + 50
  50            60
```
26a. 65   27a. 33
  b.   b.
```
  50            30
+ 10          + 10
  60            40
```
28a. 89
  b.
```
  30
+ 60
  90
```
29a. 92   b. 70 , 20 ; 90
30a. 88   b. 20 , 70 ; 90
31a. 79   b. 30 , 50 ; 80
32a. 95   b. 50 , 40 ; 90
33a. 91   b. 60 , 30 ; 90
34a. 58   b. 10 , 50 ; 60
35a. 24   b. 20

36a. 15

b.
```
   40
 - 20
 ─────
   20
```

37a. 32

b.
```
   70
 - 40
 ─────
   30
```

38a. 26

b.
```
   70
 - 50
 ─────
   20
```

39a. 41

b.
```
   60
 - 10
 ─────
   50
```

40a. 36

b.
```
   90
 - 50
 ─────
   40
```

41a. 47   b. 90 , 50 ; 40
42a. 33   b. 50 , 10 ; 40
43a. 48   b. 80 , 30 ; 50
44a. 45   b. 60 , 20 ; 40
45a. 48   b. 80 , 30 ; 50
46a. 28   b. 40 , 10 ; 30
48. less than 90
49. more than 80
50. less than 30
51. less than 50
52. more than 60

Just for Fun

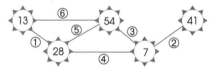

14 Checking Subtraction by Using Addition

1a. 12   b. 12 ; 28
2a. 26   b. 26 ; 63
3a. 22   b. 22 ; 48
4a. 18   b. 18 ; 51
5a. 35   b. 35 ; 77
6a. 23   b. 23 ; 82
7a. 44   b. 44 , 8 ; 52
8a. 22   b. 22 , 17 ; 39
9a. 22   b. 22 , 23 ; 45
10a. 27   b. 27 , 39 ; 66
11a. 42   b. 42 , 45 ; 87
12a. 7   b. 7 , 16 ; 23
13a. 38   b. 38 , 33 ; 71
14a. 35   b. 35 , 63 ; 98
15a. 18   b. 18 , 14 ; 32
16a. 21   b. 21 , 6 ; 27
17a. 25   b. 25 , 31 ; 56
18a. 16   b. 16 , 29 ; 45
19a. 39   b. 39   c. 39
20a. 21   b. 21 , 17 ; 38   c. 38 , 21 ; 17
21a. 17   b. 17 , 32 ; 49   c. 49 , 17 ; 32
22a. 26   b. 26 , 25 ; 51   c. 51 , 26 ; 25
23a. 13   b. 13 , 9 ; 22   c. 22 , 13 ; 9

24a. 71   b. 71 , 15 ; 86   c. 86 , 71 ; 15
25a. 25   b. 25 , 65 ; 90   c. 90 , 25 ; 65
26a. 27   b. 27 , 48 ; 75   c. 75 , 27 ; 48
27. 56 , 39 ; 17 ; 17
```
    17
 +  39
 ─────
    56
```

28. 48 , 26 ; 22 ; 22
```
    22
 +  26
 ─────
    48
```

29. 15 , 8 ; 7 ; 7
```
     7
 +   8
 ─────
    15
```

Just for Fun

1. 20 ; 35 ; 45
2. 40 ; 44 ; 46
3. 40 ; 50 ; 80

15 More Addition and Subtraction

1. 9 ; 6   2. 2 ; 10   3. 14 ; 5   4. 6 ; 12
5. 16 ; 2   6. 35 ; 29   7. 82 ; 80   8. 29 ; 36
9. 70 ; 52   10. 80 ; 34
12. 60   13. 36   14. 46   15. 36
16. 46   17. 13
18. 24 ; 44   19. 32 ; 62   20. 33 ; 53   21. 14 ; 54
22. 2 ; 12
23. 20 ; 40   24. 20 ; 40   25. 14 ; 44   26. 12 ; 42
27. 30   28. 10   29. 44   30. 40
31. 43   32. 20   33. 30   34. 26
35. 30   36. 18   37. 20   38. 30
39a. 3   b. 13   c. 23   d. 33
e. 43
40a. 6   b. 16   c. 26   d. 36
e. 46
41a. 64   b. 54   c. 44   d. 34
e. 24
42a. 58   b. 48   c. 38   d. 28
e. 18
43. 8 + 4 – 5 ; 7
44. 9 – 3 + 5 ; 11
45. 7 + 6 – 4 ; 9

Just for Fun

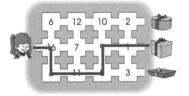

16 Addition and Subtraction with Money

1. 65   2. 42   3. 52   4. 37
5. 28
7. ✔

8. 50 , 49 ; 1 9. 100 , 85 ; 15
10. 45 , 36 ; 9 11. 75 , 56 ; 19
12. 67 , 36 ; 31 13. 76 , 46 ; 30
14. 72 , 47 ; 25 15. 28 , 16 ; 12

	25¢	10¢	5¢	1¢
16.	2			4
17.		2		2
18.	3		1	
19.	1	2		2
20.	1	1		1

21. 57   22. 66   23. 32   24. 41
25. 34 ; 34
26. 98
```
    57
  + 41
    98
```
27. 89
```
    57
  + 32
    89
```
28. 34
```
    66
  - 32
    34
```
29. 25
```
    66
  - 41
    25
```

Just for Fun

2 , 4

Final Review

1. 41   2. 45   3. 32   4. 43
5. 28   6. 18   7. 57   8. 66
9. 71   10. 55   11. 80   12. 19
13. 36   14. 69   15. 43   16. 70
17. 73   18. 27   19. 16   20. 91
21. 56   22. 42   23. 25   24. 49
25a. 63   26a. 17
  b.   b.
```
    30           40
  + 40         - 30
    70           10
```
27a. 26   b. 70 – 40 ; 30
28a. 58   b. 40 + 20 ; 60
29a. 23   30a. 23
  b.   b.
```
    23           23
  + 14         + 29
    37           52
```
31a. 16   b. 16 + 48 ; 64
32a. 46   b. 46 + 33 ; 79
33a. 32   b. 32 + 54 ; 86
34a. 25   b. 25 + 28 ; 53
35. 1 ; 11   36. 25 ; 45   37. 12 ; 42   38. 23 ; 63
39a. 3   b. 13   c. 23   d. 33
40a. 53   b. 43   c. 33   d. 23
41.   42.   43.
```
    4 3         3 8         5 5
  + 1 9       + 2 7       + 1 6
    6 2         6 5         7 1
```

44.   45.   46.
```
    6 2         5 1         5 8
  - 4 2       - 3 7       - 3 3
    2 0         1 4         2 5
```
47. 10   48. 20   49. 11   50. 5
51. 46 ; 63   52. 49 ; 23   53. 58 ; 9   54. 14 ; 27
55. B ; C   56. B ; D   57. A
58. 33 ; 33
59. 42   60. 35   61. 9   62. 34
```
    23           92           26           69
  + 19         - 57         - 17         - 35
    42           35            9           34
```
63. 83
```
    38
  + 45
    83
```

1   3-digit Numbers

1. 72, 73, 75, 77, 78
2. 98, 97, 96, 94
3. 1 3 4 = 100 + 30 + 4 = 134
4. 2 2 7 = 200 + 20 + 7 = 227
5. 3 0 9 = 300 + 0 + 9 = 309
6. 2 3 0 = 200 + 30 + 0 = 230
7. 500 + 30 + 2 = 532   8. 400 + 60 + 4 = 464
9. 700 + 0 + 5 = 705

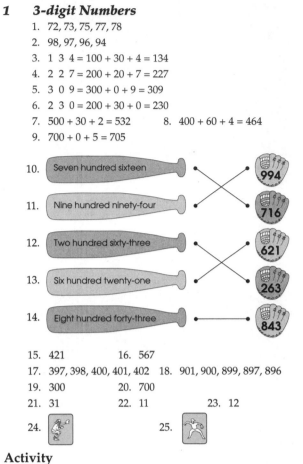

10. Seven hundred sixteen — 716
11. Nine hundred ninety-four — 994
12. Two hundred sixty-three — 263
13. Six hundred twenty-one — 621
14. Eight hundred forty-three — 843

15. 421   16. 567
17. 397, 398, 400, 401, 402   18. 901, 900, 899, 897, 896
19. 300   20. 700
21. 31   22. 11   23. 12
24. [image]   25. [image]

Activity

1. 456, 567   2. 4; 740, 704, 470, 407

2   Addition and Subtraction

1. a. 52
   b.
   ```
     1 4
   + 2 7
     4 1
   ```
   c.
   ```
     4 9
   + 1 2
     6 1
   ```

2. 36 - 16 = 20
   20
   ```
     3 6
   - 1 6
     2 0
   ```

3. 49 - 12 = 37
   37
   ```
     4 9
   - 1 2
     3 7
   ```

4. 6, 6   5. 16, 16
6. 19, 19   7. 18, 18
8. -, +   9. +, -
10. +, -, -   11. -, -, +
12. 14   13. 48
14. 8   15. 69
16. 23   17. 19
18. 64   19. 16
20. 48   21. 584
22. 598   23. 488
24. 638   25. 494
26. 382   27. 464
28. 445   29. 162

30. 184   31. 833
32. 704   33. 196
34. 320   35. 706
36. 810   37. 614
38. 621
39.
```
  3 5
-   6
  2 9
+   9
  3 8
```
40.
```
  2 2
+ 1 9
  4 1
- 3 0
  1 1
```
41.
```
  6 3
- 1 6
  4 7
+ 1 9
  6 6
```

42. 31   43. 34
44. 25

Activity

1. 27   2. 19
3. 570   4. 30
5. 41   6. 472
7. 479   8. PITCHER

3   Multiplication

1. 6, 8, 10   2. 9, 12
   5   4
   10   12
3. 12, 16   4. 15, 20, 25
   4   5
   16   25
5. 30, 40   6. 6, 8, 10, 12
   4   6
   40   12
7. 30, 40, 50, 60, 70
   7
   70

8. 3 sixes are 18.
   3 x 6 = 18
   ```
        3
   x    6
       1 8
   ```

9. 4 fours are 16.
   4 x 4 = 16
   ```
        4
   x    4
       1 6
   ```

10. 7 fives are 35.
    7 x 5 = 35
    ```
         7
    x    5
        3 5
    ```

11. 4 times 3 = 4 x 3 = 12
12. 4 times 4 = 4 x 4 = 16
13. 2 times 5 = 2 x 5 = 10
14. 7 times 2 = 7 x 2 = 14
15. Red - 1, 2, 3, 10, 11, 12, 19, 20, 21, 28, 29, 30
    Yellow - 4, 5, 6, 13, 14, 15, 22, 23, 24
    Green - 7, 8, 9, 16, 17, 18 25, 26, 27
16. 3, 6, 9, 12, 15, 18, 21, 24, 27, 30
17. 20   18. 36
19. 32   20. 14
21. 15   22. 18
23. 12   24. 24
25. 25
26. 8 x 5 = 40   27. 4 x 7 = 28
    40   28

28. 5   29. 6
30. 4   31. 5
32. 4   33. 7
34, 35.

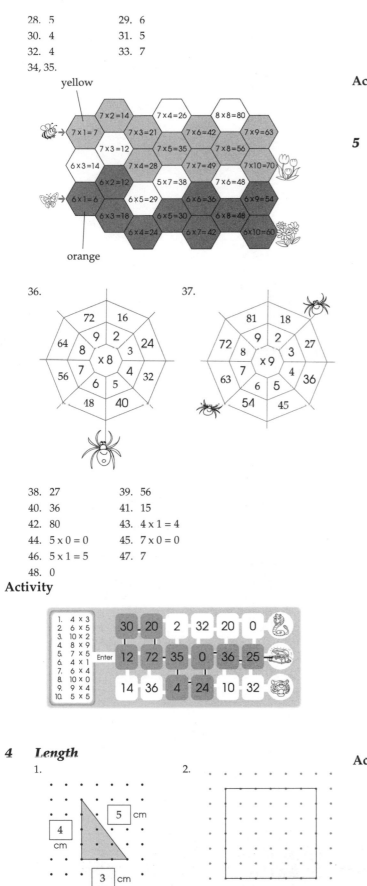

yellow

orange

36.   37.

38. 27   39. 56
40. 36   41. 15
42. 80   43. 4 x 1 = 4
44. 5 x 0 = 0   45. 7 x 0 = 0
46. 5 x 1 = 5   47. 7
48. 0

Activity

4   Length

1.   2.

5 cm

4 cm

3 cm

---

3. a. more than 1m   b. less than 1m
4. a. less than 1m   b. more than 1m
5. 12   6. 2 + 2 + 1 + 2 + 3 + 4 = 14
7. 2 + 2 + 1 + 2 + 4 + 2 + 1 + 2 = 16

Activity

4, 5, 6

5   Time and Temperature

1. D   2. B
3. A   4. G
5. C   6. E
7. F   8. 11, 10:45
9. 1, 01:15   10. 6, 05:45
11.

3
0 2 : 5 0

12. 09:05   13. 11:35
14. 5, 10   15. 15, 1
16. a.m., p.m.   17. a.m., p.m.
18. p.m., a.m.
19, 24, 25.

JULY

SUN	MON	TUE	WED	THU	FRI	SAT
			1	2	3	4
5	6	7	8	9	10	11
12	13	14	15	16	17	18
19	20	21	22	23	24	25
26	27	28	29	30	31	

20. Thursday   21. Friday
22. 13th   23. Wednesday
26. 31   27. 4
28. 7   29. February
30. 12   31. 29
32. 30, hot   33. 0, cold
34. 5, 10:00   35. 20, 12:45
36. 10   37. not likely
38. likely   39. likely
40. likely   41. likely
42. not likely

Activity

1.   2. 10:35
3. 20

6 Money

1. ✓   2.
3. ✓   4.
5. 54   6. 81
7. 81   8. 70
9. 72   10. 58

11.

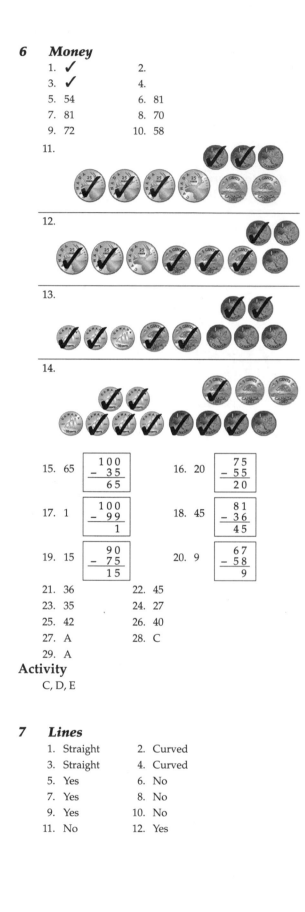

12.

13.

14.

15. 65
$$\begin{array}{r} 100 \\ -\ 35 \\ \hline 65 \end{array}$$

16. 20
$$\begin{array}{r} 75 \\ -\ 55 \\ \hline 20 \end{array}$$

17. 1
$$\begin{array}{r} 100 \\ -\ 99 \\ \hline 1 \end{array}$$

18. 45
$$\begin{array}{r} 81 \\ -\ 36 \\ \hline 45 \end{array}$$

19. 15
$$\begin{array}{r} 90 \\ -\ 75 \\ \hline 15 \end{array}$$

20. 9
$$\begin{array}{r} 67 \\ -\ 58 \\ \hline 9 \end{array}$$

21. 36   22. 45
23. 35   24. 27
25. 42   26. 40
27. A   28. C
29. A

Activity
C, D, E

7 Lines

1. Straight   2. Curved
3. Straight   4. Curved
5. Yes   6. No
7. Yes   8. No
9. Yes   10. No
11. No   12. Yes

17. 4   18. b
19. 2   20. a, d; c, e

Activity
1, 2.

3. Yes

8 2D Figures

1. F   2. A
3. E   4. C
5. B   6. D
7. 4, 4, 1, trapezoid
8. 4, 4, 0, 2, parallelogram
9. 4, 4, 0, 2, rhombus
10. 4, 4, 4, 2, square

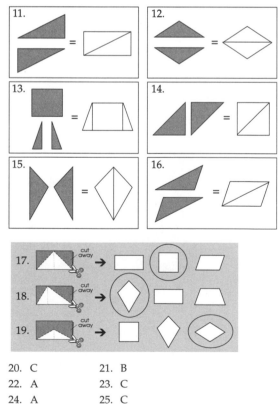

20. C   21. B
22. A   23. C
24. A   25. C

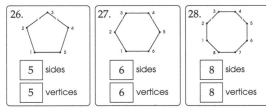

26. 5 sides, 5 vertices
27. 6 sides, 6 vertices
28. 8 sides, 8 vertices

Activity

1. 10   2. 9

9   Pictographs

1. A   2. B
3. C   4. B
5. C
6.

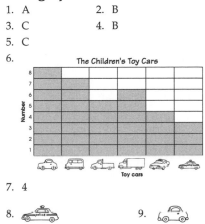

The Children's Toy Cars

7. 4

8. (police car)   9. (car)

Activity

1 ○ for 2 points

Midway Test

1. 402, 400   2. 300
3. 70   4. 8
5. 500
6. 230, 206, 203, 200, 198
7. 467, 471, 489, 500, 523
8. Four hundred twelve
9. Five hundred seven
10. Four hundred sixty
11. Seven hundred thirty-nine
12. 9   13. 431
14. 631   15. 49
16. 48   17. 38
18. 324   19. 640
20. 761   21. 18
22. 29   23. 14
24. 25, 40, 45   25. 24, 40, 48
26. 45   27. 24, 48
28. 63   29. 81
30. 0   31. 49
32. 18   33. 20
34. 6   35. 5

36. 4   37. 8
38. 9   39. 54
40. 35   41. 10
42. Hexagon, 6, 12
43. Kite, 4, 8
44. Pentagon, 5, 10
45. Rectangle, 4, 14
46. 15, 4   47. 5, 12
48. 04:35   49. 11:25
50. Sunday   51. 20th
52. Thursday
53 - 55.

```
A   Y      C      E
|   |      |    . |
|   |      |   .  |
|   |      |  .   |
B          D   F
```

56. A, 100   57. C, 5
58. B, 20   59. 58
60. 67   61. 71

	Cost	You paid				
62.	59¢	100¢	✓	✓	✓	✓
63.	64¢	100¢	✓	✓	C	✓
64.	70¢	100¢	✓	B	✓	D
65.	89¢	100¢	A	✓	C	✓

66. A   67. B
68. A   69. B

10   4-digit Numbers

1. 3000 + 300 + 20 + 5 = 3325
2. 3000 + 500 + 0 + 3 = 3503
3. 4000 + 0 + 50 + 0 = 4050
4. 4000 + 900 + 0 + 5 = 4905
5. 5000 + 0 + 70 + 1 = 5071
6. 3416   7. 7031

Activity
(suggested answers)

1. 2501   2. 1013
3. 2410   4. 3141

11   More about Addition and Subtraction

1. 581   2. 505
3. 383   4. 2
5. 4   6. 430
7. 600   8. 161
9. 681   10. 719
11. 623   12. 571
13. 208   14. 329
15. 149   16. 329
17. 307   18. 109

19. 103
20. 293
21. 128
22. 234

23. 79

```
   79
+ 132
  211
```

24. 334

```
  334
+ 129
  463
```

25. 255

```
  255
+ 259
  514
```

26. 78

```
   78
+ 329
  407
```

27. 379

```
  379
+ 347
  726
```

28. 181

```
  181
+ 169
  350
```

29.

```
  236
+  44
  280
- 143
  137
```

30.

```
  316
- 129
  187
+ 512
  699
```

31. 594, 273
32. 166, 110

Activity

1. 10
2. 19
3. 61
4. 54

12 Division

1. 4
2. 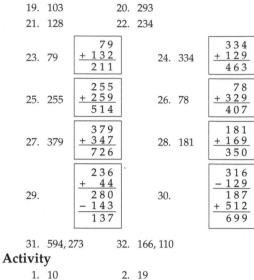 3
3. 5
4. 3
5. 3

6. 12 ÷ 3 = 4
   4
7. 20 ÷ 4 = 5
   5
8. 24 ÷ 4 = 6
   6
9. 5 with 2 left over.
   5, 2
10. 3 with 1 left over.
    3, 1
11. a. 1   b. 2   c. 3
    d. 4   e. 5   f. 6
12. a. 1   b. 2   c. 3
    d. 4   e. 5   f. 6
13. a. 6, 1   b. 4, 1   c. 2, 3
14. 2 x 4 = 8
    8 ÷ 4 = 2
15. 5 x 4 = 20
    20 ÷ 4 = 5
16. 4 x 3 = 12
    12 ÷ 3 = 4
17. 4 x 6 = 24
    24 ÷ 6 = 4
18.

```
    9 r 1
6 ) 55
    54
     1
```

19.

```
    6 r 1
8 ) 49
    48
     1
```

20. 7 r 2
21. 4 r 6
22. 9 r 1
23. 8 r 3

Activity

1. 5
2. 22

13 Weight

1. A   2. B
3. A   4. 5
5. 7   6. 5
7. B   8. A, C
9. 12   10. 30
11. 300   12. 150
13. 1400   14. 2200

Activity

1. A   2. B

14 Angles

1. b, c, a   2. b, c, d, a
3. c, d, b, a   4. d, b, c, a
5. 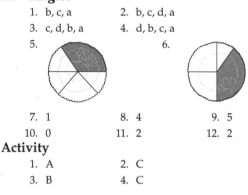   6.

7. 1   8. 4   9. 5
10. 0   11. 2   12. 2

Activity

1. A   2. C
3. B   4. C

15 Solids

1, 2.

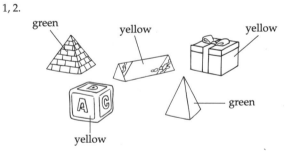

green
yellow
yellow
yellow
green

3. cone   4. cube
5. cylinder   6. pyramid
7. prism

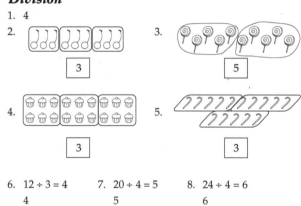

8.
9.
10.

11. 1   12. 4
13. 8   14. 1
15. 3

Activity

a.

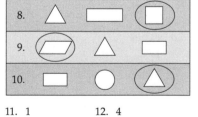

16 Block Graphs

1. 6
2. March
3. 14
4. October
5. June
6. 30
7.

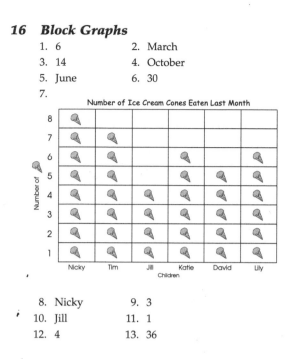

Number of Ice Cream Cones Eaten Last Month

8. Nicky
9. 3
10. Jill
11. 1
12. 4
13. 36

17 Fractions and Decimals

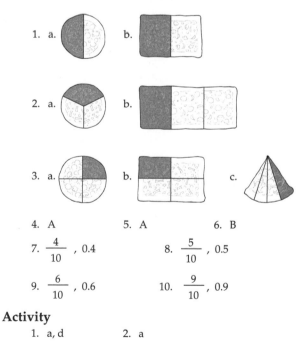

1. a.
   b.
2. a.
   b.
3. a.
   b.
   c.
4. A
5. A
6. B
7. $\frac{4}{10}$, 0.4
8. $\frac{5}{10}$, 0.5
9. $\frac{6}{10}$, 0.6
10. $\frac{9}{10}$, 0.9

Activity

1. a, d
2. a

18 Transformations

1. Slide
2. Turn
3. Flip
4. Turn

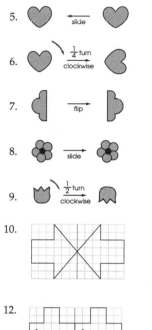

5. slide
6. $\frac{1}{4}$ turn clockwise
7. flip
8. slide
9. $\frac{1}{2}$ turn clockwise

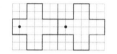

10.
11.
12.
13.

Activity

1. B
2. A

Final Test

1. 6520, F
2. 6620, E
3. 5622, D
4. 5502, B
5. 5602, A
6. 6522, C
7. 898
8. 862
9. 476
10. 167
11. 238
12. 126
13. 678
14. 485
15. 402
16. 187
17. 50
18. 326
19. 147, 220
20. 341, 133
21. 68, 283
22. 583
23. 129
24. 392
25. 187
26. 4 r 2; 4, 2
27. 2 r 5; 2, 5
28. 4 r 2; 4, 2

29.
```
      6 r 1
  4) 25
     24
      1
```
30.
```
      8 r 7
  8) 71
     64
      7
```
31.
```
      8 r 3
  7) 59
     56
      3
```
32.
```
      7 r 0
  9) 63
     63
      0
```
33.
```
      4 r 5
  6) 29
     24
      5
```
34.
```
      9 r 2
  5) 47
     45
      2
```

35. 6 x 4 = 24   36. 10 x 3 = 30
    24 ÷ 4 = 6   30 ÷ 3 = 10

37. 4   38. 5

39. 8   40. 6, 2

41. 2, 4   42. 9

43. 7   44. 7

45. 11   46. 700, 1100, 600

47.

48. Jill   49. Bob

50. Jim   51. Mike

52. 4   53. 3

54. 2   55. 4

56. 17   57. Friday

58. Tuesday   59. 25 minutes

60. 70 minutes   61. 0.4

62. 0.9   63. 0.5

64. $\dfrac{3}{6}$ 65. $\dfrac{2}{8}$ 66. $\dfrac{2}{6}$

67. B, C, A   68. B, A, C

69.

70.

turning point

1 3-digit Numbers

1. Sam   2. Craig
3. One hundred forty-five
4. Two hundred thirteen
5. 145, 178, 180, 193, 213
6. 3   7. 2
8. Peggy   9. Max
10. July   11. May
12. July and August
13. May, June and September
14. 100   15. 6
16. July, August, June, September, May
17. Six hundred seventy-four

2 Addition and Subtraction

1. 39 + 23 = 62 ; 62
2. 32 + 19 = 51 ; 51
3. 36 + 25 = 61 ; 61
4. 39 – 23 = 16 ; 16
5. 32 – 19 – 13 ; 13
6. 23 + 19 + 25 = 67 ; 67
7. 520 + 100 = 620 ; 620
8. 100 + 180 = 280 ; 280
9. 520 – 100 = 420 ; 420
10. 180 – 130 = 50 ; 50
11. 520 + 100 + 180 = 800 ; 800
12. 800 - 450 = 350 ; 350
13. 450 – 350 = 100 ; 100
14. 2nd   15. 1st
16. 2nd   17. A
18. A   19. B
20. 158 – 138 = 20 ; 20
21. 158 + 138 = 296 ; 296
22. 109 – 105 = 4 ; 4
23. 109 + 105 = 214 ; 214
24. 147 – 123 = 24 ; 24
25. 147 + 123 = 270 ; 270
26. 138 + 109 + 123 = 370 ; 370
27. 158 + 105 + 147 = 410 ; 410
28. 138 – 75 = 63 ; 63
29. 147 – 89 = 58 ; 58

3 Multiplication

1a. 2   b. 2 ; 12   c. 6
   d. 6 ; 12   e. 12
2a. 3   b. 3 ; 9   c. 9
3a. 4 ; 8   b. 8 ; 32   c. 8 ; 4
   d. 4 ; 32   e. 32
4a. 4   b. 4 ; 12 ; 12
5a. 2   b. 5 x 2 = 10 ; 10
6a. 6   b. 2 x 6 = 12 ; 12
7a. 8   b. 4 x 8 = 32 ; 32
8a. 5   b. 3 x 5 = 15 ; 15
9a. 3   b. 6 x 3 = 18 ; 18
10a. B   b. 4 ; 8 ; 8
11a. A   b. 5 x 4 = 20 ; 20
12a. C   b. 3 x 6 = 18 ; 18
13a. B   b. 4 x 3 = 12 ; 12
14. 8 x 6 = 48 ; 48
15. 7 x 6 = 42 ; 42
16. 9 x 2 = 18 ; 18
17. 4 x 6 = 24 ; 24
18. 5 x 5 = 25 ; 25
19. 5 x 4 = 20 ; 20
20. 2 x 3 = 6 ; 6

4 Money

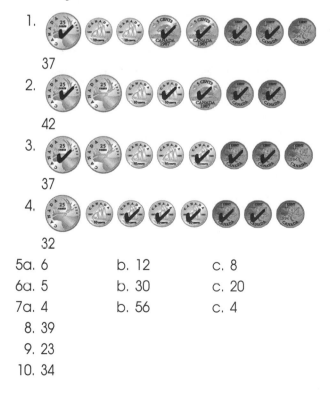

1.   37
2.   42
3.   37
4.   32

5a. 6   b. 12   c. 8
6a. 5   b. 30   c. 20
7a. 4   b. 56   c. 4
8. 39
9. 23
10. 34

11. 19

12. 23 + 19 = 42 ; 42

$$\begin{array}{r} 2\,3 \\ +\,1\,9 \\ \hline 4\,2 \end{array}$$

13. 50 – 39 = 11 ; 11

$$\begin{array}{r} 5\,0 \\ -\,3\,9 \\ \hline 1\,1 \end{array}$$

14. 34 – 19 = 15 ; 15

$$\begin{array}{r} 3\,4 \\ -\,1\,9 \\ \hline 1\,5 \end{array}$$

15. 39 + 39 = 78 ; 78

$$\begin{array}{r} 3\,9 \\ +\,3\,9 \\ \hline 7\,8 \end{array}$$

16. 23 + 39 = 62 ; 62

$$\begin{array}{r} 2\,3 \\ +\,3\,9 \\ \hline 6\,2 \end{array}$$

17. 85 – 19 = 66 ; 66

$$\begin{array}{r} 8\,5 \\ -\,1\,9 \\ \hline 6\,6 \end{array}$$

18. 34 + 34 + 23 = 91 ; 91

$$\begin{array}{r} 3\,4 \\ 3\,4 \\ +\,2\,3 \\ \hline 9\,1 \end{array}$$

19. 50 – 16 = 34 ; brownie

$$\begin{array}{r} 5\,0 \\ -\,1\,6 \\ \hline 3\,4 \end{array}$$

5 Pictographs

1. Dress shoes
2. Running shoes
3. Sandals
4. Dress shoes
5. Boots
6. 4
7. 13
8. 25
9. The Cubs
10. The Rangers
11. 3
12. The Jays
13. The Herons
14. The Lotus
15. 7

16.

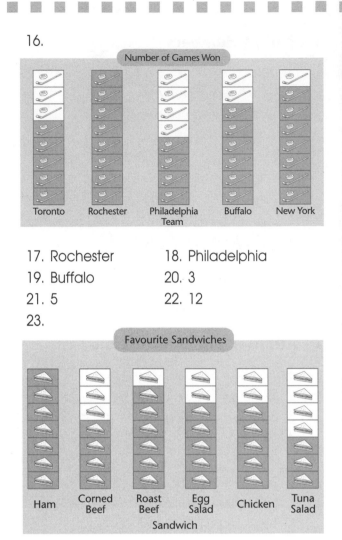

Number of Games Won

Toronto   Rochester   Philadelphia   Buffalo   New York
Team

17. Rochester
18. Philadelphia
19. Buffalo
20. 3
21. 5
22. 12

23.

Favourite Sandwiches

Ham   Corned Beef   Roast Beef   Egg Salad   Chicken   Tuna Salad
Sandwich

24. Ham
25. Tuna Salad
26. 10
27. 8
28. 2

6 More about Addition and Subtraction

1. Dan
2. Roberta
3. Roberta
4. Ada
5. 145 + 108 = 253 ; 253
6. 213 + 96 = 309 ; 309
7. 177 – 82 = 95 ; 95
8. 134 – 59 = 75 ; 75
9. Toronto
10. Oakville
11. 150 + 32 = 182 ; 182

12. 165 + 64 = 229 ; 229
13. 178 + 45 = 223 ; 223
14. 197 + 58 = 255 ; 255
15. 255 – 182 = 73 ; 73
16. 154 – 72 = 82 ; 82
17. 302 – 124 = 178 ; 178
18. 326 – 97 = 229 ; 229
19. 105 – 35 = 70 ; 70
20. 154 + 326 = 480 ; 480
21. 380 – 166 = 214 ; 214
22. 85 + 17 = 102 ; 102
23. 380 – 85 = 295 ; 295
24. 106 + 215 = 321 ; 321
25. 215 – 80 = 135 ; 135
26. 159 + 159 = 318 ; 318

Midway Review

1. 9 ; 27 ; 27
2. 5 x 4 = 20 ; 20
3. 4 x 6 = 24 ; 24
4. 7 x 2 = 14 ; 14
5. 5 x 6 = 30 ; 30
6. 8 x 2 = 16 ; 16
7. 8 ; 8
8. Pam ; Dora
9. Dora ; Pam
10. 93 ; 86
11. Pam ; Dora
12. 82   13. 3
14. 11   15. 8
16. 295 ; Three hundred twelve
17. 273 ; Two hundred ninety-eight
18. Three hundred one ; 290
19. Glenview School ; Trafalgar School
    Meadows School
20. Trafalgar School ; Meadows School ;
    Glenview School
21. Glenview School
22. 607   23. 571
24. 591   25. 17
26. Simon   27. Janet
28. 2   29. 3

30. 5   31. No
32. 3   33. 2

7   4-Digit Numbers

1. 2321   2. 3212
3. 1421   4. 2142
5. 3134   6. 2043
7. Nectarine   8. Peach
9. 2
10. One thousand three hundred twenty-one
11. One thousand nine hundred twenty-one
12. Diplodocus
13. Brachiosaurus
14. 1000
15. 2000
16. Giganotosaurus
17. Two thousand one hundred centimetres
18. One thousnad three hundred centimetres
19. 7300 ; 5206 ; 3249 ; 2375 ; 1854
20. 5208 ; 3153 ; 2005 ; 1656 ; 1054
21. One thousand eight hundred fifty-four
22. Five thousand two hundred eight
23. 2 ; 3249 and 5206
24. 3 ; 1054, 1656 and 3153
25. 2314
26. 3105
27. 1 ; 4 ; 7
28. 2 ; 0 ; 9
29. Toby's Shop
30. Ranis Retail
31. 8
32. 7
33. 5000

8   Division

1. 4 ; 4
2. 3 ; 3
3. 3 ; 3
4. 6 ; 6
5. 2 ; 2

6. 25 ÷ 5 = 5 ; 5

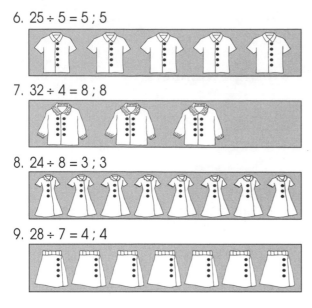

7. 32 ÷ 4 = 8 ; 8

8. 24 ÷ 8 = 3 ; 3

9. 28 ÷ 7 = 4 ; 4

10. 20 ÷ 4 = 5 ; 5
11. 27 ÷ 3 = 9 ; 9
12. 72 ÷ 8 = 9 ; 9
13. 21 ÷ 7 = 3 ; 3
14. 20 ÷ 4 = 5 ; 5
15. 10 ÷ 5 = 2 ; 2
16. 40 ÷ 4 = 10 ; 10
17. 40 ÷ 5 = 8 ; 8
18. 14 ÷ 2 = 7 ; 7
19. 24 ÷ 3 = 8 ; 8
20. 35 ÷ 7 = 5 ; 5
21. 20 ÷ 4 = 5 ; 5

9 Measurement

1a. 8:30 ; 10   b. 6:00 ; 15
   c. lower
2a. 8:45 ; 25   b. 6:15 ; 20
   c. higher
3. Tuesday   4. Monday
5. 400   6. Adam
7. Eva   8. Bob
9. 5   10. 90
11. May 18   12. 1:15 p.m.

10 More about Multiplication and Division

1. 12 ÷ 3 = 4 ; 4
2. 16 ÷ 4 = 4 ; 4
3. 18 ÷ 6 = 3 ; 3
4. 6 x 2 = 12 ; 12
5. 7 x 2 = 14 ; 14
6. 36
7. 36 ÷ 4 = 9 ; 9
8. 2 x 9 = 18 ; 18
9. 18 ÷ 6 = 3 ; 3
10. 30 ÷ 5 = 6 ; 6
11. 3 x 6 = 18 ; 18
12. 3 x 8 = 24 ; 24
13. 24 ÷ 4 = 6 ; 6
14. 4 x 6 = 24 ; 24
15. 24 ÷ 8 = 3 ; 3
16. 6 x 2 = 12 ; 12
17. 12 ÷ 3 = 4 ; 4
18. 6 x 7 = 42 ; 42
19. 28 ÷ 7 = 4 ; 4
20. 8 x 7 = 56 ; 56
21. 3 x 10 = 30 ; 30
22. 16 ÷ 2 = 8 ; 8
23. 32 ÷ 4 = 8 ; 8

11 Bar Graphs

1. Going to Cottage
2. Going to Beach
3. Hiking
4. Visiting Family
5. 13   6. 3
7. 6   8. 27
9. 6   10. Strawberry
11. Maple Walnut   12. 6
13. 3   14. 2
15. 33   16. Butter Pecan
17.

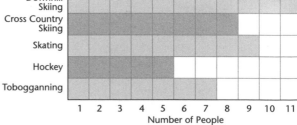

Favourite Winter Sports

Number of People

18. Downhill skiing 19. 19
20. 14   21. 2
22. 40
23.

Number of Children in Each Family

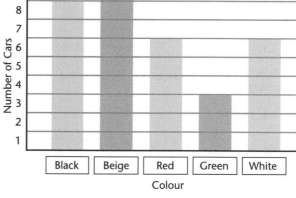

24. 2   25. 3
26. 2   27. 4
28. 16   29. 4

12 Probability

1. 2   2. 4
3. ♥   4. ♠
5. 3, 4   6. 2
7. 6   8. No
9. 2   10. ♥
11. 10   12. 4
13. 2   14. 3
15. 1   16. Vanilla
17. Lemon   18. Lemon
19. No   20. Vanilla

Final Review

1.

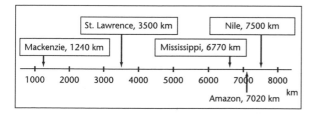

2. Nile   3. Mackenzie
4. No   5. 3
6. Mackenzie   7. Amazon
8. Yes   9. 25
10. 70   11. 45
12. 35   13. B ; C ; D ; A

14. Juice   15. Pop
16. Ice tea   17. No
18. Pop   19. Juice
20. 24 ÷ 4 = 6 ; 6
21. 24 ÷ 8 = 3 ; 3
22. 21 ÷ 3 = 7 ; 7
23. 15 ÷ 5 = 3 ; 3
24. 8 x 2 = 16 ; 16
25. 9 x 3 = 27 ; 27
26. 20 ÷ 4 = 5 ; 5
27. 6 x 5 = 30 ; 30
28. 30 ÷ 3 = 10 ; 10
29. 10 x 2 = 20 ; 20
30. 3 x 8 = 24 ; 24
31. 7 x 9 = 63 ; 63
32. 35
33. 1:20 p.m.
34. 45
35.

Number of Cars in Different Colours

(bar graph: Black, Beige, Red, Green, White)

36. 8 ; 9 ; 6 ; 3 ; 6
37. 2
38. 12
39. 32